# LEARNING RESOURCES CENTER

BLUE BELL, PENNSYLVANIA

# WELLINGTON'S SURGEON GENERAL

# WELLINGTON'S SURGEON GENERAL: SIR JAMES McGRIGOR

*Richard L. Blanco*

Durham, N.C.
DUKE UNIVERSITY PRESS
1974

This publication was supported in
part by NIH Grant LM 02189 from
the National Library of Medicine.

PRINTED IN THE UNITED STATES OF
AMERICA BY HERITAGE PRINTERS

*To my wife, Renée, and our son, Ricky (who regard McGrigor as a member of the family), I am deeply grateful for their devotion, patience, and encouragement.*

# CONTENTS

## Maps and Illustrations

# PREFACE

This work attempts to place the administrative and humanitarian achievements of Sir James McGrigor, "the father of the Royal Army Medical Corps" of the British army, into historical perspective. Although McGrigor initiated major reforms in preventive medicine and hospital care to improve the health and welfare of soldiers, heretofore his accomplishments have not been chronicled in a biography.

There is little published information about the evolution of military medicine in past centuries, particularly the role of the British regimental surgeon during the wars with France from 1793 to 1815. A study of McGrigor's colorful career helps to fill this void. Rarely in the annals of medical history is there an account matching his descriptions of sieges, battles, and sea voyages which so graphically portray the appalling conditions under which army doctors labored, and the incredible social, technical, and environmental obstacles which frustrated their efforts to cure sick and wounded troops.

On military expeditions to Europe, the Caribbean, the East Indies, and North Africa, McGrigor endeavored to protect regiments from diseases with sanitary reforms. But not until he served in Portugal and Spain under the foremost British soldier of the period, Arthur Wellesley, the future Duke of Wellington, did McGrigor have the authority to instigate significant improvements in military medicine. This relationship between a dedicated doctor and a perceptive general demonstrated the awareness of the military to the problems of medical care for the rank and file.

For this study I have relied greatly upon McGrigor's *Autobiography*, his *Medical Sketches*, and in addition, his articles in medical journals. A shy man, McGrigor was reticent about stressing his own deeds. He was equally modest about what he considered deficiencies in his scientific knowledge. Moreover, his *Autobiography* terminated in 1814, and not in 1851 when he retired from service. To fill the chronological gaps and to clarify omissions in his account, I have utilized the unpublished collection known as the McGrigor Papers—reports, notebooks, medical registers—as well as other contemporary documents. Whenever possible, I have McGrigor relate the tale in his own unassuming manner. Some of McGrigor's colleagues wrote vivid accounts of their experiences. I have also used these descriptions in order to provide a picture of the humble regimental surgeon striving to combat the ravages of pestilence and the horrors of war.

I ask the reader's indulgence in two matters—the lack of information about McGrigor's personal life, and the change, for literary purposes, of McGrigor's army title.

McGrigor wrote little about his family, and there are few clues in the documents. Aside from a brief mention of his mother, the only other woman in his life seems to have been his devoted wife, and even she is barely mentioned. There are some letters extant written by McGrigor to his eldest son, but these are too fragmentary to be useful. Furthermore, as McGrigor advanced in the army he refrained from commenting about religion, politics, or about the contemporary state of society, and aside from an occasional proud reference to his Scottish background, he described only his professional career. Due to the lack of evidence, therefore, I have been unable to delineate certain traits of McGrigor's character, although I believe that I have summarized his administrative achievements.

Secondly, there is the matter of McGrigor's title. He rose through the ranks to become inspector of hospitals, and later director general of the army medical department. As both of these descriptions are rather cumbersome and because the term surgeon general is familiar, I have modified the official nomenclature in order to describe this visionary Scot doctor as Wellington's surgeon general.

This study would not have been possible without the cooperation and assistance provided by numerous individuals and institutions. I acknowledge the financial support from two foundations for four summer research grants—the American Philosophical Society (1967, 1972), and the Research Foundation of the State University of New York, (1969, 1970). I am grateful to certain persons who encouraged me to pursue McGrigor's career through British archives and libraries. To Brian Bond, Lecturer, Department of War Studies, King's College, University of London, I owe a great debt of gratitude for aid, advice, and continual encouragement. To Malcolm M. Davies, Librarian, Royal Army Medical College, I am grateful for his kindness and for making research at Millbank so pleasant. I give my thanks to Dr. John

McKenzie, Chairman, Department of Embryology, University of
Aberdeen, who, on behalf of the Aberdeen Medico-Chirurgical Society, permitted me to utilize the McGrigor Papers. I am indebted to
Mr. Robin Price, Assistant Librarian, Wellcome Institute of the History of Medicine, for his expert help. Colonel Sir Charles McGrigor,
Upper Sonachan, Argyll, provided me with family letters about his
illustrious ancestor. Major Jock Haswell, Folkstone, Kent, provided
me with some illuminating documents. I also wish to thank Dr. Arvel
E. Erickson, Professor of History, Case-Western Reserve University,
who first aroused my interest in studying the British army as an insti-
tution reflecting social changes when he supervised my dissertation,
"The Enlisted Man—Social Aspects of British Army Reforms, 1854–
1867" (1960).

I also acknowledge the assistance of the following individuals: H. M.
G. Bailie, Archivist, Historical Manuscripts Commission; Lt. General
Sir James Parlane Baird, Director General of Army Medical Services,
1972–; Ray E. Brown, Program Officer, National Library of Medi-
cine; Lt. General Sir Neil Cantlie, Director General of Army Medi-
cal Services (1948–52); Alice Creighton, former History of Medicine
Librarian, Edward G. Miner Library, School of Medicine and Den-
tistry, University of Rochester; E. H. Cornelius, Librarian, Royal Col-
lege of Surgeons of England; Lt. General Sir W. Robert Drew, Director
General of Army Medical Services (1965–69); N. E. Evans, Assistant
Keeper, Public Records Office; Robert Ewen, Assistant Secretary
(Academic), University of Aberdeen; A. J. Farrington, Librarian,
India Office Library; G. M. Fewster, Senior Assistant Keeper, the
Prior's Kitchen, University of Durham; E. B. A. Gaskell, Librarian,
Wellcome Institute of the History of Medicine; James George, Deputy
Secretary (Academic), Aberdeen University; Ferenc Gyorgyey, His-
torical Librarian, Yale Medical Library; W. B. Howie, M.D., Aber-
deen; C. A. McLaren, Archivist and Keeper of Manuscripts, King's
College, University of Aberdeen; Major General Alastair MacLen-
nan (Retd.), Curator, Historical Library, Royal Army Medical Col-
lege, and Editor, *Journal of the Royal Army Medical Corps*; Ian Porter,
M.D., Aberdeen; C. A. Potts, Librarian, Ministry of Defense and Central Library; Julian Russell, Research Assistant, Department of Manuscripts, National Library of Scotland; Joan Stevenson, Historian, St.
Mary's, Jersey; Philip J. Weimerskirch, History of Medicine Librarian,
Edward G. Miner Library, School of Medicine and Dentistry, Uni-

versity of Rochester; Colonel Alistair G. D. Whyte, M.D., Lecturer, Department of Anatomy, University of Aberdeen; J. M. Willis-Fear, City Archivist, City of Portsmouth; John Woods, Librarian, Ministry of Defense and Army Library; Richard J. Wolfe, Rare Books Librarian, The Francis A. Countway Library of Medicine, Harvard University; Dr. Edward Maitland Wright, Principal, Aberdeen University; and the staffs of the British Museum, the Public Record Office, and the Wellcome Institute of the History of Medicine.

I acknowledge the financial support of the National Library of Medicine which partly subsidized the publication of this work.

For supervising the typing of the manuscript, I am indebted to Mrs. Diana Wedel, Secretary of the History Department, SUNY at Brockport. To my colleague at Brockport, Arnold Grade, I am grateful for suggestions to improve the style and content of chapter seven. Dr. Edward C. Atwater, Associate Professor of Medicine, University of Rochester, also suggested revisions in the first four chapters. I am obligated to Katherine E. Crowe, a Ph.D. candidate in history at the University of London, for her thorough checking of the manuscript and for her thoughtful commentaries on the material. To my wife, Irene, and our son, Richard Jr., without whose devotion and consideration this work would not have been completed, I am especially grateful.

WELLINGTON'S SURGEON GENERAL

# I

## THE TRAINING OF AN
## ARMY SURGEON

James McGrigor, a Scottish regimental surgeon campaigning with the British army during the French revolutionary and Napoleonic wars, encountered malignant diseases in many environments. He found typhus in the Germanies, yellow fever in the Caribbean, scurvy in the Indian Ocean, ophthalmia and bubonic plague in North Africa, and typhoid fever in the Lowlands. While serving under Wellington in Portugal and Spain, he initiated reforms of casualty evacuation and of hospital administration that were significant factors in limiting the high mortality rate in the army. Foremost among British army medical officers of the era, McGrigor demonstrated the importance of a medical corps and displayed a humanitarian concern for the health and welfare of the soldier.

During the Age of the Enlightenment, medicine in Britain made few spectacular advances. A scientific explanation of disease was unknown, the training of medical doctors was disorganized, and the professionalization of medicine was retarded by artificial divisions of labor. Medical concepts about the theory and practice of medicine were hampered by an adherence to venerated metaphysical dogmas about pestilence, and the medical profession itself barely experimented in the spirit of scientific inquiry. During the late eighteenth century, however, the principles of science were gradually applied to medicine. Rather than accepting traditional assumptions about disease, some physicians and surgeons made a more rational appeal to fact and to reason.

As a result of the dynastic and colonial wars during the eighteenth century, military medicine became an area of specialization.[1] During the struggle against France from 1793 to 1814, British army doctors had novel opportunities to devise new surgical techniques, to improve army hospitals, and to institute sanitary codes for the rank and file. The career of Sir James McGrigor, who became director general of the army medical department at Waterloo, exemplifies this transition in British military medicine.

In the Highlands of Invernesshire, James McGrigor, a merchant's son, was born in 1771.[2] He was reared by his parents in Aberdeen, which stands on the picturesque Don and Dee Rivers, facing the bleak North Sea. Established by the Romans, it became an important trading center for northern Scotland during the Middle Ages and the Renaissance. In the eighteenth century, the city expanded its trade with the Lowlands and the Baltic to develop into a shipping and commercial center that exported wool, hides, hose, course linen, cod, and salmon. Aberdeen became a busy seaport, and from its harbor fishing and whaling vessels sailed to the North Sea and cargo ships departed for the Americas and the Mediterranean. Although Aberdeen had granite mines, the area lacked coal and iron. Furthermore, the city was handicapped in economic expansion by long distances from other markets and by the paucity of overland trade routes. Hence, Aberdeen diversified its commerce with small industries—breweries, distilleries, tile and brick factories, and textile plants producing linen thread, sail cloth, and fine hosiery. In this bustling seaport, young James was raised.

As Aberdeen grew, it continued to be an educational center. Both King's College and Marischal College had venerable academic traditions. As Aberdeen developed closer links in the eighteenth century to Edinburgh and London, Aberdonians, emulating the careers of their famous countrymen—David Hume in philosophy, Adam Smith in economics, Joseph Black in chemistry, William Cullen, the Monros, and the Hunters in medicine—went forth to complete their education, to join the armed services, to seek professional advancement in English society, and to find opportunities in the colonies. Among these adventurous Scots was James McGrigor.

Young James was educated at Aberdeen's Grammar School, one of Scotland's oldest public schools. A superior student, McGrigor won an academic prize for his achievements, an event which he joyfully described:

At the conclusion of the five years [of study], there was an examination; and on that occasion an event occured, the most joyous . . . , of any time in my life. In the evening of that day, the whole of the pupils were assembled in the public hall, in the presence of the Lord Provost, magistrates, Professors of the University, and the clergy of the city, and my name being called aloud by the Rector, he announced to me, in Latin oration, that the first prize had been awarded to me, he then presented to me the Lord Provost who complimented me in Scottish address; and I left the public hall amidst the applause of the assembly; from which I ran to my father's house, at a quicker pace than ever I ran in the course of my life, to announce my success in having obtained the highest prize. . . . It has since been my good fortune to obtain various distinctions and honours, but with none of them have I been more elated then the prize which I then gained, when it was presented to me by the Lord Provost.[3]

McGrigor matriculated at Marischal College where he earned the Bachelor of Arts degree. He ended his formal education in Aberdeen by achieving his Master of Arts in 1788. Undecided about a career, and unwilling to enter his father's hosiery firm, McGrigor became interested in anatomy and physiology, and considered becoming a surgeon. He was impressed by the success of Scots from Glasgow and Edinburgh who made their mark in the medical world, and especially by the careers of two Aberdonian doctors who served in the army before they acquired lucrative private practices in London.[4]

Formal study in medicine was not available in Aberdeen during McGrigor's youth. Even though both King's College and Marischal had chairs of medicine, these were honorific posts, and courses in medicine were not offered.[5] Yet the lack of a local medical school did not deter ambitious youths. A lad without a university degree could apprentice himself to a local doctor and become a surgeon without a higher education; or, if he possessed a degree, he could receive clinical instruction from physicians at a local hospital and later attend lectures at Leyden or Edinburgh, which had outstanding medical faculties.[6]

And this is in general the path of training that McGrigor pursued. In a phase of education roughly corresponding to the modern internship, McGrigor worked as an apprentice to a physician at the Aberdeen County Infirmary. Although McGrigor neglected to describe his duties, presumably he performed a variety of menial tasks—cleaning bottles, pulverizing the bark and roots reputed to have therapeutic value into powders, preparing tinctures, mixing ointments, and compounding prescriptions. After acquiring the rudiments of medical lore, McGrigor was probably permitted to hold instruments during minor surgery, to bleed and to cup, to dress wounds, to accompany his master on his rounds, and to assist in surgical operations.

In addition to this practical education, McGrigor studied the medical classics and learned about chemistry and midwifery from local physicians. In order to become a physician, he increased his knowledge of medicine by matriculating at the distinguished Edinburgh Medical School from 1789 to 1791. "I attended Dr. Monro's class of anatomy, Mr. Fife's demonstrations, and Dr. Gregory's Practice of Physic," he recounted.[7] However, McGrigor never completed his medical studies at Edinburgh. As a result of overwork, his health suffered, and he left without completing the requirements for a degree.

Inspired by the state of medicine in Edinburgh and by the scientific interests of the Edinburgh Chirurgical Society, McGrigor returned to Aberdeen between university terms. On December 12, 1789, he and 11 friends founded the Aberdeen Medico-Chirurgical Society. "This did more to stimulate an effective medical school in Aberdeen than any other factor," states an Aberdeen historian. "There is little doubt that the formation of the Medical Society was the first serious properly continued medical training in Aberdeen."[8]

The society was a meeting place for Aberdeen's doctors, amateur scientists, and aspiring medical students. From their own meager resources the members contributed books, journals, botanical and zoological specimens, maintained a case book of medical histories, and presented scientific papers for discussion in which McGrigor led the list with essays on cancer, typhus, gangrene, and bloodletting. One of his papers was entitled: "Is an accurate knowledge of anatomy absolutely necessary to Medicine?" Local doctors lectured on osteology and comparative anatomy, but due to legal restrictions on dissection, the anatomical experience of the students was limited to cutting up dogs. The students sought empirical proof in their study of medicine. They distrusted unproven speculation about theories of disease, questioned the doctrines of ancient medical authorities whose dictums about the origins and cure of sickness had held sway for centuries over the medical world, and they admired such names as Harvey, Cullen, Hunter, Gregory, and Sydenham. By 1791, the society had a library, more doctors from Aberdeen and the surrounding countryside enrolled as members, and a beginning to the organized study of medicine in the city was underway.[9]

While McGrigor was studying in Edinburgh, the French Revolution erupted, and by 1792 Europe was plunged into warfare that lasted almost continually until 1814. Throughout his *Autobiography*, his letterbooks and journals, McGrigor avoided political commentary, but he left one clue about his own youthful revolutionary fervor, an enthusiasm that was soon quenched:

When I was at Edinburgh the French Revolution broke out, which was at first hailed with joy by . . . the students, by whom its merits were warmly discussed; and I brought the contagion of republicanism with me to Aberdeen, where I found it warmly advocated, particularly in the university, I advocated so much with those who advocated the revolution, as to give uneasiness to some of my friends, and I was strongly cautioned against again expressing my opinions on the subject, which in a long time, however, entirely changed.[10]

His revolutionary passions cooled, and his education in Scotland completed, McGrigor sought his fortune in London. Bidding farewell to his parents in July, 1793, he took passage on a small vessel sailing south. On the crowded ship, his precious medical books and his prized anatomical specimens had to be stored on the deck. It was a rough voyage on high seas. On one stormy day, explained McGrigor, "my baggage got loose, and along with my trunks was a small box which contained a skull and bones of the human subject. . ." To his dismay, the frail container broke open, and the contents were scattered over the deck. Horrified at the skeleton, the superstitious crewmen cursed it for causing the storm and clamored that McGrigor's specimens be heaved overboard. McGrigor refused to be bullied by the seamen, and fortunately for him the ship's captain supported the determined young Scot. "After this, contrary to the expectation of the sailors," remarked McGrigor, "we had fair weather till we cast anchor in the Thames."[11]

McGrigor's activities in London at this point are not clear. Only one letter addressed to his uncle, David Grant in Aberdeen, on September 14, 1793, provides some information. Apparently McGrigor apprenticed himself for additional training, for he commented: "I am now situated as Assistant to the surgeon 1½ miles from London, in Islington, a very pleasant village. He is an old gentleman and the first man in this place . . . but what with ye gout . . . he lets a good deal of his practice evolve on me. The salary with bed, board, and lodging which he allows me is reckoned equal to be £70 per annum, not much here."[12]

Whether McGrigor found English village life boring or the scope of his ambitions limited is uncertain. It is apparent, however, that he had been contemplating a career in the army. Anxious for an adventurous life, McGrigor was attracted to the prospect of military service, particularly at a time when England was mobilizing for war against France. "Stimulated by everything around," he commented, "I determined on service as a medical officer in the army."[13] Without bothering to become professionally qualified by taking the examination of the Company of Surgeons in London, McGrigor purchased his commission as a surgeon for £150 on September 25, 1793, in a newly formed infantry regiment—the 88th, known as the Connaught Rangers.[14]

What was the state of British military medicine during McGrigor's training? The organization of military medicine by the army medical department had barely changed in a century. A Medical Board consisting of a physician general, a surgeon general, and an inspector of infirmaries administered the department. The physician general recommended physicians for general hospitals and for staff commands. He and the surgeon general inspected medicine and equipment supplied by the apothecary general; they also presided at medical boards for military officers and examined medical candidates for commissions. The surgeon general appointed staff surgeons for general hospitals as well as regimental surgeons and surgeons' mates for the line. He shared with the inspector of infirmaries in the supervision of the administrative officers—principal medical officers, district medical officers, inspectors of hospitals—and the personnel for general hospitals such as apothecaries, purveyors, and hospital mates.

Likewise, the administration of army hospitals in the 1790's by the Medical Board was similar to that of the late seventeenth century when a regimental hospital organization developed with a surgeon and a surgeon's mate attached to each regiment. A staff structure had also evolved which comprised the medical officers attached to general hospitals that were established at major towns behind combat areas. During peacetime, permanent general hospitals were maintained at home for garrison troops and for disabled veterans. There was also an intermediary hospital between the regimental and general hospitals: the field hospital, also known as the "Marching," or "Flying" hospital. The personnel of field hospitals closely followed the regiments during an action and handled the overflow of casualties from regimental hospitals. Field hospital staff usually treated only minor injuries and ailments and sent the seriously sick and wounded to rear-line general hospitals.[15] No trained nurses or orderlies were available for hospital duty. Only when rear-line hospitals became overcrowded with casualties did something euphemistically designated as a "medical corps"—it was composed of regimental misfits and drunkards assigned to the supposedly degrading duty in the wards—gradually emerge.

Furthermore, few improvements had transpired during the eighteenth century in the evacuation of casualties. The handling of the wounded was gruesome. The traditional practice after an action was to send all casualties to the rear in order to keep an army as unencumbered as possible. During the fighting, the wounded were aided to safety by their comrades, or by regimental bandsmen untrained in the rudiments of first aid. Severe casualties could remain for agonizing hours or even days on a corpse-strewn field without receiving the slightest attention. Such tragedies occurred not because of relative indifference to suffering or contempt for human life, but because human ingenuity in the British army had not yet been applied to the problem of conveying the stricken soldier to a sanctuary. Although contemporary literature contains fleeting references to stretcher-like devices for transporting the wounded—wooden frames built to support a body, sheets of canvas connected to wooden rods, or an arrangement of blankets braced by poles or muskets—the problem of moving casualties humanely and efficiently had not been solved. Compared to the attention focused by the military on the tactics, strategy, and technology of war, relatively little attention was devoted to providing better medical care for the army.

No formal training in military medicine existed in McGrigor's youth. The Medical Board did not require its surgeons to have a specific set of surgical instruments or a minimum quantity of drugs in their medical chests. Even though medical registers were coming in vogue in the civilian medical world, few army surgeons maintained regimental records on their patients; hence the medical department was rarely able to provide generals in the field with sufficient data about the health of their men. Although visionary physicians had suggested rules of hygiene for the troops, there was not an official sanitary code promulgated, nor were there even published regulations for the supervision of hospitals. Yet there were some improvements underway in preventive medicine and in operative surgery.

Without printed manuals or medical textbooks to guide him in preventive medicine, McGrigor had to learn from accounts like *Obser-*

*vations on the Means of Preserving the Health of Soldiers* (1780). Written by
Donald Monro (1727–1802) a member of the famed Edinburgh family
of physicians and one who had served in the Seven Years War, this
work was a pioneering study of the duties and responsibilities of medical personnel during a campaign. As Monro explained: "Among the
numerous authorities of observations in the art of physic, there are
few physicians who have expressly written on the health and disease
most intendent to an army in the field."[16] Even though the army surgeon had the gruesome task of treating the maimed and butchered
casualties of battle, to Monro this aspect of a surgeon's work was less
important than the dangers of soldiering that resulted not from exposure to enemy fire, but from problems of disease caused by inadequate diet, inattention to suitable living quarters, and improper hospital accommodations. Familiar with the practice of naval medicine,
Monro suggested an analogy between the occupational perils of accidents and disease confronting both the soldier and the seaman. He
also noted the efforts made by both army and naval surgeons to establish better controls over living conditions on land and at sea.

Monro perceived a causative relation between pestilence and the
natural environment; and he noted that the hazards of soldiering subjected the men to occupational diseases usually unassociated with
civilian populations. The normal sick rate of an army's strength in the
eighteenth century before a spring offensive was 3 percent; by mid-
summer about 6 percent of the force was incapacitated; and by autumn, even if an army did little fighting, somewhere between 10 and
12 percent of a command were usually casualties, the majority of
which resulted from disease.[17] To lower this awesome depletion of
manpower, Monro offered practical advice about protecting the
health of regiments.

Monro's book is replete with information about the importance of
fresh water, means to avoid scurvy (onions, potatoes, pickled cabbage,
beer, cider, lemon, wine), suggestions for selecting camp sites and regimental hospitals, advice on clothing and quartering, and comments
about the limits of a soldier's endurance. Furthermore, he listed the
medicine and instruments needed by a surgeon, explained the precautions required before embarking troops—cleansing the ship, en-
suring enough ventilation below deck, utilizing hammocks, providing
sufficient living space, proper dieting—and he commented about the
best months for voyages to the Indies.[18] Conscious of his responsibility

of protecting the health of the rank and file in garrisons, on shipboard, and during campaigns fought on the Continent and in tropical climates of the Caribbean and the East Indies, McGrigor followed these practical suggestions throughout his career.

Monro made astute comments about the operations of regimental hospitals. He urged the establishment of numerous, small hospitals close to the line in order to prevent contagion and the overcrowding of general hospitals. He noted that "houses with small rooms [make] but bad hospitals; and damp and close places ought by all means to be avoided." Large barns or houses, and especially churches located on dry high ground, were good hospital sites. These hospitals, Monro stated, needed suitable drainage, adequate ventilation, and they had to be free from "winds impregnated with the moist putrid exhalations from the marshes." Cleansing a building selected for a hospital was vital, he claimed:

When the places are fixed upon for hospitals, every ward ought to be made perfectly sweet and clean; first by scraping and washing with soap and water, and afterwards with warm vinegar, and then they ought to be fumigated with the smoke of wetted gunpowder and of aromatics and afterwards dried and aired by lighting fires, and opening windows before the sick are admitted. After this the beds ought to be laid in doing of which great care could be taken not to crowd the ward to much, as nothing corrupts the air so much, or so soon brings on infectious disorders.[19]

Monro also listed the rules of conduct for the patients and for each member of the medical staff. A register to record the progress of the sick was advisable, he stated. Describing the uproarious condition of drunken patients who had been abetted by unscrupulous orderlies, Monro urged that strict controls be maintained "to prevent spiritous liquors . . . being clandestinely carried into a hospital." A factor in running an efficient regimental hospital, he claimed, "was in the rapid discharge of recuperated patients for duty, because recovered men are always the most riotous; because they crowd the hospitals and were in danger of catching fresh disorders from those who were sick."[20]

Another physician who strongly influenced McGrigor was Sir John Pringle (1702–82), known as the "father of military medicine." In his *Observations on Diseases of the Army* (1752), Pringle attempted to classify diseases incident to military service and to devise means to protect troops from contagion. Although intellectually trapped in his understanding of pestilence by the contemporary humoral pathology, his commentaries, written in a period unfamiliar with malignant bacteriological organisms, profoundly influenced preventive medicine during the wars of the era.

Pringle was an army physician during the War of the Austrian Succession, and served in Flanders, Scotland, and the Germanies. He made a signal humanitarian effort during the German campaign by urging that military hospitals be considered as sanctuaries during combat operations. Anxious to avoid a bombardment of his hospital on the Main, Pringle proposed that army hospitals be removed from the zones of fire and that they be regarded as havens for the wounded. The British and French commanders on the scene agreed to the experiment and as a result the model was established for future accords on military hospitals. "This agreement was strictly observed on both sides through the campaign," Pringle noted, "and although it has been broken since, yet it is my hope that in future wars, the contending parties will make it a precedent."[21]

Pringle became a baronet, physician-extraordinary to George III, and president of the Royal Society of London. He published many scientific papers; those on sepsis, antisepsis, typhus fever, and the origins of putrefaction are classics. Pringle also encouraged studies of scurvy, and he helped to popularize Captain James Cook's account of his second expedition to the Pacific (1772–75), on which, by careful attention to diet and to sanitation, the amount of disease, which normally reached fearful proportions on such voyages, was dramatically reduced.

Pringle's approach to medicine involved a desire for cleanliness, to be achieved by purifying the air and by purging the bloodstream of impurities. He ascertained that septic and antiseptic organisms were inherent in living substances, but although he pondered the problems of putrescent disease, evidently he never associated the process with living contagion. Instead, like his colleagues, he blamed pestilence on the "miasmata," or the polluted vapors of the environment.[22]

His magisterial work on military hygiene is an appalling account of how disease decimated an army to such a point that losses from combat injuries were comparably small. He divided the causes of disease incident to a military campaign into five categories—excessive heat or cold, moisture, "Putrid air," inadequate diet, and lack of rest. Sickness resulting from sudden changes in temperature, he suggested, could be avoided by suitable clothing, and supervision of bedding and barracks conditions; danger from damp and moist air could be checked by proper drainage, ventilation, and dry quarters; "putrid air" could be prevented by changing the camp sites, effective sanitation, dispersement of hospitals, personal cleanliness, exposure to fresh air, and the avoidance of overcrowding; bad diet could be changed by the quantity of the food and by providing fruit, vegetables, and vinegar; fatigue could be overcome by rest, warm clothing, and good boots. These suggestions now sound elementary, but Pringle's advice was then quite novel.[23]

Pringle's principles of preventive medicine for ships, camps, barracks, and hospitals resulted from his experience with "putrid fevers," such as typhus. One rule was to prevent the overcrowding of troops, whether on land or at sea:

The hospitals of any army, when crowded with sick, or where the distempers are of putrid nature, or at any time when the air is confined, especially in hot weather, produces a fever of a malignant kind, and often mortal. I have observed the same sort to arise in full and crowded barracks and transport ships, when filled beyond due number and detained by long and contrary winds; or when the men have been kept long at sea, and under close hatches in stormy weather. Hospital ships, for different expeditions, have for this reason been generally destructive both to the sick and those attending.[24]

Another principle developed from his experiments with regimental hospitals in Germany. "This scheme of separate regimental infirmaries," he stated, "though only intended to save the charge of the great hospitals, answered another purpose, which was that of preventing infection, the common consequence . . . of keeping great numbers of sick together." In Scotland, Pringle again tried the regimental hospital system and he remarked that "by this dispersion of the sick, and the preservation of a pure air in the wards, it was hoped that any contagions might be moderated, if not prevented. . . ." When his corps returned to Holland, Pringle remarked that "notwithstanding the violence and frequency of the flux, few people died of it; for the sick were more dispersed, the hospitals were better aired than usually, and the regimental surgeons having been taught by experience, either cured the men in the field-hospital or made them necessary evacuations before they sent them to the general hospital at Maestricht."[25]

What was the relationship of the general hospitals to the regimental hospitals according to Pringle? He suggested that an orderly and systematic handling of casualties would not only help to check disease, but would insure the better treatment of patients by a typically under-manned medical staff. "As to the general hospital," he stated, "let it receive such only as the regimental hospitals cannot accommodate, and the sick that cannot be moved with the army. Without this dis-persion of men, the great hospitals, in sickly times, be charged with some thousands, who cannot be well attended, but by a greater num-ber of physicians than has hitherto been employed by the public." The regimental hospitals, wrote Pringle, should be scattered among a number of villages, "rather than kept in one; . . . the want of pure air cannot be compensated by diet or medicines; hence appears the ex-pediency of carrying at all times, as many of the sick along with their regiments as can be easily transported." Like Monro, Pringle urged that "airy and spacious houses" be procured for the sick. "For this reason, not only barns, stables, graneries . . . but above all, churches made the best hospitals. . . . Therefore we may lay it down, for a maxim, that the more fresh air we let into hospitals, the less danger there will be of breeding contagious distempers."[26] More than any other doctor of the era, Pringle had the greatest influence on Mc-Grigor's interest in preventive medicine.

What was the level of operative surgery in the army? Along with the practical advice about hygienic measures, there was information available about the techniques for amputations, hemorrhages, the treatment of fractures, and the cauterization of wounds. Since the sev-enteenth century the number of books published in England on com-parative anatomy and on specialized aspects of surgery rose dramati-cally. Some 500 anatomical works (revisions, translations, new studies) were published in Britain during the eighteenth century.[27] But rela-tively little progress was made in the treatment of battlefield injuries. Even though the size, weight, accuracy, and sheer destructive power of artillery projectiles increased, along with refinements in musketry and in cutting weapons, the technology of operative surgery in the army barely advanced.

Until the nineteenth century, surgery was regarded as distinct from medicine. Little formal education or theoretical knowledge was re-quired for the mechanics of surgery—the treatment of wounds and the repair of broken bones merely required mechanical procedures per-formed by a craftsman. Surgery, therefore, in McGrigor's era was considered by society as an artisan skill. In contrast to the aristocratic civilian physician, the status of the surgeon in everyday life was quite low. His origins were usually humble, his formal education limited, and the scope of his medical activity severely restricted by law and custom. After centuries of a demeaning association with the Company of Barbers, the surgeons terminated this unwholesome alliance and formed in 1745 their own Company of Surgeons which was chartered in 1800 as the Royal College of Surgeons. The Crown traditionally had surgeons attached to the royal household, and some of these attained knighthood. Famous surgeons like William Cheselden, Percival Pott, and particularly the remarkable Hunter brothers, William and John, added luster and dignity to the profession by advancing surgery closer to a scientific level. Still the social prestige of the surgeons was quite low. They were not considered men of breeding, they were compromised by their long association with the barbers, and the public invariably linked them to the ghoulish "body-snatchers."

Surgery was a grim, rough-and-ready business that attracted few cultivated men. Civilian surgeons treated wounds, sprains, fractures, dislocated joints, and septic conditions. In addition, they removed cataracts, operated for hernia, acted as male midwives, and treated skin afflictions, among which numbered venereal disease. Although the surgeon could operate on the structural extremities of the body, and he "could treat with salves, plaster, linament, or lotions applied externally,"[28] he could not legally perform a major internal operation without the consent of the physician. Abdominal surgery was almost unknown, and amputations for compound injuries and severe sepsis of the limbs resulted in a mortality rate of 40 percent. The nature of the surgeon's work, states an authority, "the aura of death that surrounded him, these made him a figure from the thought of whom the patient shrank in horror—and not altogether without reason."[29] It was the surgeon's fear of increasing the agony and of causing the death of his patient that actually limited the number of such operations. Due to the difficulties of many operations, the surgeon did not operate unless he deemed it absolutely imperative. Although some surgeons were superb craftsmen and performed incredible feats of timing and dexterity, without a means to relax the patient's body during an operation and a method to protect it from infection a surgeon's chances of success in surgery were severely limited. True, he had a classical knowledge of operating on the bodily extremities, he knew of Cheselden's method of extracting a urinary stone. But usually the surgeon hesitated to enter a bodily cavity. Hence, disabilities of the body which moderns consider crippling went untreated; surgical procedures which society now regards as essential to save lives were not attempted. Yet some case-hardened surgeons who became relatively insensitive to inflicting pain on their patients and who possessed that rare degree of manual coordination necessary for such work performed some heroic feats on the operating table.

Yet the civilian surgeon was greatly handicapped in his craft by the limits of his own knowledge, the state of technology, and the restrictions of custom. He was ignorant of the process of infection, he knew nothing about the nature and treatment of shock, his understanding of pathology was minimal, and his rare experiments with blood transfusion were perilous indeed. He operated in unclean surroundings with inadequate lighting and few instruments or other mechanical devices to assist him. Furthermore, the surgeon was impeded in his understanding of the human body because three different medieval guilds controlled the practice of medicine, the craft of surgery, and the distribution of drugs. Representing these artificial divisions in the practice of medicine were the professional corporations— the Royal College of Physicians, the Company of Apothecaries, and the Company of Surgeons. These groups often discouraged creative scientific endeavors, discriminated against able men who promulgated controversial medical views, and bickered with each other about respective spheres of influence.

One result of these restraints on the modernization of medical concepts was that the surgeon remained under the hegemony of the physicians. Men of learning versed in classical medical lore, physicians were primarily concerned with diagnosis, and dealt with disease undetected by a superficial examination of the body. Problems of overt disease were generally regarded as within the province of surgeons and apothecaries, for it was beneath the dignity of physicians to operate on a patient, or to provide him directly with drugs. Determined to maintain their superior status in the profession, the physicians lorded it over the despised apothecaries who were regarded as mere tradesmen, and over the lowly surgeons who practiced a supposedly demeaning artisan craft. One result was that unless the patient was in need of surgery, a matter which the attending physician determined, a surgeon was rarely called into consultation. Thus, since the physician dominated the clinical realm of medicine, decades would pass before the surgeon had the freedom of scientific exploration to develop a conception of a localized pathology and before he had the opportunities to demonstrate his theories by empirical proof.

McGrigor was similarly restricted in the sphere of his work. But the army surgeon was essentially different from the civilian surgeon. Because the physicians and apothecaries were usually stationed only at the general hospitals, he, more than the hospital surgeon at least, was normally free of the traditional restraints on his occupation. Who else during the course of a campaign was able to provide medical advice, to practice surgery, and to pass out drugs, but the surgeon and his mate? Hence, like the general practitioner emerging in English provinces during the late eighteenth century who had a knowledge of, or qualifications in medicine, surgery, or pharmacy, McGrigor was a make-shift combination of a physician-surgeon-apothecary.

The typical army surgeon usually came from a humble background, possessed a rough-and-ready practical education in his craft, and he was often treated with contempt by the typical aristocratic officer, who often ignored his advice about sanitary matters. Barely tolerated as a mere civilian camp-follower, the surgeon occupied one of the lowest positions in the rigid social hierarchy of the army. Cited only after the paymaster and the commissary officers in the *Army List* in matters of precedent, the surgeon was usually regarded as an ill-educated "quack" who was neither a soldier nor a gentleman. Army surgery was the lowest step of the medical profession, wrote John Hennen, a prominent London surgeon. "If a man of superior merit by some chance sprang up into it, he soon abandoned the employment for the more lucrative, the more respectable and less sordid work of private practice."[30] This traditional disdain of the army surgeon, who shared none of the titles and honors awarded by the Crown for valor in battle, was apparent in a description of an event in 1788 by Robert Hamilton. He claimed that "when His Majesty [George III] reviewed the camps, no surgeon was allowed to kiss his hand."[31]

Unlike the university-bred McGrigor, the professional attainments of most army surgeons were low, and this accounted for some of the shabby treatment they received from the military. Requirements for additional medical personnel during a war were even lower than in peacetime. As the scope of a campaign widened and the casualties mounted, circumstances forced the army medical authorities to lower their already lenient standards to entice virtually any young man with the rudiments of medical or pharmaceutical knowledge to accept a warrant or a commission. As Hugh Moises, a critic of such practices stated: "I have known men who have served not many months behind the counter of a county apothecary . . . admitted to regimental practice. . . . Mere apprentice boys were appointed as surgeons and mates without exhibiting the proper testimonials of their knowledge or abilities . . ."[32]

George James Guthrie, the most famous British military surgeon of the Peninsular War, bluntly declared that inexperienced medical personnel "were appointed without having served a single day [in a regiment]. They were taken . . . to learn their profession at the expense and great inconvenience . . . of the unfortunate soldiers committed to their care. . . . Sickness and loss of life soon rendered an army ineffective, and diminished its ranks more effectively than the enemy. . ."[33]

One could view surgery attempted on wounded soldiers in the eighteenth century as virtual butchery, except that the general level of surgery performed by civilian surgeons was not much better. Major abdominal surgery was impossible unless the body was relaxed, but general anesthesia was unavailable for operative surgery until 1846, and antiseptic measures in the army were not devised until 1871. To treat casualties, McGrigor had only a limited number of instruments, and medicines. His kit consisted of knives, saws, scalpels, spare blades, tourniquets, and forceps. In addition, he had a supply of lint, sponges, linen, tow, silk and wax for ligatures, whalebone splints, pins, tape, thread, needles, adhesive plaster, some opium, submuriate of mercury, antimonials, phosphoric matches, and a canteen of wine or spirits. This equipment, then, was all that McGrigor had to repair the destruction inflicted upon the human frame during a battle.

Men of the 88th realized the excruciating consequences if they were mutilated in combat and if they reached their surgeon alive. For wounds of the chest or abdomen, McGrigor could do little except to plaster or stitch the external wounds and hope for his patient's recovery. Although civilian surgeons performed some extensive abdominal operations, the chances of survival for severely wounded men were so remote after a battle that the hard-pressed surgeon, toiling amidst scores of lacerated bodies, could not waste time on such dangerous surgery. For mangled arms or legs, the remedy was brutally simple—cut them off. The missiles fired by cannon were so destructive that an amputation was generally regarded as necessary for anything more serious than a simple fracture or a flesh wound that had missed a main artery. In his *Method of Treating Gunshot Wounds* (1744), John Ranby (1703–73), principal surgeon at the Battle of Dettingen and the First Master of the Company of Surgeons, had commented on the pathology of inflammation and of powder wounds. Recommending immediate amputation, especially when there was little hope of saving a damaged limb, Ranby wrote: "The neglecting of this juncture of taking off a limb frequently reduced the patient to so low a state . . . as must unavoidably render the result of subsequent operation, if not entirely unsuccessful, at least exceedingly dubious."[34]

The argument about the proper time to amputate had been debated for decades. Should a surgeon amputate immediately after the injury, or when the patient had recovered from shock, or possibly even some days or even weeks later? Or should he amputate as soon as the local inflammation had subsided? Even the great John Hunter, whom McGrigor greatly admired, was unclear about the timing of amputations in his classic *Treatise on Blood, Inflammation, and Gunshot Wounds* (1794). Regardless of different opinions on this matter, soldiers expected quick amputation rather than having to undergo the intense suffering of the wound and of inflammation. The general rule was to "lop off" the injured limbs as soon as the patients arrived at the field hospital, unless they were in shock. Then warmth and a glass of wine or diluted spirits prepared them for the pending ordeal.

Apart from amputation, most of McGrigor's work after an action would involve bandaging, setting simple fractures and sprains, and probing inside the flesh for foreign bodies. Probing was done with his bare fingers, and he learned to utilize special forceps to remove musket balls. Surgeons thought extraction to be easier if the patient reenacted his stance when initially hit; hence most soldiers were required to stand up for the treatment, if they could.

It seems incredible today that men would willingly submit to such torture. But in the face of death, there was no alternative to the probing, sawing, stitching, and bloodletting that occurred without any kind of anesthesia. The wine and spirits were given to strengthen the patient, not to make him insensible; opiates were provided to rest him after the operation. A soldier was expected to suffer pain, and in that era, pain inflicted in many ways upon the body was perhaps more commonplace to the average man that it is in the modern world. It was part of a soldier's code to undergo an amputation with a stoic sense of unconcern about the loss of a limb. The veteran of the eighteenth century army received little material compensation as a reward for the brutalities of army life, the horrors of warfare, the agony of the wound, the amputation itself, and the long recuperative process. Society regarded a wooden leg, a missing arm, or a patch over a soldier's eye as a badge of courage performed by a man in the line of duty.

The most significant development in military surgery resulted from the work of John Hunter, surgeon general (1790–93), who took surgery into the domain of pathology. One of the most remarkable scientists of the era, Hunter made innumerable discoveries in many fields—anatomy, geology, dentistry, etymology, and zoology. Serving with the army during the Seven Years War, Hunter pondered the problem of healing gunshot wounds. "So little has been written on the subject...," he declared, "that it deserves but little attention."[35] Yet Hunter, too, was obscure about exactly when to operate on a wounded soldier. Probably Hunter operated soon after the injury, but he was unclear about whether he operated after suppuration or after the termination of the first period of inflammation. Contrary to prevailing doctrine about the supposed uniqueness of gunshot wounds, he believed that they were essentially the same as other types of wounds. Hence, Hunter deplored the practice of regimental surgeons who dilated the wound or who attempted immediately to remove foreign bodies from the flesh.

Similar to the state of military medicine in the eighteenth century was that of naval medicine. Yet surgeons in the Royal Navy encountered somewhat different problems of operative surgery aboard warships. Moreover, their accomplishments in preventive medicine signalled a level of sanitary standards that the less progressive army medical service would emulate as it established stricter controls over conditions affecting the welfare of troops during McGrigor's early career.

Due to the vulnerability of seamen to bodily injuries during the normal course of their work, and to increased hazards aboard vessels during sea fights, naval surgeons probably treated a greater range of cuts, burns, wounds, fractures, and dislocations than regimental surgeons. It is this greater diversity of injuries treated by ships' surgeons, and the fact that screening of candidates for the naval medical service by the Company of Barber-Surgeons in London seems to have been stricter than for the army, that may have accounted for the higher level of surgery in the Royal Navy.

A ship's surgeon had to treat wounds caused by cannon balls that could smash a man's body or wrench a limb from its socket, as well as wounds inflicted by chain or grape shot. In the bloody hand-to-hand combat of boarding actions, a sailor could be injured by the fire from small arms, and by lacerations from the pike, bayonet, or the cutlass. Round shot smashing through the hulls of wooden ships often showered lancing splinters on the men that caused horrible jagged wounds. As the fire-power of men-of-war increased, and as more accidents occurred from the misfiring of guns or the unexpected explosion of gunpowder, it was common after an engagement for the surgeon to treat many seamen for severely scorched flesh. Furthermore, during an encounter with the enemy, there was the added danger of broken spars and masts, and masses of rigging toppling down upon helpless crewmen.

The normal occupational hazards of a mariner's life at sea caused serious accidents. While working atopsail, a man could fall to the deck below; he could slip on wet planks, fall down a staircase, topple down a hatchway, or be hit by oars, chains, pulleys, or anchors. During a storm, a cannon, torn from its fastenings, could crush a man's body like a massive projectile. The badly shattered limbs that resulted from such mishaps could only be amputated in most cases. As in the army, it was usually a matter of the patient's limb, or his life. Although regimental surgeons undoubtedly encountered similar battlefield injuries, naval surgeons probably treated more accidents sustained from the normal occupational dangers of life at sea.

In preventive medicine, too, the naval surgeon was probably more accomplished than his military colleague. The classic case in the eighteenth century navy of a sea surgeon's triumph over disease is the search for a remedy to combat scurvy by James Lind (1716–74). Lind's claim that he had found an antidote for scurvy was supported by naval surgeons who shared his pragmatic approach to health problems—Thomas Trotter (1760–1832), and Sir Gilbert Blane (1749–1834).

In maritime lore, there were dozens of so-called remedies for scurvy, and the supposed value of citrus fruit to ward off the disease was familiar to seamen. But until Lind's experiments in 1747, no scientific proof of the value of citrus fruit existed. Long before the antiscorbutic properties of Vitamin C were known, Lind recommended that oranges, lemons, wine, cider, raw onions, pickled cabbage, sauerkraut, fresh vegetables, and so forth supplement the sailor's fare of dried and salted foods. Unfortunately, the great discovery was virtually ignored by naval authorities because of Lind's error in heating the juice before bottling it, the skepticism of other surgeons, the obstinacy of the Navy Victualling Board, and the erroneous experiments comparing citrus fruit and other remedies that were conducted on Captain James Cook's second voyage to the Pacific (1772–75). Not until 1795, in fact, after being convinced by Blane and Trotter of the value of citrus fruit and citrus juice, did the Admiralty provide its crews with such rations. Due to his great achievements in preventive medicine, Lind justifiably ranks as "the father of naval medicine."

The careers of Lind, Blane, and Trotter demonstrate the growing importance of naval medicine in eighteenth century naval warfare. Ship's crews were more frequently exposed to malaria and yellow fever in the Caribbean, to scurvy and the Guinea worm in the Indian Ocean, and to typhus and malnutrition during the grueling blockades of French ports. As physician to the fleet on the West Indian Station during the American Revolution, Blane instigated many improvements in the diet, living quarters, and the hospital care of seamen. Through his compilation of sickness and mortality rates in the fleet, he demonstrated the value of medical statistics to determine the comparative health of the navy. As physician of the Channel fleet during the French Revolution, Trotter studied sea diseases, he innoculated crews against smallpox (1795), and he promoted Dr. Edward Jenner's method of vaccination, which the Admiralty adopted in 1800. These sanitarians, and their lesser known colleagues, persuaded the Admiralty to establish stricter hygienic controls aboard naval vessels— the inspection of recruits; the promulgation of sanitary codes; provisions to improve the cleanliness of crews by the issuance of free soap, more clothing, and by the installation of bathing facilities; betterment of the seaman's diet by careful attention to victualling; efforts to clean, drain, fumigate, and ventilate the ships; and methods to improve the storage and purification of water.

The reasons for the superior level of medical care in the navy compared to the army are not clear. But one may speculate on the influence of various factors upon naval medicine such as the impact of global expansion, the influence of the merchant marine, the relationship of naval architecture, the isolation of a surgeon at sea, and the early organization of naval medical services.

As merchant, privateering, and naval vessels explored strange areas of the world in the sixteenth and seventeenth centuries, ship's surgeons invariably encountered new maladies, strange drugs, exotic spices and herbs, and novel methods of prevention and cure; they discovered that an unknown disease could be as arbitrary as the winds and tides, and as unpredictable as a mysterious coast. During the era of overseas expansion, the sea surgeon probably was the first to encounter tropical diseases. The impact, then, of exploration and of oceanic trade upon nautical medicine was profound. Merchant marine captains serving the great mercantile associations—the Levant Company, the Company of Merchant Adventurers, the East India Company—rigidly supervised the health of their crews. In fact, the East India Company in the seventeenth century had a medical organization that apparently was the forerunner of naval medical services.

It appears that the design of warships was also a factor. As sailing vessels, representing the peak of European technology in the pre-steam age, journeyed on longer voyages, and as they increased in size, weight, and complexity due to architectural modifications, inevitably more man-made environmental problems emerged at sea. Great care had to be exercised in the storage of water, the preservation of food, the location of cargo and supplies, and in the allotment of rations. Moreover, on a large three-decked man-of-war carrying scores of cannon, 600 to 900 men were crammed into tiny spaces and compartments. Such crowded conditions, along with the dangers of poor drainage, constant dampness, and inadequate ventilation created conditions leading to contagious and respiratory diseases. Hence, it was essential that the surgeon (under the watchful authority of the captain) establish strict sanitary regulations. Perhaps, in the self-contained world of an ocean vessel, the ship's officers could more easily regulate living conditions than army officers during a land campaign.

Furthermore, except when he worked on a hospital ship or at a shore hospital, the naval surgeon was probably professionally isolated from his colleagues, for outside medical aid was rarely available to a vessel on the ocean. Thus, the surgeon was almost quite alone with his responsibility on the high seas, and it was this degree of isolation and the urgency of solving critical problems that forced him to delve into the realm of internal medicine and to the dispensing of drugs, regardless of the traditional restrictions on these activities by the physicians and apothecaries. Although it is doubtful that the training of naval surgeons was superior, or that the navy attracted a superior caliber of candidate, or that more naval surgeons made the service their career than did regimental surgeons, perhaps the responsibility for the health of a crew falling upon the surgeon, the freedom while at sea from normal occupational restrictions, and the necessity of keeping men fit and healthy—for seamen were almost irreplacable during a long cruise—may have fostered a more pragmatic attitude as the naval surgeon ventured frequently into medicine.

Apparently the navy pioneered in establishing an early public health service. Due to the distribution of squadrons scattered over the oceans, and to the continual flow of sick and disabled seamen through home ports, the Admiralty in the late sixteenth century developed a comprehensive medical organization for its seamen. The navy had a Sick and Hurt Board in 1653; in 1703 rules for hospital ships were issued; and in 1731 the navy had regulations for the conduct of surgeons and for the care of the sick and wounded. Decades before the army, the navy had standardized the equipment required in a surgeon's chest. And nothing in the military world matched the care of the sick, aged, and infirm at Haslar, Greenwich, and Plymouth hospitals. The state of naval medical services, in fact, was unmatched by the army until the early nineteenth century. McGrigor and his fellow regimental surgeons had the task of elevating military medicine to the level of naval medicine.

Soon after McGrigor joined his regiment at Chatham for the first time, he had opportunities to test his new skills in curing the sick and in healing the wounded. Confident of his abilities and anxious for adventures overseas, the ambitious Scot was determined to make a reputation in the army as a dedicated surgeon and to emerge from the forthcoming campaign with distinction.

But during his first night in the barracks, two drunken officers had a bitter argument that resulted in the death of one of the hot-heads. "This incident," recalled McGrigor, "took great hold of my mind, and doubtless of life after, by making me cautious and studious to avoid brandy-and-water parties at night." Virtually abstaining from drink, McGrigor tried to avoid the carousing activities of some of his fellow junior officers. Nevertheless, to his dismay, McGrigor learned that regimental tales about his supposed enormous drinking capacity were common knowledge and that according to the gossip, he was "not the least affected by the immense potations I had shared in." After convincing his commander of the truth, the embarrassed McGrigor swore to avoid heavy drinking. These events, he recalled, "made a deep impression on my mind; and during the eleven years I remained in the 88th regiment, as well as afterwards, I was known as one of the most temperate members of the mess."[36]

In June, 1794, the Rangers were ordered to active duty on the Channel Island of Jersey. Jersey was then a refuge of Frenchmen fleeing the Reign of Terror. "And the island teemed with exiles," stated McGrigor, "boats coming daily from the opposite coast with fugitives, males and females, and not a boat arrived without bringing account of fresh victims of the guillotine . . . ."[37]

On Jersey, McGrigor encountered a mysterious foe far more insidious than the French enemy across the Channel—the dreaded typhus. Commonly known as jail fever, ship fever, camp fever, or hospital fever, typhus was the scourge of European armies. The pestilence thrived on a combination of factors such as cold, filth, dampness, undernourishment, unsanitary and overcrowded living conditions that prevailed whenever large numbers of men were confined or assembled under unhygienic conditions. It invariably occurred whenever their clothing was vermin-ridden or when their daily companions were rats. A decisive breakthrough in the conception and practice of medicine had not occurred, and few physicians speculated on a germ theory of disease. Nor did they suspect that the deadly intracellular typhus parasite was transmitted by the all-too-familiar louse that infested the bodies, garments, and quarters of sailors and soldiers.

Fifty men from the 88th died on the island, and McGrigor himself contracted the disease. He was treated by Dr. Robert Jackson, the surgeon of the 3rd Foot, who alternately applied cold water to McGrigor's body and caused his skin to blister.[38] The second phase of the treatment was to induce the patient to regurgitate for prolonged periods, and to extract large quantities of his blood in order to remove the so-called "impurities" from the circulatory system.

While recuperating from his illness, and from the treatment, McGrigor learned that his regiment was sailing for Holland. Although unfit for duty, nevertheless, McGrigor pleaded for permission to accompany the Rangers and convinced his superiors that he would soon be cured. His first adventure with the 88th began as he voyaged in July to the Dutch coast.

# II

## THE FLANDERS CAMPAIGN

Since April, 1792, Austria and Prussia had unsuccessfully waged the War of the First Coalition against the French Revolution. Their invasion of France was routed in September, and Jacobin armies poured into the Rhineland and into Flanders. Ideologically opposed to the Revolution and fearful of French aggression in the Low Countries, England allied with the conservative monarchies and contributed an army to the struggle. In March, 1793, Frederick (1763–1827), the Duke of York and Albany and the second son of George III, landed in Holland with his command.

During the first year of the British effort on the Continent, York fought an indecisive campaign; by the spring of 1794 his command clung to defenses along the Scheldt. Then the French smashed the Austrian and Prussian positions and cracked the Anglo-Dutch force in Flanders. Unable to hold a line in Belgium, York's army retreated in July over Holland's rivers and estuaries. As British reinforcements were landing during the summer on the Dutch coast, the entire Allied right flank disintegrated. Placing an army between the English and the Austrians, the French lunged up the Flemish coast and then proceeded to attack Dutch ports such as Bergen-op-Zoom where the 88th and other regiments were disembarking.[1]

The Rangers soon found themselves huddling behind Bergen's ramparts against the enemy's bombardment. In the besieged city, McGrigor encountered the mysterious typhus fever carried by sickly troops from Chatham, Jersey, and Southampton in damp, crowded ships. The infection spread rapidly through the louse-ridden ranks, and soon the young surgeon had to treat 200 incapacitated men. Searching for a building in which to house them, McGrigor displayed a degree of initiative that typified his activity during an emergency. With the aid of a sergeant's guard, the young Scot commandeered a chapel, and, ignoring the furious protests of the indignant minister and congregation, converted it into a hospital.

Clinging to a 90-mile front in Holland as the Austrians retreated further and further to the Rhine, York garrisoned five fortresses—Bergen, Breda, Hertogenbosch, Graves and Nijmegen. Yet under constant attack, the defense of Bergen became untenable, and York had to withdraw his troops from the city. At Williamstadt, the 88th was inspected by the worried York, who asked McGrigor about the health of his men. The Rangers were then ordered to reinforce a Dutch-Hanoverian force under Lieutenant General Johan Ludwig von Walmoden at Nijmegen, the key to the defense of the Waal River.

In the meantime, Amsterdam and The Hague capitulated to the French, who swept up to Dutch coastline to cut off York's army. After capturing Bergen, the enemy proceeded to invest the next fortresses in the allied line. By luck, the French discovered a weak line at Boxtel, and here they probed for an opening. At Boxtel, on September 14, Arthur Wellesley, a young lieutenant colonel in the 33rd Infantry, demonstrated his coolness in battle as he skillfully extricated his regiment from the attack.

As the Jacobins attacked the fortresses in September, the condition of the English army, cut off from supplies and left without assistance in bleak and hostile terrain, became desperate. Mrs. Elizabeth Harcourt, wife of General William Harcourt, a staff officer with York, predicted that "winter quarters on the frontier of Holland would ruin our army. The effect would be like the West Indies, and disease would destroy those the sword has spared."[2] In a similar vein, Captain William Harness of the 80th regiment lamented in a letter to his wife that "the season is very wet, and men become sickly. We have three hundred in the hospital."[3]

The troops arrived in Nijmegen where they expected to find respite from the campaign and a haven during the winter. Writing in early October, the observant Mrs. Harcourt described the difficulties in defending the city:

The town stands on a gravely hill along the river; the country is dry and hilly . . . very unlike the rest of Holland. A branch of the Rhine River runs close to the town, over which, at a place which is 350 yards broad, our troops have built a bridge, not of boats, but of ships, to facilitate a retreat. The position of the army is alarming; the French are in immense force on the other side of the Muese. The river is narrow in the part, so that in four hours, the enemy can, if they choose, throw pontoon bridges over it in several parts, at once, and attack where they think it most advantageous.[4]

By October 27, Nijmegen was under heavy attack. "Day after day," commented McGrigor, "the enemy advanced their approaches... and at length, the place was completely invested from one side of the river to the other..."[5] General Walmoden sent out troops on November 4 to repel the French penetration of his outer defenses, but the Jacobins ringed the city even tighter. One night, remembered McGrigor, the entire horizon was lighted by the intensive bombardment:

An immense French force hemmed us in daily closer and closer. The cannonade from the walls became constantly heavier, as we endeavoured to annoy them in advancing their second parallel. Their shot at length took effect on many parts of the town, and in some streets the houses were completely riddled. The large church, in which my sick and wounded, with those of other corps were placed, was not spared; although an hospital flag was on the steeple. While engaged in dressing the wounds, I saw several cannon go through the walls, and some shells burst into the church.[6]

As the French penetrated Nijmegen on November 7, Walmoden prepared to evacuate his men over a bridge crossing the Waal. McGrigor was in the trenches with his regiment when he discovered that the army was withdrawing from the city. After waiting agonizing hours, the Rangers were finally ordered to evacuate their positions before the moon rose. "All had hitherto been darkness," stated McGrigor, "but as we were crossing the bridge, the moon began to rise."[7] The garrison scurried along the collapsing bridge as the French lobbed shells along the line of retreat. As the allied regiments retreated over the river, the last of York's fortresses toppled, and his army was forced to defend the north bank of the Waal in freezing weather.

The French did not halt their offensive and repeatedly probed for an opening. Describing his arduous duty, Wellesley wrote that "The French kept us in a perpetual state of alarm we turned out sometimes twice a night; the officers and men ware harrassed to death. I have not had the clothing off my back for a long time and generally spend the great part of the night on the bank of the river."[8] Quartered in sodhuts on the river's edge, the troops lacked food, fuel, and clothing, while typhus and dysentery took a heavy toll of the shivering and emaciated men.[9]

The key factor in the defense of the swift-flowing Waal was that ice had not formed to provide a passage for the French. In Arnheim, Mrs. Harcourt stated: "I hope no frost will come to make a bridge for the French over the Waal, and things may mend. Trouble for us if it freezes."[10] Until late December, the British maintained their precarious position and repeatedly repulsed French efforts to land troops on the north banks. But in the meantime, the Dutch armies surrendered, the Austrians retreated to the Rhine, and the Prussians withdrew from the war; and in late November, to avoid placing the stigma of defeat on His Royal Highness, York was recalled to London for consultation. To add to the difficulties of the demoralized redcoats, the coldest winter since 1739 swept over the Lowlands and now the Waal became passable for the French. "The ice was so strong," wrote Captain L. T. Jones, "that regiments of cavalry with the heaviest cannon, could cross without the least fear of its giving way."[11] As rivers, polders, and canals froze in late December, the Jacobins swept up these icy highways, seized the entire Dutch coast, captured the Orangeist fleet in the ice of the Zuider Zee, and drove the enemy out of Holland. In a new intensity of cold and bitterness, the battered British staggered out of the Lowlands hoping to reach the distant ports of north Germany.

In the tragic retreat of the doomed Anglo-German forces in 1795, the ministerial neglect of the army became painfully apparent. The supply lines, manned by the newly formed Royal Corps of Waggoners, a collection of ruffians called the "Newgate Blues" in dubious honor of the famous prison, began to collapse. The inadequacies of medical services—shortages of personnel, lack of medicine, and mishaps in the conveyance of the sick—were all revealed. Dumped into open wagons or canal barges in freezing weather, casualties were carelessly transported to general hospitals at Rhenen and Arnheim, and to the few remaining Dutch ports still held by the British. Stunned by his visit to embarking ships filled with dying men, Sir Jeremiah Fitzpatrick, the inspector of health for the Land Forces, wrote Home Secretary William Dundas that "the unfortunate men were. . . . inhumanly treated." In his former post as inspector general of prisons in Ireland, Fitzpatrick had often witnessed the degradation of convicts, but he was shocked at the state of hospitals at Arnheim, where "such misery and wretchedness as I found can scarcely be described."[12]

The general hospital system typical of eighteenth century military operations, usually adequate for a relatively static campaign, failed because the steady retreat of troops across the Lowlands necessitated the constant shifting of casualties to new hospital locations at the rear of fluid battle lines. Furthermore, as McGrigor put it, "the want of system at this time, and the inexperience of the medical officers were at this time striking."[13] Civilian physicians, appointed to supervise the general hospitals, were unfamiliar with army routines and were unable to supervise the handling of thousands of sick troops; they could not even maintain discipline in the wards. As supervision in the hospitals deteriorated, the treatment of patients worsened, and as a consequence, the general hospitals became notorious for their reputedly callous treatment of helpless men. William Fergusson, a surgeon with the 80th regiment, claimed that "regimental hospitals were all but unknown, and in the general hospitals, there was neither system, or control, or rule of management. As soon as circumstances pressed, every hospital consequently became a pest house—a deadly drain upon the effective strength of the army."[14]

"In these hospitals," remarked McGrigor, "disease, particularly typhus fever, became general. Our hospitals were filled with overflowing and the mortality among medical officers was particularly great."[15] So infamous was the reputation of the general hospitals, called "slaughter houses" by the rank and file, that orders for the sick to report to infirmaries were regarded as virtual death-warrants.[16]

The scarecrow army was further handicapped by a scarcity of shelter from the wintry blasts. "Our troops," remembered McGrigor, "raw and composed in a great measure of new levies gave way under the harassing marches, bad quarters, and the toil to which they were exposed."[17] So great was the primitive need for housing that some British troops fought with their own countrymen to determine which regiment could occupy a barn or a farmhouse during a storm. Even help from the Dutch, many of whom were Jacobin sympathizers, was not forthcoming. Many Dutchmen, more partisan to the French cause than to the Allied and furious at the looting by English-German troops, refused them aid. Under these circumstances, Walmoden's officers feared leaving their sick with the peasants. "In many instances," reported Captain Jones, "[the Dutch] were so barbarous as to let the troops die at their doors, sooner than offer them shelter . . ."[18]

Through the German states the retreat continued with the French in close pursuit. From Deventer on January 22, Mrs. Harcourt, gamely accompanying her husband, remarked "The march of our army, over the most dreary wastes . . . was shocking beyond description. No tree, no house was there to shelter our troops, nothing but wild heather, covered with snow, and the severest frost that was ever known."[19] Driven over the Leck and Yssel rivers, the remnants of York's command staggered to the Ems in early February. "The strongest men," explained McGrigor, "worn down by harassing fatigue succumbed daily, and thinned our ranks. In the extreme cold, the soldiers lay down in the snow by the road-side, overpowered with drowsiness and all the entreaties of the officers could not make them move on."[20] So enormous was the sick-list, and so helpless were the medical contigents, that carts full of dying soldiers were left behind to perish in the frozen wastes. "Without covering, without atten-dance," exclaimed the horrified Corporal Brown of the Coldstream Guards, "and insufficient shelter from the weather, they are thrown together in heaps, unpitied and unprotected, to perish by conta-gion."[21] Writing to his family on February 26, from Osnabruck in Hanover, McGrigor lamented that "of the 1000 poor fellows, who came to the Continent with the 88th we this day muster only 100 fit for duty. . . . The enemy still continued to pursue and we to retreat in the best manner fighting now and then."[22] For the young surgeon, the harrowing journey over a foreboding white landscape strewn with broken wagons, frozen pack-horses, and piles of human corpses was an unforgettable nightmare.

After weeks of misery and privation, the remains of York's com-mand in late March neared the Weser. Exhausted from marching, McGrigor and two officers stumbled upon a farmhouse that provided shelter for the night. Desperate for sleep, McGrigor was grateful for a bed. He forgot his own medical training, for he neglected to re-move his wet clothes and wearily tumbled to rest. "When the drums beat to arms at a very early hour in the morning," the Scot noted, "I felt very ill; my limbs benumbed, and with a deadly faintness, I was sensible at once that I had got the deadly typhus, which had so thinned our ranks." Unwilling to leave their surgeon to the French pickets, McGrigor's companions dragged him onto a horse, and placed him prostrate across the animal's back. With the aid of soldiers to hold his head and feet, McGrigor was carried off with his regiment. "Awful as my position was," he admitted, "I found that after re-maining in the open air, I had revived a good deal since starting."

His sickness worsened as the 88th neared the coast, and the de-lirious McGrigor had to be placed in a horse-drawn cart. Awakening two days later in a mud-hovel, the fever-stricken surgeon was startled to learn that his regiment was embarking. Insisting that he be conveyed to the harbor, McGrigor was placed in a wagon and taken to the docks. A naval officer spied McGrigor, helped him into a long-boat, and with the aid of a chair and pulley, assisted the sick man onto a ship. "At sea," McGrigor said, "I gained appetite and strength wonderfully; and by the time we cast anchor at Yarmouth, I was able to come on deck."[23]

This horribly bungled expedition, which tragically revealed the weakness of British military power on the Continent, ended with the complete evacuation of the remaining 16,000 British troops from northern Europe. Not until 1808, in fact, were the British able to maintain a foothold on the Continent against the French juggernaut. Although the Flanders campaign had little immediate effect in improving the medical department, it inspired the disillusioned Duke of York, an inept strategist but a capable administrator who became commander in chief (1798-1809; 1811-1827), to initiate a series of military reforms for the army. The humanitarian York gradually reformed the demoralized regiments, but a sarcastic British public, less impressed by his talents, lampooned the duke for the Flanders fiasco in a famous doggerel:

> The noble Duke of York
> He had ten thousand men,
> He marched them up to the top of the hill,
> And he marched them down again.

In the Flanders campaign were at least two other military officers who became famous. Major General Sir Ralph Abercrombie, who trudged with his men to north Germany, later led an expedition to the West Indies with the Connaught Rangers and then commanded a British army in Egypt. In Flanders too was Arthur Wellesley (1769–1852), the future Duke of Wellington. Entering the army in 1787, Wellesley, by influence and purchase, became a lieutenant colonel in six years. His first campaign, the retreat across Holland through Germany, was a dreary affair for him. When asked in 1839 what he had observed in the Lowlands about warfare, Wellesley replied: "Why, I learnt what one ought not to do, and that is always something."[24] On another occasion, Wellesley remarked that "the system was wretched. I learned more by seeing our faults and the effects of our system in the campaign in Holland than anywhere else. It has always been a marvel to me," he concluded, "how any one of us escaped."[25] In his introduction to war, Wellesley had seen a campaign fought under the worst circumstances—a divided command, untrustworthy allies, an inefficient supply line, a civilian population that preferred the enemy to its defenders, and the results of a prolonged and chaotic retreat during a harsh winter when disease decimated an army. Although the British lost 6,000 troops in the retreat from Holland, only one-tenth of this number died from combat injuries.[26] The rest were stricken by typhus and other diseases.

What is particularly significant about the defeat of the unreformed British army in this disaster is that it was pitted against Jacobin forces, animated by a fiery patriotism and determined to win decisive victories in a single season rather than to retire to winter quarters, as soldiers had done for centuries, to await the spring harvest of grain for men and the availability of forage for horses. In the Flanders campaign, the British army, cut off from its winter cantonments, had to retreat across hostile country in the bitter cold, short of transport and unaided by the civilian population. Thus the novel French method of seeking quick victories would require adjustments in the medical organization of the British army to match the changing nature of warfare.

For McGrigor, embittered by the inefficiency of the medical department and the callous treatment of the men, the expedition was a morbid initiation to medical practice during warfare. Over half the men in his own regiment had perished during the campaign.[27] Like Wellesley, McGrigor also learned "what one ought not to do." His efforts to improve military medicine, to alleviate the misery of the sick and wounded, and to dignify the medical profession began in the ordeal of the Flanders campaign.

# III

## THE WEST INDIAN CAMPAIGN

After the Flanders campaign, McGrigor remained in the 88th. During the spring of 1795, the regiment was strengthened with additional recruits, and it was ordered to another garrison. In May, the Rangers marched to Norwich, the leading provincial center of republicanism in England, in order to reinforce troops stationed there.

A quasi-Jacobin club known as the Norwich Revolutionary Society flourished in that traditional stronghold of religious dissent and of independent craftsmen.[1] The Norwich Revolutionary Society modelled its program and activities on the pattern of the London Corresponding Society and the London Constitutional Society, which stressed the necessity of reforming an oligarchical Parliament and the urgency of redressing numerous social and economic inequities. By 1795, the popular agitation for the transformation of an unjust society into a humanitarian brotherhood of man became increasingly vociferous in leading provincial manufacturing centers like Norwich, Bristol, Sheffield, and Birmingham. There, political clubs voiced increasingly radical views about society because of an economic recession in industrial areas, the phenomenal popularity of Tom Paine's *Rights of Man* in the ranks of literate workingmen, and the inevitable comparison between an unreformed Parliament in London and the democratic National Convention in Paris.

By May, when Rangers reported for duty in Norwich, English Jacobin activity, in the view of the Crown's minister, was seditious, treasonous, and increasingly dangerous to a nation fighting revolutionary France. As a loyal officer who had overcome his youthful sympathy for radicalism, McGrigor remembered the difficulties that his regiment encountered in Norwich:

On our first arrival, the officers could hardly appear in the streets without insults from the populace. At night, if they went out, they were knocked down; and attempts were even made to sow dissaffection among the soldiers. Desertions became frequent, and at length so numerous, that it was not an unusual occurrence for twenty or thirty men of the garrison to desert in a night. We found that there was a society in Norwich for the encouragement of desertion. It was amply supplied with funds, and the members of this society provided them with . . . clothes and money, and then dispatched them to their respective homes. . . . [But] in the course of time, and after the soldiers had many encounters with the townspeople, we got the mastery of the democrats or levellers as they were then called. . . . and an association of respectable tradesmen was formed against republicanism.[2]

However, the young surgeon was more concerned with the health of his men than with the turmoil of local politics, for that perennial enemy, typhus, struck the garrison. The Medical Board instructed McGrigor to establish a temporary hospital, an administrative duty that he fulfilled until relieved by an army physician. Soon cured of the disease and reinforced with more Irishmen, the Rangers moved to Southampton to join troops preparing for an expedition to the West Indies. At Southampton, as the 88th prepared for the next adventure overseas, its new commanding officer arrived—Lieutenant Colonel William Carr Beresford.

Beresford was a tough soldier who assumed that most of the injuries and diseases in regimental ranks were feigned by shiftless and untrustworthy troops, and that the sickness of soldiers generally resulted from their own slovenliness, their drunkenness, and from what was usually termed "other irregularities of the men." McGrigor noted that "from the hour the new Colonel arrived to take command of the regiment, his temper appeared bitter, and his conduct harsh. He was perhaps dissatisfied with the state in which he found the regiment." Beresford repeatedly complained that the daily sick roll was incorrect, and that it exaggerated the actual degree of sickness. In a particularly foul mood one day as he perused McGrigor's morning report, Beresford blurted: "This state of things must not continue. I will not have such a number of sick in my regiment, and I am sure the greater part of them are not sick."

Beresford's reproach hurt the sensitive McGrigor. Due to his academic training, his military experience, and his study of current medical literature, he regarded himself professionally qualified. In contrast to the filthy living conditions in the barracks, over which he had no jurisdiction and which he regarded as "a nursery for disease," McGrigor, an ardent disciple of Sir John Pringle, had labored to maintain hygienic standards in his regimental hospital in order to prevent typhus:

With the constant arrival of recruits, not in the cleanest state, accompanied with numerous families, I saw the probability of the reappearance of an old enemy—the typhus, from the habitual drunkedness and other irregularities of the men. There was much fever prevalent, which, I foresaw would degenerate into typhus, and I did everything to keep the hospital sweet and well ventilated. I think that I succeeded, for its clean and cheerful appearance attracted the notice of all the officers.[3]

Although McGrigor insisted that the men listed on sick call were actually ill, he was unable to convince the skeptical colonel, who stormed that the troops were shirking their duty. Beresford then made an unannounced inspection of the regimental barracks, and in the process he became increasingly angered with his line officers for neglecting to supervise the cleansing of the quarters. McGrigor anxiously waited until his temperamental commander passed through the sick wards, and then he asked Beresford for suggestions to improve the hospital. To his delight, Beresford made no criticism; on the contrary, he praised McGrigor's hospital and ordered his staff to consider it as a model of cleanliness for the regiment.

Yet the tension between the colonel and his surgeon increased. Beresford berated McGrigor for missing a parade inspection. McGrigor stoutly contended that his first duty was to the sick and not to a military formation. Weary of the incessant quarrelling, McGrigor contemplated an "exchange" into another regiment. Beresford was astounded when he discovered that McGrigor planned to quit the 88th. The colonel apologized for his outbursts and informed the disgruntled surgeon that the medical department was the only satisfactory one in the entire regiment. "In short," McGrigor concluded, "we became friends, warm friends, and continued so ever after."[4]

In August, Beresford led the Rangers to Portsmouth where an army under the command of Sir Ralph Abercrombie was preparing to embark for the Caribbean. Abercrombie's expedition was part of a steady stream of men and ships sent to the West Indies since 1793 to seize French colonies—an effort that had been blunted by the fatalities of troops from the ravages of disease, the insurrections of slaves clamoring for emancipation, and the activities of French revolutionaries in Caribbean waters.

In a global war with a European colonial power, the traditional opening move by Britain in the eighteenth century was to attack enemy possessions in the Caribbean. The colonies were relatively easy to assault and were generally difficult to defend. William Pitt the

Younger, the prime minister, reasoned that the seizure of the French sugar isles would hurt the economy of the French Republic. As France increased her hegemony over Europe, Pitt enlarged British territorial ambitions in the Caribbean to encompass the seizure of the West Indian possessions of Spain and Holland. Moreover, the Ministry could not ignore pleas from influential British West Indian planters in Jamaica and Barbados, who were horrified at the bloody insurrections of ex-slaves in the French-Spanish colony of Hispaniola (Haiti and Santo Domingo), and who feared invasions by revolutionaries with their negro and Black Carib cohorts.[5]

Although the British had battled their enemies in the Indies for over two centuries, their naval and military forces were ill prepared for campaigning in the tropics. England had lost thousands of seamen and soldiers in West Indian warfare to malaria and yellow fever. "The Caribbean Islands have always proved unhealthy and fatal to the European constitution," lamented Dr. John Rollo of the Artillery in 1780, "but none so peculiarly as the Soldier. The Nature of his Duty exposed him to meridian heat, and midnight Air, to every Species of Fatigue and to every Cause which can possibly produce Disease."[6] Dr. John Hunter of Jamaica (no relation to his more famous medical namesakes) published in 1788 some evidence about the enormous sickness and mortality rates of troops stationed in the Indies. He demonstrated that within four and a half years during the American Revolutionary War over 5,000 troops perished from disease on Jamaica without participating in combat.[7] Similar proof of the morbidity of the Caribbean environment was provided by Gilbert Blane, physician to the fleet, who stated that from 1780 to 1783, naval vessels on the West Indian station lost 3,200 men—exclusive of deaths from encounters with the enemy. These casualties were due to fever, "fluxes," scurvy, ulcers, smallpox, dysentery, rheumatism, and "pectoral"complaints.[8]

While the navy, under the inspiration of James Lind, Gilbert Blane, and Thomas Trotter, had progressed in preventive medicine, the army lagged behind. In a significant work on military hygiene written in 1791, John Bell, a former surgeon of the 94th Infantry in the Caribbean, stated the necessity for an official army sanitary code to match that of the navy:

. . . as I thought it was much wanted from having observed the little attention paid to preserving the health of soldiers, compared with that which is bestowed on the navy. . . . We have had several books written on the diseases of the army, containing observations equally applicable to the treatment of the same diseases among any other description of men. But the peculiar causes which ruin the health of the British army in the West Indies, so far as I know, have neither been fully stated, nor has any attempt been made to effectively remove them.[9]

A major difficulty in checking the destructiveness of a pestilence like yellow fever that obliterated regiments from the Barbados to Grenada was that tropical medicine was unrecognized as a medical specialty, nor was it an object of scientific research. Furthermore, army surgeons were unable to differentiate from among a bewildering variety of fevers and other symptoms, and they were totally unaware of the bacteriological origins of diseases carried by malignant microscopic organisms found in water, and on insects and rodents. Although scurvy was gradually being eliminated in the services since the 1770s and smallpox would be checked in both the army and navy after 1800 due to Dr. Edward Jenner's discovery of vaccination, no cure was discovered for yellow fever. Only preventive measures could limit the effects of yellow fever—called Black Vomit, Yellow Jack, Havana Fever, Guinea Fever, Benin Fever, or Boullam Fever. Similar to the prevailing confusion in describing a variety of dietary diseases such as scurvy, attempts to classify fevers had resulted only in confusion.

There was general agreement, however, about the treatment. Venesection was usually recommended along with blistering, sudorifics and emetics. Medicinal remedies consisted of doses of opium, mixtures of antimonials diluted with wine, or Peruvian Bark compounded with wine or rhubarb. Peruvian or Jesuits' Bark was the cinchona from which quinine was extracted after 1820, but the drug was difficult to digest, it was unpalatable, and medical authorities in the eighteenth century disagreed about its remedial virtues. Not until 1854, in fact, was the efficacy of Peruvian Bark recognized in medical circles as a valuable prophylactic against fever. Still another panacea given to feverish patients was the famed Dr. James's Powder, a mixture of antimony and phosphate of lime, known as the aspirin of the eighteenth century. Army doctors lacked an understanding of the underlying pathology of disease, and they followed the contemporary climatological belief that pestilence lurked in the "miasmata," and in the supposedly poisonous vapors of swamps, marshes, and rivers.

Hence, they tried to cure their patients with such drugs, bled them, induced profused sweating, and administered body-wracking purgatives to remove the so-called impurities of the blood. For virtually all diseases that afflicted soldiers in the tropics, from colic to ulcers of the legs, as well as fevers, the surgeons used such medicines and treatments.

However, certain environmental factors, if controlled by man, could have eliminated some dangers. Army surgeons were aware of the problems due to insect-bites, dietary deficiencies, impure water, unhealthy barrack locations, primitive lavatory facilities, and overcrowded conditions aboard ship. Medical writers pondered the peculiarities of diseases in the tropics, but official army handbooks, containing "common sense" instructions about hygiene and sanitation, were not available. Not until 1795, for example, did the War Office issue sanitary regulations about troopships.[10] By then, the authorities were considering Sir Jeremiah Fitzpatrick's suggestion to replace the traditional rule of alloting two tons of a transport's tonnage per soldier for a more sensible and humanitarian standard of a specific amount of cubic feet of space per man.[11]

Soldiers often spent weeks on a vessel before sailing, many months at sea in damp and crowded quarters, and they seldom had enough fresh provisions, or sufficient room or ventilation below decks. As a consequence, an expeditionary force, usually with some sickly recruits from the start, invariably was stricken by disease on a voyage. Many troops arrived at their new posts incapacitated for general duty. Although the best sailing times for passage to Bombay or Barbados were common maritime knowledge, and although admirals attempted to take advantage of sailing with favorable winds and of landing in the Caribbean during cooler months, the exigencies of naval warfare often altered such plans. Like the seasonal aspects of European land campaigns, seaborne expeditions were also conditioned by the rhythm of the seasons for each geographical area. Although the Royal Navy endeavored to determine the safest time to embark, convoy, and land troops on a distant shore, inevitably there were obstacles to such foresight. The operations of the Admiralty in reassigning scarce shipping to other areas of war, the delays in mobilizing an army for overseas duty, and the hazards of unexpected storms at sea that could force a fleet to spend additional weeks on the ocean, often drastically altered the most judicious plan for a campaign. Due to such unpredictable circumstances, instead of leading fresh and acclimatized troops into combat, a general often found himself relatively immobilized with a sickly army that was ill from weeks of close confinement at sea, or that was landed during the rainy season or in the hottest month.

Warfare in the tropics was different from campaigning in Europe, but nevertheless officers accustomed to cooler climates determined strategy in the Caribbean. As a result, a number of factors relating to the West Indian environment were often overlooked. The necessity of seizing a key enemy bastion, as in European wars, also operated in the Indies, but citadels and garrisons on the sugar isles were inevitably located near pestilential lowlands areas. Surgeons were aware of an apparent causative relationship between a regiment's health and its location at higher and cooler hill stations, but the strategic necessity that a military bastion be located near the coast predominated over the health factor. As William Fergusson commented about his service in Santo Domingo:

In the West Indies, I found medical opinion equally at discount. The convenience of the engineers, the whim of the Quarter Master General or General Commanding, and the profit of the contractor seemed alone to be considered. There was not a station in the command where the health of the troops seemed to have been thought of, or a health opinion asked for.[12]

Likewise, little thought was devoted to a comfortable uniform, to a suitable diet, or to problems of the sheer physical limitations of white men in a hot climate who were required to march and to fight as if they were in northern Europe. Troops still wore the traditional redcoat and cumbersome headgear as they stood guard or in parade under a broiling sun. They usually ate the same daily ration of hard biscuit and fresh or salted meat served as the traditional diet to generations of troops, even though the Caribbean provided an abundance of fish, fowl, fruit, and vegetables. To quench their thirst, they often drank brackish water or inferior grades of rum. On a campaign, troops laden with gear marched through steamy jungles and hauled ponderous cannon through insect-infested terrain. Yet, regardless of the heavy casualty rates, the islands were considered well worth the enormous cost in men and money.

As Britain enlarged her West Indian garrisons during the Seven Years War and the War of the American Revolution, navy and army surgeons described their experiences in the Caribbean and pointed out the necessity for prophylactic measures to protect the health of troops in this seemingly morbific environment. On the eve of the French Revolution, numerous medical works by Lind and his naval colleagues and at least five studies by army doctors provided advice about acclimatization in the Indies.

Although intelligible descriptions of yellow fever had existed since the seventeenth century, and although other treatises on tropical medicine were written in the English language during the eighteenth century, James Lind's *Essay on Diseases Incidental to Europeans in Hot Climates* (1768) was the first scientific treatment of tropical disease, and his work became the standard commentary on the subject for the next fifty years. Devoting a chapter in his book to diseases of the West Indies, Lind described these maladies by their prevailing gruesome nomenclature—Black Vomit, the Bloody Flux, the Dry Belly Ache. Appalled by accounts of yellow fever during a British attack upon Havana in 1763, Lind warned of the dangers emanating from stagnant water, from a careless selection of an anchorage near a pestilent coast, the putrefaction of food under a torrid sun, and the irritating bites of flies and mosquitoes. In this pioneering handbook of survival techniques in the tropics, Lind noted that "a total ignorance of these important matters, or inattention to them, are in commanders-in-chief, highly blamable, as well as extremely dangerous: the lives of thousands may be lost by it."[13]

Apparently, the first British army doctor who wrote from actual experience about military medicine in the West Indies was John Rollo, a surgeon on St. Lucia from 1778 to 1779, whose essay was published in 1783. Noting the lack of medical information available to combat disease in the Caribbean, he stated: "We acknowledge, that we met with many difficulties, and often regretted our Deficiency in Experience...." Writing in the typical climatological fashion of the period, he commented that "in general, we believe those who reside in the Windward parts of the Island, and those Parts not exposed to the noxious Effluvia of Marshes and Woods, are in the most salutary Places of Abodes."[14]

Another of these writers was John Bell, whose study appeared in 1791. Bell was less concerned about theories of disease than about offering practical suggestions concerning improving hygienic standards for troops. He advocated a canteen system, the improvement of hospital diet, the establishment of an army medical school for regimental surgeons, and he recommended that medical officers be consulted in the building of barracks and hospitals in the Indies. His most important contribution, however, was to castigate the cherished army practice of providing daily issues of rum to the troops. According to popular legends, rum and other spiritous liquors were supposed to have regenerative powers necessary to sustain a white man in the tropics. The army apportioned rations every morning to entire garrisons from the youngest drummer boy to the most hardened veteran in order to enable the men to withstand fatigue and to ward off the supposedly pernicious effects of the morning fogs. Bell criticized this practice which he claimed inevitably contributed to the physical debilitation of the rank and file. He urged that troops be provided with a daily breakfast before duty, and that the rum ration be severely curtailed or that it be replaced by porter.[15] But Bell's suggestions were virtually ignored until the 1830s.

Judging from the number of editions, the most influential work in this field of medicine was written in 1788 by Dr. John Hunter of Jamaica. He staunchly advocated standards of cleanliness and also hospital registers to record the progress and treatment of disease. "A plan of this kind," he explained, "may greatly contribute to improving our knowledge of disease, in all the various climates to which the possessions of the British empire extend, and by enabling us to take better care of the health of seamen and soldiers, prove a national benefit."[16] Hunter urged the compilation of a medical handbook on hygiene because ". . . the useful experience of one war has been lost before the commencement of another. It would seem to be a proper time at the conclusion of the present, to collect the useful lessons we have so dearly purchased, and to deduce from them the best regulations for preventing similar misfortunes in future."[17] Though baffled about the origins, prevention, and cure of diseases, army surgeons thus offered some sensible advice about the adaptation of an army to the Caribbean. But whether military officers heeded this advice is difficult to determine.

The war in the West Indies began in April, 1793, when the British quickly captured Tobago from the enemy. Taking advantage of the inability of French authorities on Hispaniola to quell the racial war underway between ex-slaves and their former masters, the British invaded the island and seized some coastal settlements. But an English effort in June to seize Martinique was repulsed, and the British command in Barbados requested reinforcements in order to renew the campaign.

The Pitt Ministry had decided that the opportunity to dominate the verdant Caribbean isles, which offered Britain a veritable cornucopia of valuable raw materials, was even more vital than a decisive victory in Flanders. Hence the government dispatched an expedition in November consisting of 6,000 troops under General Sir Charles Grey and Admiral John Jervis to the Barbados.[18] Due to limited evidence, it is difficult to determine whether Grey heeded medical authorities in his preparations for the expedition. On October 8, 1793, John Hunter, the surgeon general, (1790–93) offered the following advice to Grey about the tropics:

Doctor Hunter's "Observations on the Diseases of Jamaica", being generally approved as containing many useful Hints for the Practice of Military Hospitals in Tropical Climates, I would recommend that Copies of this Work be provided for each, of the Garrison Surgeons in Jamaica, and the Leeward Islands, of the Twelve Commissioned, and Eighteen NonCommissioned Officers of the Medical Staff for the Forces, under the Command of Sir Charles Grey; and of the Surgeons of Regiments forming the said Armament.[19]

It is apparent that Grey antagonized the Medical Board which succeeded Hunter, the surgeon general, by appointing his own medical staff and by promoting his own candidates. "In all his medical arrangements," complained the board in July, 1795, to the Duke of York, "He did not once consult or take the advice of any medical officers, not even of the Director General of his own hospital."[20]

Yet, the military operations in the Caribbean proceeded successfully. From Carlisle Bay in early January, 1794, Grey's army consolidated its foothold on Santo Domingo and invaded the French colonies. By May, the redcoats had advanced to Port-au-Prince (Haiti), and had swept over St. Lucia, Marié-Galante, Martinique, and Guadalupe when the rainy season brought an end to the 1794 campaign. In his report to London, Grey boasted that "we are now in complete possession of the Windward and Leeward Charibbee Islands."[21]

By June, however, Grey's command was barely clinging to Guadalupe as the French and their black allies tried to drive the invaders into the sea. On Hispaniola, hordes of blacks, led by André Rigaud and Toussaint L'Ouverture, successfully repelled the British occupation of this crown jewel of the French colonial empire. Then insurrections erupted in the British colonies of Dominica, St. Vincent, and Grenada.

Grey was confronted with the dilemma of trying to retain the captured islands, while simultaneously attempting to suppress numerous rebellions throughout the Lesser Antilles with a dwindling troop strength. Victor Hugues, a dedicated French revolutionary who arrived in the Caribbean, augmented Grey's problem. He offered weapons and inspiration to Republican sympathizers and stirred up insurrections by the restless Maroons in Jamaica and by disgruntled French settlers on Grenada, St. Lucia, and St. Vincent.

More dangerous than Jacobins was the yellow fever which decimated Grey's army. Army surgeons were helpless in combating the pestilence, and throughout 1794 they pleaded repeatedly for more drugs and hospital equipment and complained about long delays in receiving medical supplies from England. Hugues's capture of an English hospital ship laden with supplies added to the difficulty of the British surgeons. In the navy, ships leaving Barbados for the Leeward Islands were also hit by the disease. Off Guadaloupe, one squadron lost 20 percent of its crew in six months.[22] Describing the near epidemic which eventually killed nearly 1,200 seamen during the campaign, Lieutenant Bartholomew James, on board the *Acorn*, remarked:

In a few days after I arrived at St. Pierre [Martinique] I buried every man belonging to my boat twice, and nearly all of the third boat's crew, in fevers, and, shocking and serious to relate, the Master, Mate and every man and boy belonging to the *Acorn* transport that I came from England in. . . . The constant affecting scenes of sudden death was in fact dreadful to behold, and nothing was scarcely to be met but funeral processions in this town of both officers and men.[23]

The yellow fever which destroyed British crews and regiments throughout the Caribbean virtually terminated the campaign. When the exhausted and dispirited Grey sailed home in November, 1794, he had lost three-fourths of his command within a year.[24]

The next major West Indian expedition—18,000 men and 200 ships under Abercrombie and Admiral Charles Christian—was destined to sail in the summer of 1795 to reinforce the deteriorating British position. But months of delay resulted from the mustering of soldiers, the gathering of provisions, the collecting of transports off Spithead, and the dispersing of some regiments from the Southampton encampment to other areas of war.[25] Consequently, the departure of the fleet was postponed until the autumn. Abercrombie's orders had been altered four times, but on the eve of his departure he was finally instructed to pacify Grenada, St. Lucia, St. Vincent, and then to seize the Dutch colonies of Essequibo and Berbice (for the overseas possessions of France's ally, the Batavian Republic, were now fair game). In addition, he was ordered to assist another force of 9,000 troops, sailing from Cork under Major General John Whyte, in the conquest of Santo Domingo.[26]

The Abercrombie expedition was a step in the advancement of military medicine, for it was probably the first on which medical experience from previous Caribbean campaigns was officially utilized.[27] Abercrombie selected an experienced medical staff, relied upon the advice of naval surgeons, and decreed sanitary regulations to be enforced aboard ship and in tropical garrison.

As the troops prepared to board the transports in late September, an army sanitary board, one of the first of its kind, met in Southampton to devise hygienic standards for the expeditions. Its membership consisted of Dr. John Hunter; Thomas Young, a veteran of Flanders and the Indies who was appointed as inspector of hospitals in Barbados; John Weir, an inspector of hospitals; Dr. John McNamara Hayes, director of the army's temporary hospital in Southampton; and Lieutenant Colonel Frederick Maitland, a veteran of the Grey expedition. While serving on Martinique in 1794, Maitland had written a sanitary code, stating that "soldiers are the most inconsiderate Beings on the Face of the Earth and if left to themselves are in many Respects helpless." He urged that officers enforce a strict standard of hygiene and added: "Without this supervision, the wilest measures, and the most judicious Regulations, must prove nugatory."[28]

Noting that other recent military expeditions had sailed without such rules, and that officers were generally careless about supervising hygiene, the sanitary board noted that "the present circumstances of Sir Ralph Abercrombie's Command seems to offer the most convenient means of Supplying these great defects in our Military System."[29] To protect the health of the troops on the Barbados passage, the board urged the following: that the regiments selected for the expedition be screened so as to exclude the lame and that some troops already acclimatized at Gibraltar join the armada; that additional medical officers be attached to the expedition; that the fleet depart in early October to insure six months of military operations before the onset of tropical storms that usually brought the "sickly season"; that the troopships be well ventilated, have abundant space below deck, be fumigated before departure and be provided with hammocks for the soldiers; that hospital ships accompany the fleet and remain in Caribbean waters during the expedition; and that the men bathe and exercise daily on ship and be provided with a diet (rice, soup, sugar, barley, vinegar, sauerkraut) adequate to ward off scurvy. Upon landing in the Indies, officers were to supervise the cleaning of living quarters, and to provide their men with ample quantities of fruit, vegetables, fresh meat, cocoa, coffee, and to determine that the rum for the soldier's ration was at least one year old. Furthermore, the regulations warned against excessive exercise under the tropical sun, advised frequent changes of clothing to avoid bodily chills at night, and suggested lime juice as a remedy for insect bites.

The board noted the recent success of the Royal Navy with similar sanitary measures, for the navy was then sending vessels on long voyages around the world with comparatively slight incidences of sickness and disease "when formerly in a few months one-half of the crew perished." The reason for "this wonderful Difference," claimed the sanitarians, "is only to be ascribed to the unremitting attention to many small Matters, often apparently trifling, and which severally considered, appeared of little importance. It would be unpardonable not to profit by the experience."[30] With Abercrombie's support to these measures, his expedition to the Indies was the best prepared military force, from a medical standpoint at least, that had ever sailed from British shores.

Abercrombie was satisfied that adequate medical personnel were on hand (a surgeon, an assistant surgeon, and a mate for every regiment) that a vigorous inspection of the troops was underway, and that the enforcement of the sanitary code would help to avoid the tragedies of the Grey expedition. He wrote on October 27 to Dundas: "Regulations for the care of the men on ship board, and on their arrival in the West Indies have been framed by military and medical men of Judgement and Experience and no Pain or Expense have been spared to furnish the troops every article for their Accommodation and Comfort, in health and Sickness." The expedition was ready to depart, Abercrombie confided to Dundas, "and if the weather should provide favorable . . . the whole of the Infantry might be embarked on Thursday morning."[31]

By early November, however, the transports were still waiting for the boom of cannon to signal the departure of the fleet to the Caribbean. With the Rangers on the *Jamaica*, McGrigor was occupied in supervising the cleaning of the vessel's passenger accommodations and in inspecting recruits who arrived daily to join the 88th. One evening, McGrigor was instructed to examine some men on a nearby ship. After completing his assignment, McGrigor attempted to return to the *Jamaica* by longboat. Unable to do so because of the heavy seas in the anchorage, he spent the night ashore.

McGrigor awoke to the sound of cannon which signified the sailing of the expedition. Off Portsmouth preparing to depart were two separate fleets—200 vessels under Abercrombie and Christian, and another 500 ships destined for the Mediterranean. Although the signal was supposed to alert the larger fleet to weigh anchor, many skippers of the West Indian fleet misunderstood their instructions and immediately set sail. "Much confusion ensued; so that a great many of the transports for the West Indies got under way," McGrigor remembered "in the belief that the signal was for us."[32] Scurrying to catch his ship in this comedy of errors, McGrigor, along with several other officers in the same predicament, boarded a small sloop. After hailing several vessels in the convoy without locating the *Jamaica*, McGrigor transferred to the transport *Betsy* as it passed the Isle of Wight; and on the *Betsy* McGrigor remained for the entire voyage not knowing whether he followed or preceded the ship of his own regiment. After an uneventful passage of six weeks, he arrived on December 25 at Carlisle Bay.[33] To his dismay, McGrigor later learned that the *Betsy* was the only vessel in the entire armada to arrive, that the initial signal had been a mistake, and that the navy had caught up with the other vessels and guided them back to Portsmouth.

Off Spithead, bad luck plagued Abercrombie's expedition. When the fleet departed on November 16, it encountered a severe storm that wrecked numerous ships on the Dorsetshire coast; the rest of the battered ships had to find sanctuary in Portsmouth. The armada sailed again on December 9, but a tempest again buffeted the vessels. Many ships were sunk, others were scattered over the ocean as some craft were blown back to the Solent, some to Gibraltar, and a few were even driven by the storm to the French coast to be captured by the enemy. Although Christian battled the storms for eight weeks, he had to return to Portsmouth for repairs. Abercrombie and Christian made another effort to cross the stormy Atlantic in early March, 1796, and this time, they were successful. In April, Abercrombie's ship arrived in the Barbados, and within a few weeks Carlisle Bay was filled with masts of the fleet.

Unfortunately for the soldiers, the additional weeks in cramped quarters below decks and the lack of fresh provisions at sea had been instrumental in contributing to an outbreak of disease. At Carlisle Bay, McGrigor and other regimental surgeons examined the disembarking troops and placed incapacitated men in the newly erected "portable hospitals" (wooden sheds brought from England). Dr. George Pinckhard, deputy inspector general of hospitals, remarked that the men "were in a sickly state [after], their long confinement on Board . . . ," but "being regularly exercised, they will have the advantage of becoming in some degree, seasoned, previous to their being ordered upon actual service."[34]

Assured that his troops were fit for duty, and anxious to attack before the start of the next rainy season, Abercrombie dispatched expeditions throughout the West Indies. "Grenada, we were told," related Pinckhard "was almost wholly in possession of the brigands, St. Vincent in imminent danger from the Charibs, and Guadaloupe, if not St. Lucia, so Strengthened by reinforcements from France as to bid us defiance."[35] Sir Ralph sent reinforcements to British garrisons on Santo Domingo, ordered Major General Whyte to seize Berbice, Demarara, and Essequibo in Guiana from the Dutch, while he himself led troops to quell insurrections in the Windward Islands. In late April, Abercrombie and Colonel Sir John Moore, destined to become a famed military hero, invaded and conquered the French island of St. Lucia. Leaving Moore to pacify the colony, Abercrombie bypassed Guadaloupe and seized St. Vincent. After these victories, Abercrombie sailed to Grenada, in turmoil since early 1795 because of predatory raids by French-negro bands called the "brigands."

The southernmost of the Windwards, Grenada had originally been a French possession, but after its cession to Britain in 1763, French planters on the island were required to swear loyalty to George III. During the War of the American Revolution, when the colony fell again under Bourbon occupation, cultural ties with France were renewed, so that when Grenada reverted to the English in 1783, the French population, accused of collaborating with the enemy, was subject to political discrimination. Thus, French settlers, disgusted with inept British rule and excited by the news from revolutionary

France, were on the verge of revolt. In March, 1795, Julien Fedon, a mulatto planter of Grenada and a follower of Hugues, arrived from Guadaloupe with weapons, liberty caps, and revolutionary cockades to instigate an insurrection. Fedon armed the French, proclaimed the emancipation of the slaves, and proceeded to transform Grenada into another Santo Domingo by burning towns and pillaging plantations in an orgy of destruction while the small British military detachment was unable to check the revolt. Then torrential rains hampered the guerrilla activity.

By February, 1796, Fedon held most of the island settlements except the town of St. George's where a small garrison waited for reinforcements from the Barbados. In March, a relief force of 400 men, including detachments of the 88th accompanied by McGrigor, arrived from Carlisle Bay. But this support was still inadequate to break the siege. In April, Brigadier General Oliver Nicolls landed with another 800 men, and now the British took the offensive. Nicolls pushed the enemy back from the seacoast, and then, in a series of bloody skirmishes, he tried to seize Fedon's camps in the hills.

On one such foray into the jungle, the Rangers suddenly discovered that they were about to be ambushed by the rebels. "We were in an awkward position," related McGrigor, "for, undiscovered by us, we had pushed beyond a body of the enemy, which now fired on us from the rear; and we were now actually almost surrounded." While the 88th tried to extricate itself, McGrigor assisted the wounded. To his astonishment, he noted that all his able-bodied comrades were fleeing from the enemy. "I lost no time in joining them," he admitted, "and I confess I never made better use of my legs. The bullets absolutely tore up the ground close to us on each side; how we escaped was to me a miracle."[36] Fortunately another regiment quickly came to their support. The troops rallied and drove Fedon from his fortress sanctuary.

Nicolls then assaulted the brigands' main stronghold near Marquis Bay before French reinforcements arrived from Guadaloupe. In a tough, no-quarter fight, in which McGrigor accompanied his charges through musket fire, the British dislodged Fedon from his mountain lair just as French schooners neared the beach below. Sickened by dysentery after this encounter, McGrigor returned to St. George's and was not a witness to the final pacification of the island.

In the last phase of the campaign on Grenada, 5,000 British troops cut off the insurgents' escape by sea and trapped the last 300 brigands at Fedon's remaining bastion high in the mountains. By the time Abercrombie arrived in June, Nicolls was mounting his last attack on the rebels in the interior and soon the insurrection was quelled. The remnants of the brigands were hunted down, shot in the bush without mercy, or were hauled off for speedy execution in Georgetown's marketplace in a manner that sickened the compassionate McGrigor.

After the fighting on Grenada ended, Abercrombie terminated his campaign for 1796. But another danger, far more formidable than French partisans or rebellious slaves now struck the British regiments—yellow fever. As McGrigor explained, the fatalities from disease were far greater than from combat:

When quiet was restored, and inaction of the troops in quarters succeeded to the active operation in the field, where all was excitement; then, as I believe had ever happened in similar situations, much disease appeared. It now presented itself with overwhelming force, and with hideous mortality, being more fatal to the army by far than the enemy. The number that died of yellow fever was four times that of those who fell by the bullet and bayonet. . . . The disease, however, appeared in more aggravated or hideous form among the troops when the rebellion was checked. They were numerous, too much so for the accommodation for them in the island, and, consequently, they were much crowded in many places . . . .[37]

Although McGrigor wrote no other commentary about his experiences with yellow fever on Grenada, it is possible to comprehend his bewilderment in treating the disease. For example, one specialist on yellow fever was Dr. William Wright of Edinburgh, a civilian physician appointed to the West Indian expedition. In charge of the main general hospital at Carlisle Bay, to which hundreds of stricken men were sent from garrisons throughout the Caribbean, Wright attempted to make a detailed classification of the types of fevers he encountered. As a cure for yellow fever, he advised liberal doses of opium, and mercury.[38]

Dr. Colin Chisholm, who served with the Ordnance on Grenada, wrote a controversial book on yellow fever. Chisholm claimed that the "Malignant Pestilent Fever" was not the so-called yellow fever, but that it was "Boullam Fever" brought to the Caribbean in 1793 from West Africa by a slave ship. He also prescribed hearty doses of calomel, a mercury compound, to cure it. Chisholm's description of the inexperienced army doctors, their confusion about remedies, and the chronic shortages of drugs provides a rare commentary on the medical department:

The medical staff of Sir Ralph Abercrombie's army was composed of young men, who had little or no practice and who were totally unacquainted with the climate and its diseases, and of the few who had particularly resided in the country and who had no experience in the treatment of disease incident to it in the capacity of surgeons to regiments [sic]. Unhappily for the army, a diversity of opinion prevailed among the gentlemen [about the proper cure] . . . .[39]

On Santo Domingo in 1796 as an assistant inspector general of hospitals was Dr. Hector M'Lean. He stated that the yellow fever was not a new or peculiar "distemper," but that it was "the common Remittent Endemic of the island applied to the English Constitution, and accompanied occasionally with yellowness, as an accidental symptom."[40] He was embittered about the negligent administrative preparations at Port-au-Prince. Troops there, he claimed, were forced to spend hellish weeks aboard steamy transports "where an infectious fever raged, and made great havoc among the men."[41] Preparations for landing medical stores and hospital equipment, he insisted, were careless, and "the consequence was that numbers perished, and that little army, which originally consisted of five thousand men was very shortly reduced to fifteen hundred." M'Lean was a caustic critic of the waste, expense, and the over-crowded and unsanitary conditions of general hospitals on Santo Domingo. He was particularly disgusted by the undisciplined ward attendants. The hospital orderlies, M'Lean lamented, had access to the wine and liquor supplies for the sick, and they would "enliven their meetings by a constant share of gaiety. In this manner the sick are often totally neglected, in spite of every vigilence of the part of those who attend them."[42] Conscious of the slipshod supervision and the low moral standards of the hospital orderlies, M'Lean was one of the first army doctors to urge the creation of a medical corps for hospital duty:

No duties are more sacred, [than] that of attending to the sick; no duties require more strictness of manner, or greater decency and fitness of deportment. But instead of forming this body [of medical corpsmen] on this principle, they were made of outcasts from all the regiments; either of men, whom disease had incapacitated for army duty; or of those fitter for Botany Bay, or the hospitals of invalids, than employment requiring humanity or action.[43]

Serving as superintendant of military hospitals on Jamaica between 1792 and 1797, William Lempriere remained on the island as a civilian practitioner in Spanish Town. After summarizing the various prophylactic measures necessary to preserve the health of troops, he stated: "It is generally acknowledged by physicians of eminence and candour who have long practiced in the West Indies, that all fevers endemical to tropical climates, exist only where marsh exhalations prevail; and that these are produced by the action of heat, or moisture. . . ."[44] Yet, by preventive measures and assiduous supervision of army hospitals, he stated, it was possible to check yellow fever and to gain some knowledge of the pattern of disease by keeping medical registers on the condition of patients. Puzzled by the variety of fevers, he wrote: "Yet the symptoms are so ambiguous, and contradictory in different subjects, are marked with so many distressing circumstances and often are so rapidly and unexpectedly felt, that they too frequently baffled the exertions of the most judicious, and the oldest experienced physician."[45]

McGrigor's friend, Robert Jackson, was the most famous army surgeon of the period who described his experiments with yellow fever. Jackson had published a book, *A Treatise on the Fevers of Jamaica* (1791) based upon his earlier experiences in the Caribbean and North America, that made him an acknowledged expert on tropical medicine, and hence a logical choice for an administrative post in the West Indies. Jackson had sailed to Santo Domingo with General Whyte in February, 1796, and served there until 1797. He improved the hospital diet, reformed the system of stoppages (deductions from a soldier's pay) for medical expenses, established a regimental hospital system, and experimented with cold affusions of water on feverish patients. Although Jackson's theories about the origins of disease and his treatment of yellow fever failed to exemplify scientific standards, the popularity of his books, and his efforts to improve army hospitals and the welfare of the rank and file, distinguished him as a leading medical department reformer.[46]

Perhaps the most harrowing account of the yellow fever which struck Abercrombie's men came from Dr. George Pinckhard, who nearly died of it while serving in Surinam. Describing his efforts to cure himself, Pinckhard admitted that no medical remedies seemed to help. "Bark, mercury, bleeding, bathing, and a variety of other remedies have been amply tried; but in vain, for all have proven equally ineffective. . . . Nor did it appear within the power of man to prevent [the fever]."[47] Homeward bound in 1797, Pinckhard visited the learned Jackson at Port-au-Prince. After lengthy discussions with him, Pinckhard became convinced that "early venaesections" were the surest remedy to treat the fever. Dr. Jackson, wrote Pinckhard, "esteems it important to the cure that the quantity drawn at first bleeding should be ample."[48]

Regardless of the efforts to protect the troops—the issuance of a lighter uniform, and the establishment of cooler hill stations to enable sick men to recuperate—Abercrombie's regiments, like Grey's, were wracked by disease. From St. Lucia, Sir John Moore stated on August 30, 1796, that "the sickness among the troops is dreadful . . . the deaths upon the Morne Fortune are from sixty to seventy a week."[49] And that same month, Moore, a dedicated champion of the enlisted man, wrote to his father in England that: "It is not the climate alone that kills troops in this country; it is bad management. We seem as ignorant as if we had never before made war in it."[50] Shaken by the enormous mortality rates, Major General Charles Graham reported on October 10 from Martinique to Dundas that the incomplete sick returns of troops on Grenada and St. Lucia, which he enclosed for ministerial perusal, "will show how severely this army had suffered from an unwholesome climate which is more to be dreaded than the most sanguinary enemy."[51] And Abercrombie, who had to return briefly to England in late 1796 in order to recover his health before commencing his 1797 campaign, confided to Dundas that "perhaps this expedition has been undertaken too lightly. We had not sufficient information, and to lay [sic] the best, it is not easily attained."[52]

Regardless of the fearful toll of lives, the campaign against Britain's enemies in the Caribbean went on until 1802. By then, the Dutch West Indian possessions of Curacao and Surinam had fallen to the English along with the Danish islands of St. Thomas, St. Bartholomew, and Santa Cruz.[53] After Spain joined France in the War of the Second Coalition, Abercrombie was ordered to attack His Hispanic Majesty's colonies in the West Indies. Although he conquered Trinidad (February, 1797), Abercrombie was repulsed in his invasion of Puerto Rico. On Santo Domingo, also, the British suffered defeat after defeat, and like the French and Spanish, they too evacuated this pestilential island.[54] Yet, after all this appalling waste of manpower, the irony of these seemingly senseless campaigns is that at the Peace of Amiens (1802), Britain restored to her former enemies all her recent Caribbean conquests, retaining only Trinidad. As Bryan Edwards, an historian of the British West Indies, stated in 1819: "The dreadful expenses of human life in such enterprises is beyond all the compensation that the most splendid victory can afford."[55]

The total number of British casualties in these West Indian campaigns is difficult to determine without sufficient documentary evidence, but there are some reliable estimates. Edwards claimed that "no less but probably rather more than thirty thousand soldiers were victims of pestilence and sword. . . ."[56] Chisholm estimated that from March, 1796, to April, 1797, Abercrombie lost 30 surgeons, 341 officers, and 13,809 rank and file. By adding to these figures the 6,000 soldiers who perished on the Grey expedition, Chisholm claimed that some 20,000 troops died on these enterprises, but that only 2,000 expired from combat.[57] For Sir John W. Fortescue, the military historian, who totaled up the casualties of seamen and soldiers, their steady stream of reinforcements, and the losses of troops on Santo Domingo, the figure was even higher. "After long and careful thought and study," he asserted, "I have come to the conclusion that the West Indian campaigns . . . which were the essence of Pitt's military policy, cost England in Army and Navy, little fewer than one hundred thousand men, about one-half of them dead, the remainder permanently unfit for service."[58]

After the Peace of Amiens, the collapse of Napoleon's attempt in 1804 to reconquer Santo Domingo, and the gradual obliteration of French maritime strength from the seas, the danger to the British hegemony of the Caribbean faded. The West Indies henceforth occupied only a minor role in future naval and military operations in the war period. But Britain kept thousands of men guarding the valuable sugar isles, and sickness and casualty rates continued to be enormous.[59]

To what extent these West Indian expeditions initiated military and medical reforms is difficult to determine. Certainly Abercrombie and Moore, ever zealous in improving the lot of their men, labored to improve sanitary conditions in the army, but whether such examples influenced the typical military officer stationed in the tropics is debatable. As Hector M'Lean concluded:

It is a pity that Officers in Command, do not read such parts of medical works, as treat of the health of soldiers. This kind of knowledge, in warm and unhealthy climates, would prove highly useful. The General of an army, ought to be well informed, in whatever regard the Encampment, diet, or Exercise of his soldiers. It is not in the power of medical men, to pursue extensive plans, without the support of the Commanding Officer; they can only recommend, but cannot execute.[60]

Yet, the mishaps of the Flanders and Caribbean campaigns led to improvements in the treatment of the rank and file. In 1798, the Medical Board issued sanitary rules and hospital regulations. In addition, the military paid more attention to the "seasoning" of troops in the Mediterranean before embarking them to the Caribbean, to the need of rotating regiments from the Indies to the healthier environment of British North America, to the utilization of black battalions for duty in pestilent areas,[61] and to improvements in diet, dress, and in barracks construction. Even though the experiment of utilizing soldiers as hospital attendants failed on Santo Domingo, and though there is little evidence of similar trials until 1808, at least some army surgeons became familiar with this attempt to improve the management of hospitals. Regardless of heated disagreements by doctors about the origins and the treatment of such diseases as yellow fever, dysentery, hepatitis, and pulmonary ailments, there was increasing agreement in the medical profession that prophylactic measures for seamen and soldiers were necessary, and that in some still inexplicable manner, the great killer, yellow fever, was linked to the environment of hot, swampy, insect-infested areas. It is also apparent that army surgeons gained valuable experience in treating thousands of men stricken with similar diseases in its hospitals, and the accumulated statistical evidence, gathered from hundreds of medical registers, provided some clues about the nature of disease.[62]

The remnants of the 88th on Grenada, whose ranks were greatly diminished by yellow fever, embarked on July 20, 1796, aboard the *Betsy* for England. Carrying 140 soldiers and seamen, the vessel anchored off Tortola on July 29 with other transports gathering for the homeward passage. The ship's crew was so apprehensive about the pending hurricane season that in the frenzied preparations for sailing the vessel was carelessly provisioned. During the hurried activity before departure, McGrigor, fearful of being trapped on a fever-stricken vessel at sea, inspected every individual aboard the *Betsy* and excluded from the voyage any man "who had the least appearance of disease or debility."[63] Regardless of his precautions, yellow fever appeared on

August 6 as the ship left the Caribbean. The captain and first mate perished and one quarter of the troops soon became sick.

Not only were the crew and passengers stricken with fever, but the vessel was unseaworthy, or as McGrigor termed it, "an old crank transport, of the worst description, and, as afterwards appeared, ought never to have been taken up for the service." The former second mate, now the acting captain of the *Betsy*, was "not only grossly ignorant of navigation, but likewise intemperate. We found him not infrequently lying dead drunk opposite the companion door." Thus, McGrigor found himself with only pork and biscuit to eat, trapped on an undependable vessel with a sick crew and with a drunken skipper. Then to add to the difficulties of the voyage, the *Betsy* was battered continually by severe Atlantic storms:

Our tub of vessel rolled about fearfully and appeared quite unmanageable. . . . At this time our situation was anything but enviable: the billows were running high, our cabin in total darkness, and occasionally admitting water; our acting captain almost always drunk; some men dying daily and thrown overboard; and I endeavoring to read the service over them. . . . Our vessel was very crank; and the crew and soldiers dispirited.

During one perilous tempest, the army officers, fearing for their lives after weeks at sea, finally removed the intoxicated captain from command of the vessel. They entrusted the future of the *Betsy* to one of their army comrades, Captain Richard Vandeluer, who had been a midshipman in his youth.

"With all the externals of a skipper," McGrigor wrote, Captain Vandeleur set to work in handling the vessel, and as the weather moderated, he began to take observations on the ship's location. Even though it was foggy and no landmark was in sight, Vandeleur announced to his delighted companions that the ship was in the English Channel. But after three more days without sighting the coastline, the *Betsy* encountered an American merchant ship bound from New York. "How near Dover are we?" hailed the *Betsy*. "Dover!" replied the Yankee, "you are in St. George's Channel; the mouth of the Mersey not far off." Thoroughly disillusioned about Vandeleur's navigation, the dismayed officers put the ship about and managed to steer through the Channel until they finally sighted the Irish shore.[64]

After this horrendous voyage, the *Betsy* anchored on September 23 in the Cove of Cork.[65] On shore, McGrigor and his friends enjoyed the hospitality of a local inn and pondered their good fortunes in ever reaching land. Yet McGrigor was still not free of the accursed *Betsy*. Even though the vessel was condemned by Admiralty officials for being unseaworthy, it was the only ship available to convey the 88th to England. Wondering to what extent he could trust his luck after his recent hardships at sea, McGrigor boarded the dangerous vessel for the last stage of the voyage to Portsmouth.

From his Caribbean experiences, McGrigor learned that mysterious fevers in hot climates could decimate an entire army, and he was reinforced in his belief that sanitary reforms were necessary to protect the health of West Indian garrisons. McGrigor also realized how little the medical profession really knew about tropical diseases.

# IV

## THE EAST INDIAN CAMPAIGN

The Rangers disembarked at Portsmouth in October, 1796, and marched to their regimental headquarters at Halifax, Yorkshire. Mc-Grigor was granted a leave to visit his family in Aberdeen and did not rejoin his regiment until the spring of 1797. By then, the 88th was preparing to move to Portsmouth from where it would sail for Jersey. But while traveling to that great naval base, the Rangers learned that seamen of the Royal Navy at Spithead had mutinied.

After brewing for months, the mutiny at Spithead erupted on April 15, and it soon spread to other naval bases on the eastern coast. Involving one half the crews of the North Sea and Channel fleets, the Naval Mutiny of 1797 was a severe crisis for a nation at war. As the defiant ships at Spithead refused to hoist sail, Britain's maritime shield of sturdy wooden walls against revolutionary France seemed to splinter as the rebellious seamen conducted the first mass sit-down strike in modern history. Fighting the War of the First Coalition, a struggle plagued with military and diplomatic failures since 1793, the Pitt Ministry found itself deprived of the kingdom's major strategic weapon against the enemy.

Unable to acquire a foothold on the continent, the Ministry had witnessed the erosion of the alliance against the Jacobin Republic. Prussia quit the war in 1795. The United Netherlands was a French satellite termed the Batavian Republic. Fearful of British designs in South America, Spain became an ally of France. Russia, which had not entered the war, still refused to participate in the struggle. In southern Europe, General Napoleon Bonaparte defeated the Italian states and negotiated an armistice with Austria that left England without a fighting ally. Virtually the only encouraging news in London concerned naval victories. Near Ireland in 1794 and off Portugal in 1796, English fleets had triumphed over the enemy's navies.

Regardless of these naval defeats, French privateers sunk and captured hundreds of English vessels. The Directory massed an army on the Channel coast and probed for weaknesses in English defenses by abortive invasions of Ireland (1794) and Wales (1797). On the defensive as the First Coalition collapsed, England relied heavily upon her maritime power in the duel with France.

The navy seemed to disintegrate as the seamen at Spithead rose in protest at their miserable plight. Goaded beyond endurance by hunger, severe discipline, and brutal working conditions, and inspired by democratic ideas emanating from the Irish, French, and the American revolutions, the crews refused to weigh anchor until their barbaric conditions were ameliorated. Delegates from the lower decks formed committees to present their complaints to the Admiralty and to Parliament. To the astonishment of Britain's rulers, the mutineers ejected officers from the ships, established forecastle governments, seized control of Portsmouth harbor, hauled flags down from the rigging—the royal standard, the Union Jack, and admirals' pennants—and hoisted up the red banner of revolution.[1]

Arriving at the height of the turmoil in Portsmouth, McGrigor explained that "we found a great number of troops, and everything in a critical state on board the fleet, the officers having been sent shore, and the crews' delegates ruling everything in Spithead."[2] Even the city of Portsmouth seemed to be rebellious to such loyal officers of the Crown, for its civilian population seemed genuinely sympathetic to the mutineers. Portsmouth was tired of war, its streets had been inundated for years with hordes of destitute wives and families of unpaid seamen, and its householders, burdened with additional taxes for poor relief, had been unable to convince Parliament to provide the borough with financial support. To many townsmen, the chief difference between a fleet controlled by the Admiralty or by the seamen was that the sailors, wearing red cockades or gilded ribbons inscribed with revolutionary slogans on their hats, came ashore in greater numbers to make speeches and to frequent the shops and taverns. As McGrigor explained, the townspeople of Portsmouth were sympathetic to the mutineers:

Great numbers of the sailors were on shore, roaming in the streets . . . in a mutinous and drunken state, their language and conduct most insubordinate and treasonable. At this time it was not thought prudent to interrupt them much; in fact a great part of the inhabitants of Portsmouth and its neighborhood, and all the owners of public houses and of slop shops, with the dissolute females of the town, appeared to be of their party.[3]

The tension in Portsmouth was such that officers hesitated to attend local theaters in uniform because they were likely to be greeted with boos and jeers of the riotous seamen in the audience. "Troops were pouring daily into Portsmouth," remembered McGrigor, "and we foresaw that the season for action was approaching."[4] But a major clash was averted because the military controlled the shore batteries, and because a Seamen's Bill to improve the wages of the lower deck, hastily passed by an alarmed Parliament, was announced to cheering sailors. Then the Cabinet sent a special emissary, Lord Richard Howe, venerated as the sailor's friend, to negotiate with the fleet. Arriving May 10 in Portsmouth, "Black Dick," as the men fondly called him, came with a royal pardon and a promise of naval reforms. Howe achieved a formal reconciliation between the Crown and its seamen in an historic episode of collective bargaining.

Although the mutiny at Spithead terminated in May, it spread to Yarmouth, Plymouth, and particularly to the Nore where "a Floating Republic" was established by defiant seamen who were more radical than their Spithead brethren. By July, however, the mutineers at the Nore and other bases lost their support, the mutiny was crushed, and its leaders executed. The threat to British naval security was thus averted. The same crews that had participated in the mass harborside strike put to sea in July with the Union Jack at the masthead to resume the blockade of Brest and to achieve a decisive victory in October, 1798, over a Batavian fleet off the Zuider Zee.

In the meantime, the 88th embarked on May 20, 1897, for Jersey where the regiment would be stationed for the next 18 months. Although McGrigor slights his activities on Jersey in his *Autobiography*, from documents one can trace his career there. Writing to his uncle on June 2 from Jersey, McGrigor remarked that his regiment had been on duty at Portsmouth, "as you may imagine not in a very tranquil state," and that since his arrival on June 6, he had been stricken with "a kind of fever peculiar to the island."[5] The Rangers, he later informed his uncle, were part of a force stationed on the island to defend England against a French attack. Some 7,000 soldiers were on guard, and "a very strong squadron of Frigates stationed there under Sir Richard Strachan, and we are not under the smallest apprehension for the island."[6] The threat of a French assault was apparent in a letter of May, 1798, when he wrote that "the troops were terribly harrassed night and day and we are all kept in a continual state of alarm. Every inhabitant from 15 to 60 years of age is now obliged to carry arms."[7] Although the English were not yet aware of their enemy's change of plans, the danger of an invasion in 1798 had faded. Upon the recommendation of Napoleon, who commanded the expeditionary force on the Channel Coast, the Directory cancelled a crossing and ordered an army to strike at the Near East.

As the threat of invasion subsided, McGrigor had the opportunity to compile a medical case history of the 88th during its service on Jersey. Although the techniques of maintaining such records would be commonplace today, the procedures for recording the causes, symptoms, and treatment of diseases were only then coming into vogue in the medical department. Beginning with his first case book compiled at Halifax, and throughout his service in the East Indies and in Europe, McGrigor indicated his fascination with statistics. In his descriptions of the origins and progress of diseases, he inadvertently demonstrated his bewilderment about the actual sources of contagion.[8]

When typhus, his old enemy from the Flanders campaign, struck his regiment in July, 1797, McGrigor, proud of the previously healthy state of the men, was unable to check the pestilence. Searching for a remedy, McGrigor, assiduous about reading the current medical literature, found evidence for a cure advanced in an article written by Dr. Carmichael Smyth (1741–1821). Smyth, a famous London physician, claimed that he had prevented the spread of typhus when he was superintendent of the prison at Winchester and again at Sheerness on the Navy's hospital ship, *Union*. Awarded a grant of £5,000 from a grateful Parliament and appointed physician-extraordinary to George III, Smyth recommended fumigating the clothes and quarters of typhus-stricken men with fumes of nitrous acid.[9] McGrigor wrote to Smyth on October 8, 1797, explaining that he had previously lost 50 men from typhus on Jersey in 1794, and that he was delighted to discover Smyth's suggestions:

As Surgeon to the 88th regiment, I have for these last four years, been witness to the dreadful ravages of an infectious fever in different parts of the world. In England, in the island of Jersey, on the continent of Europe, during a voyage to, and in different islands of the West Indies, this fever has been the scourge of the regiment of which I have the honour to belong, and after a trial of every mode of practice which I could learn, it proved extremely fatal.

On my return from the West Indies, having seen in Duncan's Annals of Medicine, an account of your work on fever, I determined to take the earliest opportunity of giving a trial to the mode which you recommend, of weakening and destroying contagion. . . .

The effect of the nitrous fumigation, is evident, not only in the diminished numbers of cases, but also in their degree of virulence. . . .[10]

After an enlisted man died of typhus in July, McGrigor quickly put into effect Smyth's ideas. Although he resorted to the traditional remedies for dealing with so-called "gaol-fever"—Peruvian Bark, James' Power, emetics, blisters—McGrigor and his two mates fumigated the bedding and clothing of the sick, as well as the barracks and hospital. Furthermore, as he wrote to the Army Medical Board, "I determined, therefore, immediately to separate everyone, complaining of any symptoms of fever, from those in health, and for this purpose had several tents pitched at some distance from the barracks . . . in a dry and airy situation about a mile distant."[11] McGrigor explained that there was only one fatality out of sixty-five cases, and he attributed his success to the use of nitrous vapors.

McGrigor demonstrated in this case history an empirical attitude toward medicine—a skeptical view of traditional systems of the monistic pathology of disease, an emphasis on more accurate clinical observations, and a stress upon autopsies. Although a germ theory of disease and a knowledge of the cellular structure of the human body were still unknown, the rationalism of the Enlightenment was gradually applied to late eighteenth century medicine. During the Napoleonic wars, army surgeons, familiar with the hospital methods of the civilian colleagues, utilized in their own case histories the precision, the techniques, and the knowledge derived from recent discoveries in the basic sciences. McGrigor was representative of this new age of hospital medicine. He indicated that he was anxious to publicize the results of his findings on Jersey because "the confirmation or refutation of an opinion in medical science, especially of one that so nearly concerns mankind in general, as a mode of obviating contagion, is no less useful than a new theory, a new medicine, or a new mode of curing disease. . . ."[12]

McGrigor's attempts to explain the causes of disease were not based on scientific evidence. He attributed the outbreak of typhus in the regiment to the location of the barracks (on a damp, marshy meadow near the beach at St. Owens Bay), and to a variety of climatic factors such as the prevailing winds, the prevalence of fogs, and the degree of moisture in the air.[13] Fascinated by climatology that typified much of the contemporary learned medical writing of the day, McGrigor kept a medical register in which he dutifully recorded the weather and the temperature. "It is a curious correspondence [relation]," he noted, "and that struck me, that on looking at a register which I have kept, and examining the days on which men were taken ill . . . on every day, I have found a wonderful correspondence [with the type of weather]."[14]

He claimed that one of the major factors which contributed to the disease was the poor health and the unwholesome living habits of the recruits. The unfitness of recruits for army life was a perennial problem throughout the French revolutionary wars, because the English, unlike the French in this era, still drew most of their troops from a very narrow segment of the population—the inhabitants of slums and villages, many of whom probably had pulmonary disorders and deficiency diseases upon entering the service—and because the army, training these recruits in old-fashioned cantonments and then cooping them up in crowded vessels, neglected to condition them for rigorous overseas campaigning. McGrigor also cited other factors to explain the spread of disease—the poor quality of the drinking water, the excessive amount of exercise to which the men were subjected in order to prepare them for an inspection, and the degree of intemperance in the ranks due to the fact that gin "of a very bad quality" was smuggled into the barracks.[15] Pleased that the troops had recovered their health by the spring, McGrigor wrote to his uncle that the regiment "has of late been healthy, yet I have been much taken-up . . . with practice among the natives here. I have been of late been asked by them to give up the army and settle among them, but have not made up my mind to that yet."[16] Fortunately for the future of military medicine, McGrigor changed his attitude about entering civilian practice on Jersey, for he was soon engaged in another great adventure—an expedition to the East Indies.

How the war against France was extended to the Indian Ocean is a fascinating tale. Unable to defeat the Jacobin Republic in Europe, Pitt opened diplomatic negotiations in July, 1797. But the militant Directory that assumed power in September refused to make concessions and terminated the peace talks. Although France had won stunning victories on land, she was confronted by a stubborn Britain, still dominating the seas and intent on creating a new coalition, and by a rearmed Austria, determined to recover her territorial losses. France had to defeat Britain before Pitt formed a Second Coalition, or the Directory faced the awesome prospect of a seemingly perpetual war.

The French could have mounted an invasion of the British Isles, or they could have launched attacks upon England's overseas empire, damaged her commerce and eventually forced the enemy to sue for peace. The quickest and most decisive blow to Britain was a cross-Channel invasion, but such a plan required that the French control the Channel for a few days. Yet the French fleets were no match for the superior British men-of-war. Furthermore, mastery of the Channel, with the concomitant unpredictabilities about winds, tides, difficulties of communications, and the mobilization of an armada from many ports on the Continent, presented insurmountable difficulties.

An alluring alternative blow to Britain, an attack on her colonies, was also dangerous. But an expedition to the Mediterranean, particularly Egypt, was an area with fewer risks. Although a crusade to the East would be a maritime gamble, the Directory reasoned that Turkey was militarily weak, and that Britain had no permanent fleet in the Mediterranean; the opportunity of extending Republican influence to the Aegean and the Holy Land was indeed tempting. And if victorious in Egypt, France could win another colony and bargaining power at a diplomatic settlement. Hence, in March, 1798, the Directory ordered Napoleon to mobilize an expedition destined for Malta and Egypt.

Napoleon sailed with his fleet on May 17 from Toulon. Eluding a British squadron, his armada captured the island of Malta in early June and then sailed on to the coast of Egypt. Landing near Alexandria in early July, Napoleon marched his troops up the Nile. By a stunning victory over Ottoman armies at the Battle of the Pyramids, he became master of Cairo and of the Lower Nile.

Admiral Horatio Nelson discovered that the French armada had eluded him at Toulon and pursued Napoleon to Egypt. Finding no evidence of an enemy invasion of North Africa, and unaware that he had passed the slower-moving French armada in the darkness, Nelson sailed to the Levant, and then on to the Aegean Islands in search of his elusive prey Hearing of Napoleon's landing near Alexandria, the infuriated Nelson headed back to the Egyptian coast. On July 31, he surprised the enemy ships in Aboukir Bay and virtually obliterated the French fleet. Nelson's decisive victory drastically altered the course of the war, for it encouraged Continental nations to join in a new alliance, crushed the Directory's dream of making the Mediterranean into a French lake, handicapped the French occupation of Egypt, and isolated Napoleon's army in the Near East. But Napoleon was still master of the Nile.

The French schemes in the eastern Mediterranean affected strategy in the Indian Ocean and accelerated wars of the British East India Company against native states. Although the British had seized French trading posts in India, French influence was still strong. France maintained diplomatic links with Anglophobe Indian rulers, and French officers trained native armies in the states of Mysore, Hyderabad, and the Mahrattas Confederacy. From Mauritius in the Indian Ocean, French privateers raided British commerce throughout the East Indies.[17]

Lord Mornington (Richard Wellesley), the governor general of India, believed that if Napoleon acquired a naval base on the Red Sea and if he coordinated an invasion of India with a native uprising inspired by Tippo Sahib, the Sultan of Mysore, the British hegemony in the East would be jeopardized. To check French influence, Mornington ordered Major General Sir David Baird and Colonel Arthur Wellesley (Mornington's younger brother) to conquer Mysore.

In the meantime, the British sent reinforcements to the Presidencies, swept the Indian Ocean of enemy vessels, acquired naval bases in the Red Sea, and made treaties with the rulers of Persia, Zanzibar, and the sultanates of southern Arabia. To demonstrate the power of the Royal Navy to Arab rulers, British ships blockaded the Red Sea and bombarded the French-held port of Cosseir.

Hence, in India, the Indian Ocean, and the Red Sea, French plans of conquest were frustrated. Hoping to achieve glory in the War of the Second Coalition underway in Europe, Bonaparte left Egypt in August, 1799, for France. Although the French still had troops at Suez and ships at Mauritius, their inability to move men and material from Egypt allowed the British to score a major colonial triumph in India and to operate in the Indian Ocean and the Red Sea without interference as the net tightened on Napoleon's trapped army in Egypt.

It was this enormous maritime advantage which enabled Britain to transfer armies from one strategic area to another with relative ease. In fact, the inability of the British to maintain a foothold on the European continent (with the exception of Gibraltar), and the mobility of their seaborne forces in this era tempted the government to use its military force in a variety of daring, and often unsuccessful, expeditions to other destinations. As a result of such ambitious ventures, medical staffs of the services had to prepare for a wide range of health-related problems in unfamiliar and sometimes exotic environments. Thus, McGrigor's experiences in the East Indies indicate the enormous difficulties confronting army doctors concerned about protecting their regiments confined for months aboard cramped ships on long voyages.

Accompanied by the adventurous McGrigor, the Rangers departed on Christmas Day, 1798, from Portsmouth aboard two vessels—the *Carnatic* and the *Taunton Castle*. In his capacity as inspector of health, Sir Jeremiah Fitzpatrick examined these ships before they cleared port. He was horrified at their filthy condition, the lack of accommodations for the troops, and the disgusting state of the provisions. Fitzpatrick was particularly vehement in describing the overloading of the transports with extra passengers. Both ships, he insisted, had a maximum capacity of only 180 soldiers.[18] "But to have stored 396 Men, with a proportion of Women and Children, independent of the Crew, on board the *Carnatic* so encumbered, and 411 on board the *Taunton Castle* was one of the most unreasonable acts ever committed and would have been better classed with those of the darkened age than those of the enlightened 18th century...."[19]

McGrigor described how the men fared on board the 1,200 ton *Taunton Castle*. "Those in the *Carnatic* found a healthy and well-regulated ship," he said, "but this was by no means the case in the *Taunton Castle*. A fever of the typhoid form had prevailed there several weeks before the soldiers came on board, had pervaded the ship's company, and proved fatal to many of them." In February, 1799, as the ship sailed through the South Atlantic, the mysterious fever struck most of the passengers. "At this time, dysentery appeared," McGrigor reported, "and afterwards continued the prevailing disease, until our arrival at the Cape of Good Hope."[20]

Arriving on March 27 at Cape Town, a port of call on the passage to India, the *Taunton Castle* took on fresh provisions. "A three weeks stay at the Cape," stated McGrigor, "nearly recovered all our sick."[21]

In a letter written from South Africa to a relative at home, however, McGrigor commented on nonmedical matters:

After nearly four months we dropped anchor in Table Bay and I have just set my foot on terra firma, luckily there is a neutral vessel here just getting under for England I cannot let slip the opportunity of sending you one of my scrawls.... at length we have luckily obtained orders to proceed to the place of our destination which is said to be Bombay. The Cape, tho' very pleasant, is very dear and consequently a bad quarter for a soldier—the Army in India it is said have already taken the field, and the Malabar Coast will certainly be the first scene of action.[22]

Departing from the Cape in April, the vessel provisioned again at the Coromin Islands in the Indian Ocean. To prevent an outbreak of scurvy on the ship, McGrigor had the troops exercised ashore for a few days and had their ship-diet fortified with coconuts, fruit, and vegetables available on the island. Not only scurvy, but severe cases of dysentery and hepatitis plagued the ship on the passage to Bombay, and before the vessel sighted the Malabar Coast, 28 men had perished on the voyage. McGrigor carefully recorded these events and forwarded his account to his former professor in Edinburgh, Dr. James Gregory, who read the narrative of the *Taunton Castle* to his medical students.

Arriving at Bombay on June 10, 1799, too late to participate in the Mysore campaign, the 88th was quartered on Colabah Island, two miles from the city. For the next 15 months, the Rangers resided in Colabah's unhealthy barracks, "located on the only low situation on the island; a situation that during [the rainy season] is almost always swampy," McGrigor commented.[23] From Colabah, the regiment marched to Bombay's main fortress. In October, 1800, the Rangers exchanged quarters with the 86th and then lived within the fortress for a few months.

McGrigor continued his medical register, meteorological readings, records of dissections, and compiled from his journals comprehensive reports for the Bombay Medical Board about the diseases that afflicted the regiment: tetanus, cholera, dysentery, hepatitis, scurvy, pneumonia, measles, venereal ailments, ophthalmia, and the "guinea worm." Pondering the causes of the alarming amount of illness, McGrigor sought an explanation in environmental factors such as the seasonal variations of the weather, the degree of daily temperature, and the diet of the troops. "It appears, that, on the whole, the months to which the change of the season falls are the most unhealthy. July and August when the rains set in are the most so. October is the most fatal month; and September the next to it in destructive influence."[24] In addition to the seasonal climatic changes, McGrigor believed that variations in the daily temperature had some pernicious effect on health. Yet he admitted that the men were even healthier during the hottest months. "If heat be noxious, something in this instance obviated its effects. Was this exercise?... Heat of itself, then, does not appear to be the principal cause of the prevailing diseases."

Perhaps the diet of the soldiers was a factor, he reasoned, claiming that the men were provided with too much "animal food," instead of the sensible native diet. "There can be little doubt, that the nearer we approach to the mode of living of the natives, the more nearly we shall attain their state of health." As proof of a European habit that had disastrous results in the tropics, he explained that sickness increased immediately after pay-day when the men could purchase from the natives additional quantities of arrack (a fermented toddy of coconut milk) in addition to their daily allowance of one half pint of spirits during the rainy season. "Intemperance had hitherto always prevailed as a principal cause of the diseases which prevailed," he maintained.[25] Hence, some inexplicable combination of heat, moisture, exposure to the sun, and dietary customs seemed to account for the awesome death toll for one year of 43 soldiers, 5 women, and 13 children attached to the regiment. Yet this loss of life out of 500 men, McGrigor stated "is as small a proportion as most newly-arrived European corps have suffered in the same period." As a sanitarian anxious to establish better controls over living conditions in the barracks, he concluded in his report to the Bombay Medical Board:

Yet this proportion of deaths is very considerable, and, if continued, would, in a short period exhaust a corps. In a political and economic view, this waste of men is alarming. And, were we to calculate what the loss of forty-three European soldiers amounts to, it would be highly worthy of the Honourable East India Company to take measures to lessen this waste of men; and, that the gentlemen who direct the medical affairs in the country could suggest those measures, there can be no doubt. Though, to newcomers, sickness is, in a great many cases, unavoidable; yet, perhaps, in as great number of cases, the causes of sickness might be, if not always obviated, often lessened.[26]

While the 88th guarded Bombay, Mornington planned another conquest. With southern India pacified, the governor general contemplated an attack on Mauritius, the only threat to the British hegemony of the Indian Ocean and the nest for a dozen bold French privateers. But Admiral Peter Ranier, commander of the fleet in India, wished to sail with an armada to capture the fabled Manila galleons in the Spanish Philippines, and Dundas in London wanted to complete the annexation of the Dutch colonial empire by seizing the Spice Islands. Hence, Mornington wavered for months before ordering an expedition either to Manila, to Java, to Mauritius, or to the Red Sea. Furthermore, Mornington was anxious to assist the career of his ambitious brother, Colonel Wellesley, by providing him with a suitable command for his talents. Mornington also had to consider the rival claims of General Baird, the hero of Seringapatam and a bitter rival of Colonel Wellesley, who insisted upon his prior right to command. By April, 1800, Dundas overcame Mornington's indecision, upon the express command of George III, who ordered that an army be sent from India to occupy the Dutch East Indies. Thus, Mornington assembled a force under the command of Colonel Wellesley at the best anchorages on the west side of Bengal—Trincomalee and Point de Galle on Ceylon.[27]

Along with other European and native regiments sent to Ceylon was the 88th. Embarking from Bombay in December, 1800, McGrigor and his companions seemed destined for voyages on a series of wretched ships. Their vessel was the tiny *Minerva*. Just before the 1,100 ton *Minerva* sailed from Portsmouth to the Indian Ocean a year before, Sir Jeremiah Fitzpatrick, zealously inspecting troops transports, had reported that the vessel had a very limited passenger capacity. "This was a Spanish frigate and is very ill calculated to carry Troops . . . [and] on the whole I consider my duty to mention that, She is not calculated to carry more than 300 men. . . ."[28] Yet when the 150 crewmen, 450 Rangers, and numerous native followers were aboard the *Minerva* in Bombay, there were over 800 men squeezed together on the passage to Ceylon. So limited was the space that 200 men had to remain above deck for the entire voyage. "From the weather, the men suffered severely," complained McGrigor. "I am thus particular, as I think the sickness which prevailed during the next and following month is principally to be attributed to the situation of the troops on board the *Minerva*."[29] Landing on Ceylon in January, 1801, the 88th fortunately was quartered in a dry and well ventilated cinnamon warehouse. Meanwhile other contingents arrived to join Wellesley's command.

The actual destination of the army was still indefinite for months until a dispatch from London overruled Mornington's vacillation and his concern for his brother. Officers on the expedition had assumed that Arthur Wellesley would command the army in the capture of Batavia and Mauritius. On Mauritius, stated McGrigor, "every one expected to be enriched by the plunder to be found there."[30] But in February, a vessel from Bombay carried startling news to Ceylon—a new expedition to Egypt.

Dundas feared the consequences of Napoleon's recent victories in Italy and the possibility that French reinforcements would be sent to Egypt. Hence he ordered Mornington to transfer the army back to Bombay. From India, a force under General Baird, with Colonel Wellesley as second in command, would be transported to the Red Sea in order to join in the conquest of Egypt. Delighted with the prospect of voyaging to Africa, McGrigor explained that when the 88th discovered their new destination, "all was joy—for fighting and promotion were considered the certain results of an expedition to that quarter." Thus back to Bombay the army sailed.

The strategy involved a romantic three-pronged offensive at the French army in Egypt. But the strategists minimized the difficulties of campaigning on unknown African deserts and the logistical problems of linking widely dispersed English, Turkish, and Indian armies.[31] While the main British army would land at Aboukir Bay, Turkish allies would advance from Syria to assist the redcoats in the capture of Rosetta and Alexandria on the Nile delta. To complete the trap of the French, the expedition under Baird and Arthur Wellesley would sail to the Red Sea and disembark at Suez. From here, Baird's army would cross the Arabian desert to the upper Nile, where it would participate in an attack by British and Ottoman troops marching on Cairo.

While Baird's army of 7,500 English and Indian soldiers mobilized at Bombay, 16,000 troops under Abercrombie, transported from England, Gibraltar, Portugal and Malta, underwent intensive training in landing operations on the coast of Asia Minor. Supported by the Royal Navy, Abercrombie landed at Aboukir Bay on March 8 and quickly established a beachhead. At Canopus, Abercrombie defeated a French force which withdrew to Alexandria. Meanwhile, an Ottoman army of 16,000 men under the grand vizier crossed into Egypt from the east, occupied Damietta and marched up the right bank of the Nile.

Leaving the blockade of Alexandria and Rosetta to subordinates, Lieutenant General John Hely-Hutchinson, the new commander replacing Abercrombie who fell in battle, advanced up the left bank of the Nile. Supported by another army of Turks, he forced the French back to Cairo. Although the British had vastly underestimated the strength of enemy garrisons, were stricken by disease and were short of siege guns, the disheartened French in Cairo were ready to capitulate. Facing the threat of rapidly advancing enemy armies from the north, Napoleon's dispirited generals exaggerated the reported danger from the south of a British landing on the Red Sea. By late June the French prepared to surrender.

Meanwhile in India, Baird and Wellesley had supervised the hurried mobilization of regiments for the expedition to Africa.[32] In March, an advance contingent of 700 European and Sepoy troops sailed from Bombay to the Persian Gulf. In April, the rest of Baird's army followed. Sick with the "Malabar Itch," and perhaps wary of serving under the quarrelsome Baird, Wellesley resigned from the general's staff to remain in India finding future opportunities for his talents in the Mahrattas Wars. McGrigor (who met Wellesley briefly during the preparations for the voyage) had many influential friends on the Bombay Medical Board of the East India Company. This fact, in addition to his demonstrated zeal in regimental sanitary matters, may have accounted for his unprecedented promotion from a mere army surgeon to become head of the medical department for the East India Company in Baird's command.[33]

The expedition sailed on April 3 from Bombay to the Red Sea. Aboard the *Minerva* McGrigor left a brief account of the voyage:

In consequence of an overland despatch from England, we hurried off from Bombay without having completed our water, and some corps left behind them their mussacks for its conveyance. The guinea-worm still raged on board; and I found that in the vessel in which was Mr. Bruce [McGrigor's assistant surgeon] it had spread to a greater extent than in that in which I was, having ran through most of the soldiers, several of the ship's crew and attacked Mr. Bruce himself, who suffered much torture from one in each leg. The disease is a very extraordinary one, and was new to me when I first met with it, although I was very well stocked with books, having had, I have reason to believe, a larger stock than most surgeons when we went to India. I looked in vain for an account of this loathsome and painful disease: I found mention merely of its name and antiquity, and that the only treatment was to pull it out daily.

A steady wind brought in past the opening of the Persian Gulf, and in a little time into the Straits of Babelmandel, We were then becalmed opposite the island of Socotra, which appeared a mere barren rock. . . .

We touched both at Jedda and Mocha. In going into the former place we struck on a sand-bank, and got off with some difficulty. In the same place, we found the LaForte frigate aground; she was subsequently lost in the Red Sea.

At Mocha we took on board a stock of its far-famed honey, which was most rich and famous. From Jedda to Cosseir the weather was bad; it blew fresh, and some accidents happened to the shipping before we anchored opposite Cosseir. [34]

While provisioning at Mocha on April 26, Baird heard of Abercrombie's victory near Alexandria. Then at Jedda in early May, Baird received a dispatch from Admiral John Blankett, cruising off Suez, informing him that because of pending monsoons, the Red Sea squadron would anchor at the Egyptian port of Cosseir to protect the landing of the Indian army. Baird also learned that an advanced party supported by ships from Capetown had already disembarked at Cosseir where it was procuring water bags, food supplies, and pack animals.

When McGrigor arrived at Cosseir on May 18, a hundred vessels were unloading their cargoes of men, cannon, provisions, oxen, cattle, horses, and barrels of water. Cosseir, a small village of mud huts, was once a marble quarry for the ancient Pharaohs. In recent times, Moslem merchants made it a trading depot in the exchange of Egyptian grain for Arabian coffee and Indian muslins. By June, however, Cosseir was transformed into a large military encampment as reinforcements arrived from the Cape. As the army prepared to cross the mysterious desert, the troops were still relatively healthy. "Yet the heat was intense," remembered McGrigor, "the regular duty severe, and preparatory to the march to the Nile, there was duty of fatigue, which for want of native followers . . . was done by the soldiers themselves." [35] To McGrigor's dismay, after supervising the welfare of 8,000 men at Cosseir, a newly arrived army physician from Capetown superseded him. Offered a postition as second in command of the medical department in the Indian army, McGrigor indignantly refused. With Baird's support, a compromise was reached. "It was decided that I should conduct the duties and superintend," wrote the proud Scot, "till the army crossed the desert and had joined the English army in Lower Egypt." [36]

Informed that Hely-Hutchinson had advanced up the Nile and that he had ordered the Indian army to assist at the siege of Cairo, Baird assembled his command for an historic event—the first attempt in modern times by a military force to cross the 130 miles of desert from the Red Sea to the Nile. The "route over the desert of Thebes," noted McGrigor in the only medical account of this stirring adventure, had been "unattempted by an army for perhaps two or three thousand years."[37] Baird was aware that the success of the expedition depended upon careful estimates of the physical capacities of the troops and upon adequate shelter and provisions for the march over the hot sands. He plotted the location of seven stations on the desert. Located about eight to twelve miles apart, these sanctuaries were at natural water wells, or were provided with portable water carried in leather bags and wooden casks by camels.[38]

The little army, accompanied by thousands of pack animals laden with water containers, sacks of rice, and jugs of wine, began to cross the barren country on June 19. Dividing his force into small units, Baird sent his men across the desert in stages. As each group reached a depot, it found food and water left by a previous party of soldiers. Marching only at night and resting during the day in tents, the expedition lost only three men from heat exhaustion, and within a week journeyed over the desert to Keneh on the Nile. Due to the careful preparations by McGrigor, Baird and Beresford, the army had made the dangerous crossing with few casualties. Citing the difficulties of the march, McGrigor stated:

There was but little sickness . . . , and yet almost every exciting cause existed. The heat was intense. In the currents of dust, much of it went into the stomach and lungs, and occasioned nausea, which was likewise occasioned by the hot destructive winds. To this the Arabs and even the camels turned their backs. . . . The fatigue on the march has perhaps never been exceeded by any army.[39]

Resting his army at Keneh, Baird learned that the enemy had already surrendered on June 28 in Cairo. Yet the French in Alexandria still defended the city, and Baird hoped to share in the glory of that last major siege of the Egyptian campaign. Baird gathered scores of native boats for the trip down the Nile. On July 29, the expedition began the 400-mile voyage to Cairo. Upon landing on August 12 at Gizeh, Baird discovered that he was again too late. The French in

Alexandria were contemplating surrender. On September 1, the enemy capitulated, and the fighting was over.

Ironically, France had defended Egypt and Britain had invaded it to strengthen their respective bargaining positions at the peace negotiations. But Napoleon realized that his Egyptian army was trapped, and the fall of Cairo had little effect on the armistice. The resulting treaty, the Peace of Amiens (March 27, 1802), marked the end of the War of the Second Coalition and the first halt in nine years of continual fighting. The Coalition powers recognized Napoleon's satellite republics in Europe and returned all the French colonies overseas along with the captured Dutch and Spanish colonies with the exception of Ceylon and Trinidad. Less significant than the conclusion of a war, but crucial in military morale were the victories in Egypt. The British army had inflicted upon the enemy in Egypt the single greatest defeat suffered by the French in the wars. Although Baird's army had barely fired a shot at the enemy, the expedition contributed to the rapid deterioration of the French will to fight. Moreover, the expedition caught the imagination of the English public for it dramatically revealed the feasibility of utilizing Sepoy troops, transported outside of the East Indies to a European theater of war for the first time, and it demonstrated that with adequate attention to medical care, a British army could cross an African desert.

The Egyptian campaign is important in medical history because the generals supported their surgeons' efforts to protect the health of troops, and because the expedition along the Nile introduced British medical doctors to the relatively new environment of North Africa. Due to his experiences in the Lowlands and the Caribbean, Abercrombie made careful preparations with an experienced medical staff. Yet regardless of Abercrombie's intentions, the military operations over vast and unfamiliar terrain resulted in innumerable difficulties for the medical department. Many of the troops, kept for weeks in crowded transport vessels, landed unfit for duty; the usual confusion typical of past campaigns with respect to shortages of medicine, personnel, and casualty conveyances characterized this expedition; and the great distances covered by troops marching rapidly along the Nile added to the problems of the hard-pressed surgeons trying to establish hospital stations close to the army.[40]

In the development of preventive medicine, the expedition was significant because British troops in Egypt and at other Mediterranean stations (Malta, Corsica, Sicily, Gibraltar) were the first overseas military contingents to be vaccinated against smallpox. Furthermore, doctors encountered two diseases generally familiar to them only through historical descriptions and not through personal observation—the deadly bubonic plague last seen in Western Europe in the 1720s and the debilitating ophthalmia of North Africa that caused partial or total blindness.

Prevalent in the filthy and squalid living conditions of native populations along the Nile since the ancient Pharoahs, eye diseases like trachoma, conjunctivitis, and ophthalmia struck French, Turkish, and British troops during the Egyptian campaigns and deprived thousands of soldiers partially or totally of their vision. Such diseases have now been specifically identified with precision by modern ophthalmologists. However, because medical men compiled evidence about these afflictions in the prescientific era of medicine, it is difficult to determine exactly what eye diseases these surgeons were describing. Dominique-Jean Larrey, surgeon in chief of Napoleon's Army of the Orient, had tried to cure the epidemic of eye diseases that swept through the French ranks. But he and his colleagues failed to detect the contagious nature of the diseases. Baffled by the pestilence, Larrey ascribed it to certain environmental conditions—the sun's rays, the warm south winds, the hot white sands, the daily temperature changes, and "the immoderate use of liquor and the women."[41] When the British arrived at Alexandria in 1801, over 1,000 French troops were either partially or totally blinded from the loathsome afflictions.

Naval and army surgeons in Abercrombie's army, also untrained in ophthalmology, were similarly perplexed by the nature of the disease which swiftly incapacitated hundreds of Turk and British troops. Through the efforts of McGrigor and other medical men (John Vetch, George Power, Henry Dewar, Arthur Edmonston) the first comprehensive studies of ophthalmia based on hundreds of cases were compiled. Their endeavors to study the disease promoted the establishment of the first ophthalmic hospitals in England. Although at least four other naval and army surgeons on the expedition are credited with studying the disease in a scientific manner, "the best and most complete report on ophthalmia during the campaign of 1801 was produced by James McGrigor . . ." stated Dr. Max Mayerhoff in 1934 for the British *Journal of Ophthalmology*.[42]

McGrigor's description of the disease corresponds to that of an acute purulent conjunctivitis, usually followed by a complete loss of the eye or by corneal specks and a chronic inflammation that lasted for months. "After the plague," McGrigor noted, "the most formidable disease in the army was ophthalmia. In the 10th and 88th regiments there were upwards of 350 cases. The total number in the [Indian] army exceeded six hundred."[43] McGrigor seems to have suspected the contagious nature of the disease:

Several gentlemen thought that this disease, in Egypt, was contagious. So singular an opinion I would hesitate to offer on slender grounds. However, the remarkable prevalence of the disease in particular companies of regiments, while the same general causes prevailed everywhere, will not be easily accounted for, without admitting something of the kind. . . . I believe that several diseases are contagious which are not suspected to arise from such a cause: the theory of contagion is but very imperfectly understood. . . . It could not escape observation how rarely officers were the subject of this disease. . . . I lay most stress on the attention which officers pay to cleanliness. In the 88th regiment where I believe, forty men did not escape an attack, only two officers out of thirty had ophthalmia.[44]

Among the numerous commentaries about the disease, one of the best was by a military officer, Lieutenant Colonel Robert T. Wilson, who restated the general ideas about eye disease held by the French. "The disease is believed to originate in the nitrous particles emitted from the ground by the force of the sun, which are of a quality so pungent and penetrating, as to endanger the fine vessels at the corner of the eye."[45] Yet Wilson aptly noted that ophthalmia was partly due to "the barbarous inattention of parents" to their children who "have from earliest infancy at the corner of their eyes great quantities of little insects continually settled."[46] Extracting information about eye diseases from the medical reports, Wilson reported that the British soldiers "have suffered considerably, one hundred and sixty being totally blind, and two hundred having lost one eye irrecoverably."[47]

These sightless British victims were eventually repatriated to England and were treated at a special army hospital at Chichester. Due to the great incidence of ophthalmia among returning army veterans, the spread of the disease in barracks in Britain among regiments disbanded after the Peace of Amiens, and the consequent appearance of the malady in lower classes, many practitioners in Britain became familiar with ophthalmia.[48] Matching the degree of medical specialization in smallpox and obstetrics that was underway, a civilian hospital which studied eye diseases opened in 1805. In 1821 the London Ophthalmic Hospital was founded, and in 1827 it received royal patronage. "The contagious nature of the disease, not admitted by French surgeons," concluded Mayerhoff, "was discovered by several surgeons of the British army and navy . . . and established by judicious observations."[49]

McGrigor maintained a great interest in eye diseases, and he frequently corresponded about the maladies.[50] Yet his handling of the bubonic plague enhanced his reputation as a practical hospital administrator. After the evacuation, in September, 1801, of the French forces from Egypt, one half of the British army was transferred to Mediterranean stations while the remainder, including the Indian army, remained on occupation duty. The Rangers were posted to Rosetta where McGrigor, guarding the medical stores for his regiments, became comfortably ensconced in a desert setting resembling the encampment of an Old Testament patriarch.

I had upwards of a dozen Indian servants with their wives, besides my English soldier servant; and for my stock, three cattle, two horses, twenty-four sheep, three goat etc. My own large Indian marque was in the centre, and around were small Arab tents, which my Indian servants had raised for themselves. In another quarter were found all my animals, and a stores tent, in which some of the servants nightly kept watch, and made rounds to see that no marauders made incursions upon us. . . .

But McGrigor's idyllic life at Rosetta soon terminated. He was restored to the superintendence of the medical department of the Indian army and moved to Baird's headquarters at Alexandria to assume his duties. Worried about the amount of sickness in the ranks even though the men were relatively inactive, and about the fearsome plague that perennially smote the Nile population, McGrigor initiated sanitary measures to protect his men.

My first measure was to take steps to meet the appearance of the plague for although no case actually existed, I thought it right to make the necessary preparations. I made immediate representations to General Baird, and, with his sanction, made immediate arrangements for pesthouses, houses of observation, as well as for the formation of a board of health.[51]

McGrigor's precautions were barely established in September when the dreaded pestilence struck the army hospital in Alexandria. He persuaded Baird to envoke emergency quarantine provisions: removal of the sick to isolated areas, transfer of the regiments to cleaner quarters of thatched, well-ventilated huts outside of the filthy native towns, fumigation of regimental living accommodations, and daily inspection of the troops. McGrigor's actions helped to check the spread of the plague. "From the time the sick of the 88th regiment were separated," he reported, "and from regulations regarding cleanliness and fumigation being rigidly adhered to, the progress of the contagion was effectively suppressed in that regiment."[52] During November, 1801, the disease spread to all the other British units along the Nile, and one fourth of the army was stricken with the disease. Gradually, as other surgeons followed McGrigor's leadership, the plague began to diminish in intensity, and the numbers of deaths from the pestilence declined sharply. The real heroes of this combat with the mysterious foe (carried by flea-infested rats) were the regimental surgeons. Thirteen of them volunteered for duty in the "pest-houses" of quarantine with their patients, seven of the doctors caught the infection, and four died from it.

Cured of the plague by March, 1802, Baird's army was ordered back to India. The force left Alexandria on May 2, marched up the Nile, and encamped by the pyramids.[53] By traveling only at night, the well-provisioned army reached Suez without mishap and sailed on June 2 for Bombay. Delighted that only a relatively small number (10 percent) of his men had perished from diseases on the entire expedition to Egypt, and gratified by the support in preventive measures that he had received from Baird and Beresford, McGrigor commented:

During an uncommonly long voyage, in a march over extensive deserts, in a country and climate described the most inimical to the human race, the Indian army enjoyed a considerable degree of health, and suffered only a small mortality. . . . In no army, perhaps, was the health of every man in it more the care of every officer, from the general downwards than in the Indian army. . . . To conclude, never, perhaps, was there an army healthier than the Indian army when it embarked on its return from Egypt.[54]

By the time Baird's army arrived at Bombay on August 13, 1802, McGrigor was entrusted with a new responsibility. The Bombay Medical Board feared that a contagion could be carried from Persia where another horrible plague was raging. It ordered that every vessel sailing to India from the Red Sea and the Persian Gulf anchor at Butchers Island in Bombay harbor for a medical inspection before proceeding further. Writing to Baird on June 16, the Medical Board had assigned this task to McGrigor: "the Senior Surgeon attached to the troops

daily expected from Egypt [to] be appointed to the Medical Duties of the Lazareeto at Butchers Islands and that he take charge of
the office immediately on his arrival."[55] Supported by a company of
Marines and an East India Company cruiser to enforce the quarantine
decrees, McGrigor spent six months on the island station. He inspected scores of ships until the danger of the plague had passed. Fortunately, the pestilence had not accompanied the ships bound for India, and McGrigor stated that he found no trace of the plague on ships
coming from the Persian Gulf.[56] Thus, while handling a crucial post
for the East India Company, McGrigor had augmented his reputation
as a medical administrator and had gained more experience in regulating public health measures.

After his duty on Butchers Island, McGrigor was posted to the 88th
stationed in Bombay. During his last months in India, he experimented with remedies for syphillis and for dysentery, completed an audit
of the medical department account for the Indian army in Egypt, and,
during his leisure, began an account of the Red Sea expedition.

On March 7, 1803, McGrigor and the Rangers sailed homeward on
the small *Cambrian*. The vessel arrived at Capetown on May 19 after
an uneventful voyage, and on June 27, departed from South Africa.
While passing through the South Atlantic in September, the *Cambrian*
encountered an American vessel which informed the surprised regiment that Britain was again at war with Napoleon and that French
privateers were in nearby waters. In order to deceive the enemy into
believing that the *Cambrian* was a man-of-war, her captain had dummy
wooden cannon constructed, the rigging altered, the sides of the vessel
repainted, and the army officers paraded on the decks in full dress uni-
forms in order to present the appearance of naval officers commanding
a well-armed frigate. Some unidentified vessels followed the *Cambrian*
for several days, but the deception evidently duped the pursuers who
veered off, leaving the vessel free to complete its voyage to Cork.

While at sea, McGrigor continued to write his manuscript, and
during a leave of absence after his return to Britain he completed his
narrative. Three colleagues, William Wright, Sir Walter Farquhar,
and Gilbert Blane, encouraged the modest McGrigor to publish his
work. Writing to a colleague in Edinburgh on November 5, 1803,
Wright stated:

I am hoping to introduce you to my excellent friend Mr. James McGrigor,
surgeon of the 88th Regiment who had the medical direction of the Indian

Army when in Egypt. He has everything to recommend him as a gentleman, a philosopher, and a physician. He has a vast number of medical communication and observations on the plagues and other fevers of Egypt and of India. His extreme modesty, I fear, may prevent him from arranging and publishing his materials; but I shall continue to urge him doing so, because I know they will be extremely useful.[57]

McGrigor discovered that no other medical officer in Abercrombie's army had written an account of the expedition. In 1804, he published *Medical Sketches of the Expedition to Egypt*, a work closely modeled on Sir John Pringle's *Observations*. Worried about his writing style, McGrigor stated:

Of the numerous imperfections of the Sketch, I am abundantly sensible. The life of a medical man in the army is at no time very favourable to literary pursuits; mine has been peculiarly unfavourable; and I had little time or opportunity since I first entered the army to attend the ornaments of diction. For the last fifteen years of my life . . . my time has been occupied in a laborious attention to my duty in the army.[58]

And equally modest about his knowledge of medicine, he noted:

I have purposedly avoided doubtful speculation and hypotheses. Anxious, above all, to adhere closely to fact, and keeping them unmixed with notions of my own . . . as statements of facts, from which everyone can form deductions for himself, as they stand, they appeared to be much more useful than any conjection which I might hazard to advance. It is to be feared that too often, facts and details are made to bend to preconceived opinions and theories. . . .

On the causes of disease, I have dwelt a short time that to some may have appeared unnecessary. But I thought that, while the general causes of the diseases of soldiers and sailors have been ably handled by a Pringle, and a Lind, a Cleghorn, and a Huxham a Blane and a Hunter,—from me, little could be expected.

On grounds that appear not slight, we suspected that several of these diseases were propagated by contagion. But I have no intention of entering on the discussion of contagion; an obscure subject, and on which I do not presume to think that I could throw any new light. If ever the veil which covers it be removed, the late discoveries in chemistry bid fair to do it. The accurate knowledge which we have acquired of the composition of bodies, and in particular of the constitutional parts of the atmosphere, have opened new fields of inquiry to the philosopher and to the physician.[59]

In this work, McGrigor revealed his fascination with climatological influences on disease that characterized his earlier writings. "I am decidedly of opinion that in the peculiar soil and climate of Egypt. . .

we are to look for the principal causes of disease which prevailed the most in that country."[60] He believed that a variety of interrelated environmental factors caused disease. Foremost was the miasma in the atmosphere caused by the prevalence of "hydro-carbonate" gases emitted by decaying vegetable matter. Secondly, the unhealthiness of the Nile Valley resulted from the yearly subsiding of the river itself: "There is a great exhalation from the mud, and from putrid animal and vegetable matter left behind. The effluvia of these substances, acting upon the human body, will readily account for most disease." A number of other pertinent factors that also accounted for the prevalence of sickness among the troops—"the extreme filth of the inhabitants of Egypt," "the dry parching wind," the "noxious moisture from the marshes, the heavy dews, and improper diet, and the excessive consumption of hard liquor."[61]

Beyond this discussion of disease based on a traditional miasmatic and climatological pathology, McGrigor added a new element to army medical history by stressing the heretofore unsung bravery of army surgeons who fought deadly sickness in pestilent hospital wards:

From the nature of the prevailing disease, the campaign in Egypt was, in a peculiar degree, a service of danger. To their regret, the Indian army arrived too late in Egypt to share in other dangers than those arriving from the diseases of the country; and here, the medical gentlemen had the post of honour. The zeal, attention, and perseverness displayed, particularly by those employed in the plague-establishments, deserves every praise. Nothing can so possibly incite the exertions of medical men, in such circumstances of danger, as the consciousness of co-operating with the best and most enlightened of mankind for the alleviation of human misery. Intrepidity is more than a military virtue; but seldom I believe has there been a greater display of it than among the medical officers in Egypt, whose duty it was to reside in the pest-houses.[62]

Another major point that McGrigor emphasized was the necessity for surgeons to keep detailed case histories of their patients. This record-keeping, he insisted, was extremely useful in acquiring a knowledge about a disease such as the plague. "Thus, the history of the disease, in most of its points," he stated, "came to be investigated; and previously to entering a pest-house, before his tour came round, every [surgeon] had acquired some knowledge of the plague, and of the success of other practitioners."[63] In a passage that indicates McGrigor's passion for requiring medical registers in the army, he wrote:

I think it is a matter of regret that such journals are not more perfectly kept throughout the army; with a little industry on the part of the profession they might always be so. Had such records been always faithfully kept, many practical points would not, as they are now, be involved in doubt and uncertainty. We should not now be so ignorant of some diseases of the countries where we have so often made campaigns or of which we have so long been in the possession. Humble as the labours may seem and confined as the abilities of an individual may be, were he only faithfully to relate observations made with care, to compare them with his contemporaries, and by these to correct the opinions of his predecessors, he would perform no mean service to his art.[64]

McGrigor also demonstrated the necessity for close cooperation between the military and the medical in order to protect an army's health. He cited the reforms in naval hygiene of Lind, Bland, and Trotter, and the improvements in army sanitation of the Medical Board and the commander in chief. As an example of how to curtail sickness at sea, McGrigor stated that he had protested to the East India Company authorities at Trincomalee over the overcrowded condition of the *Minerva* on the passage from Bombay to Ceylon. As a result, the company provided additional vessels for the return voyage. On the trip to Egypt, he explained, the provisions that he had distributed to the troops helped to preserve their health at sea—"Potatoes, onions, breadfruit, pickled vegetables, often rice, and pepper which were regularly served to all."[65] Lecturing to the generals about the proper care of their troops, McGrigor concluded: "The fact cannot be too often repeated or too generally known, that nothing conduces more to the health of a corps, than the preserving a good internal economy of it. A good commanding officer has, in general, a healthy regiment."[66]

Thus, McGrigor chronicled his adventures in the East with a landmark in military medicine. He wrote a comprehensive medical history of a significant campaign in an exotic environment, and he also provided military officers with practical lessons in army hygiene. Furthermore, he had acquired a reputation as a farsighted administrator of hospitals, and as one of the foremost sanitarians in the army.

# V

## ADMINISTRATOR OF
## ARMY HOSPITALS

McGrigor rejoined the 88th in November, 1803, for a bleak winter at Helsham, Sussex. Deprived of an assistant surgeon, and overwhelmed by the work of curing many sick Irish recruits, McGrigor "found the duty irksome and heavy...."[1] After supervising the medical affairs of an entire army in North Africa, the overworked surgeon relished a promotion to another corps in order to demonstrate his administrative talents.

Now a seasoned veteran of overseas campaigns, McGrigor transferred in February, 1804, to the Horse Guards Blue at Canterbury. After a decade of the Rangers' rough and ready life, he smiled at the ornate and resplendent dress of these Household troops, and at their punctilious military code. Ludicrously attired in the field dress of his new regiment, recalled McGrigor, "I burst into laughter at my own appearance, equipped as I was with a broad buff belt, jack boots that came high up my thighs, and stout leather gloves which reached nearly to my elbows, with a large, fierce-looking cocked hat, and a sword of great weight, as well as length."[2]

In the spring, the Blues moved to Windsor, where the formality of military ritual was even more rigidly maintained. To his dismay, McGrigor discovered that at court functions involving his regiment, he was required to wear a very ostentatious uniform instead of the simpler attire for medical officers recently ordered by the Duke of York. Uncertain about what costume he was supposed to wear, and unable to purchase a new outfit from his meager pay, McGrigor had to borrow a comrade's uniform. Yet his superiors still chastised him for being improperly dressed for royal balls. Disliking pomp and ceremony and resenting distractions from his medical duties, McGrigor admitted that while serving with the aristocratic Blues, "military etiquette interfered to annoy me not a little."[3]

The Blues delighted their sovereign, George III, with their displays of martial valor demonstrated in drills and parades. The king took a keen interest in the regiment—he often inspected the horsemen on reviews, visited their quarters, and appointed himself a captain of a regimental troop. Showing a concern for the rank and file, His Majesty occasionally questioned McGrigor about the health of the soldiers. To the joy of the ambitious surgeon, he discovered that the king was familiar with his service record. "I was questioned by him about the continent when I served under the Duke of York," remembered McGrigor. "He asked me about the state of slavery in the West Indies, about India, and made many inquiries about Egypt."[4] Bothered by a severe inflammation of the eyes, the king prepared to leave Windsor in August for the supposedly beneficial sea air of Weymouth. As he inspected the troops before departing, His Majesty noticed McGrigor, and referring to his own eye ailment, said to the surgeon: "Aye, aye, this is one of the fruits of the expedition to Egypt."[5]

McGrigor's work in the East had also attracted the attention of William Dundas (1742–1811). Formerly treasurer of the navy, home secretary, secretary of war, Dundas was ennobled as Lord Melville in 1802. In 1804 Melville was first lord of the Admiralty and was also president of the Board of Control for India. In 1805, he attempted to create a fourth Indian Presidency at Penang, Malaya, to be called Prince of Wales Island. As "the uncrowned king of Scotland," and controller of patronage for India, Melville had placed relatives and followers in many government posts, and he planned to nominate McGrigor, a fellow Scot, as head of the medical department for the new colony. McGrigor was aware that he would have to resign his army commission in order to qualify for the lucrative appointment with the East India Company. But after decades of an active political life, his patron Melville had a horde of enemies. A Parliamentary committee, the Tenth Committee of Naval Inquiry, charged that Melville's administration of public funds while serving as naval treasurer was suspect, and in April, 1805, impeachment proceedings were instituted against him.

Opposition Whig periodicals denounced Melville with vitriolic comments about the projected Presidency. His antagonists called the new colony "Nova Scotia" and predicted that it would be looted by Melville's hungry Scot countrymen. Although Melville was acquitted of the charge of malversation by the House of Lords (June 12,1806), the previous year McGrigor withdrew his own candidacy for the medical post. Embarrassed by the publicity, and conscious that company doctors opposed his appointment, McGrigor had informed Melville that he wished to remain in the army.

Although he lamented the loss of a prized opportunity in the East, McGrigor was soon reconciled by an unprecedented promotion to a supervisory office. The advancement of a meritorious surgeon was usually to the rank of staff surgeon, and then, after some years in grade, to the rank of physician to the forces. On February 20, 1804, McGrigor was awarded his M.D. degree from Marischal College with a thesis on regimental hospitals, and undoubtedly, the title of "Dr." further qualified him for a promotion. On June 27, 1805, he was named deputy inspector of hospitals for the northwest district of York. Dr. McGrigor now had the opportunity to initiate reforms in medical care, to establish improved standards of performance by his subordinates, and to correlate statistical data on the health of many regiments in his jurisdiction.

Explaining his duties as an army hospital inspector, McGrigor commented that after his initial tour of regimental facilities, he pondered "turning the reports and returns made by the surgeons to the purposes of professional and scientific information...." To his dismay, the Medical Board did not require statistical reports about the health of regiments, nor did it attempt to improve the professional level of its surgeons. Instead, the board stressed economy in hospital accounts and treated its surgeons like mere clerks:

The most minute and scrupulous attention was not only exacted in the number of ounces of soap, salt, oatmeal, etc. given to each patient, but an error even in the fractional parts brought down the animadversion of the board...; while no notice was taken of any new or extraordinary feature of prevailing disease, no propositions ... nor any injunctions issued to notice post mortem appearances.

To counteract the board's accounting mania, McGrigor lectured to his staff on current medical literature, and he demonstrated his techniques for compiling medical registers. He stressed that "a military hospital was the best for trying the effects of all new remedies . . . because, there the patient was more under the control and observation...." Caustic with the lazy surgeon and complimentary to the diligent, McGrigor endeavored to instill in his men a sense of pride and professionalism that heretofore was lacking in the medical department.[6]

McGrigor's work won the praise of Francis Knight, the inspector general of hospitals, and the commendation of the Duke of York, who urged that the capable inspector be rewarded with a more responsible position. Transferred on June 27, 1806, to the southwest district, Mc-Grigor now supervised a larger area—Hants, Dorset, Wiltshire, Somerset, Gloucester, Worcester, South Wales, and Hampshire. He also administered the general hospital on the Isle of Wight, and supervised the embarkation of troops from Portsmouth. Although his responsibilities were enormous, McGrigor relished his new role. "For this I could not complain of," he explained, "for from boyhood I ever delighted to traveling, and I found an inspection tour a great relaxation, after much writing duty, and my regular course of reading at headquarters."[7] His administrative duties also encompassed the supervision of medical services for the ophthalmic hospitals, a prisoner of war camp, recruiting depots, and the inspection of army and militia garrisons in his district. "I was not dismayed, however, by the extent and formidable nature of the duties..." he wrote. "At this time I courted such a charge, I was full of activity and zeal, and full of confidence. ...If I grasped at much, my appetite was soon gratified."[8]

In addition to these duties, McGrigor had to oversee the provisioning of medical supplies and the staffing of medical personnel for military expeditions that assembled at Portsmouth for overseas destinations. In a revealing passage about his inspection of ships, McGrigor wrote:

I had to examine each of the transports appointed for the reception of the troops, the quantity of the provisions, and particularly the water on board; also the accommodation for any sick that might occur during the voyage, and the supplies of medical comfort as well as of medicine, together with the stock of chirurigical material and instruments supplied and embarked for the expedition. I had furthermore, to examine, and inspect each corps as to its health when it arrived, to receive each of the medical officers of the staff . . . and finally, to survey each transport and inspect each corps after embarkation . . . in fact, I placed the medical concerns of every expedition in an efficient state in the hands of the inspector, or principal medical officer of the expedition, before he sailed from Portsmouth, leaving him little to do while there.[9]

At Portsmouth, where British armies sailed for the Iberian Peninsula, McGrigor in December, 1808, encountered an awesome task—providing staff and hospital accommodations for the returning veterans of a tragic campaign in Spain. Sir John Moore's army had been driven from the Peninsular port of La Coruña by the relentless Napoleonic juggernaut that was sweeping over Spain. Now the medical department quickly prepared for the arrival of Moore's shattered army.

By 1808, the Peninsular War had developed into the major theater of war between France and Britain. Napoleon had regarded the Peace of Amiens as a mere truce. Although he suffered a severe maritime defeat at Trafalgar in 1805, his military machine rolled on as he smashed the Austrians and the Prussians and Russians. With the Treaty of Tilsit (1807), Napoleon imposed his peace on Europe.

Yet some states still eluded him. Britain defiantly mocked his plans for a Channel invasion. Both Portugal and Spain remained independent and resisted efforts to cooperate in Napoleon's Continental System. Yet Napoleon duped the inept Bourbon rulers in Madrid and made a treaty that provided for the joint occupation of Portugal between France and Spain. As his troops crossed the Pyrenees, he then proceeded to acquire all of Iberia. While French armies marched to Lisbon in November, 1807, Napoleon also dispatched divisions to occupy cities in northern Spain. Forcing the royal family to abdicate and assured of an easy conquest, Napoleon sent a force to Madrid and proclaimed his brother, Joseph, the new king of Spain.

French marshals proceeded to occupy the Spanish provinces with ease. But on May 2, 1808, the entire nation erupted into a vast xenophobic outburst of defiance against their conquerors. Although the French defeated Spanish armies in June and July, a Spanish victory at Bailen smashed the myth of this invincibility. Stunned by the resistance, the French withdrew to the Ebro River in the north to await reinforcements. Now Britain had her long awaited chance to land a force on the mainland. The Portland Cabinet ordered Lieutenant General Sir Arthur Wellesley, home from his triumphs in India, to command a British army for service in Portugal. Wellesley won a decisive victory over the French and opened the road to Lisbon. Although he planned to push the enemy out of Portugal, Wellesley was checked by his more cautious superiors on the scene who granted the French there an armistice.

In the meantime, the British government, emboldened by Wellesley's victory in Portugal and anxious to assist the beleaguered Spanish from the French invaders, gambled on a daring scheme proposed by Sir John Moore. Moore—leading an army composed of divisions un-

der Generals Sir John Hope, Sir David Baird, and William Carr Beresford—began an heroic 400-mile march in October through the Portuguese highlands to Spain in order to cut the enemy supply line at the
Pyrenees.

As Moore converged upon Salamanca in early November, Napoleon, enraged over his reversals in the Peninsula, reinforced his armies
in northern Spain. Anxious to recover lost prestige over "the Spanish
Affair," as he termed it, Napoleon stormed into Vitoria on November
7 to personally direct the conquest operations. By late November, as
Moore was still marching toward the Pyrenees, Napoleon had
smashed the entire Spanish army in the north and by early December,
he issued a conqueror's decrees from occupied Madrid. By Christmas,
Moore was at Sahagun, north of Salamanca, when he suddenly realized that enemy armies and the great Napoleon himself, forcing his
Imperial Guard through blizzards in the Sierra de Guadarrama
mountains, were hurrying to trap him.

In a nightmarish march through winter storms, Moore withdrew
his tired army over the Esla River and pressed on to Astorga in Leon.
With the French only 36 hours behind, Moore pushed his hungry and
exhausted men on a harrowing retreat unparalleled in the Peninsular
War. As the demoralized British hurried to the seacoast, they pillaged
villages for bread and wine. Regimental morale began to collapse under the stress of constant marching through the bleak terrain, the prevalence of disease in the ranks, and the constant pressure on their trail of
the relentless French. "A malignant fever was raging . . . among the
Spanish troops that joined the retreat," wrote Dr. Adam Neale in one
of the few published medical accounts of the campaign, and "our men
half-famished, half-frozen, desperate . . . were altogether furious, and
no longer under any sort of control."[10] After a horrifying journey to
the coast on which bodies of men and horses, guns, and baggage were
strewn all over the route to safety, Moore's army staggered out of the
cold mountains on January 10, 1809, to the temporary haven of the
Spanish seaport of La Coruña. Here transport vessels awaited to rescue them. Unable to evacuate because stormy winds delayed the
docking of the rescue ships, the British made a desperate last-ditch
resistance at La Coruña as the French bombarded the town. Unable
to crack the determined British defenses and appalled by his severe
casualties, Marshal Soult, who directed the attack, withdrew and permitted the British to evacuate from the coast. Again the army, saved

once more by the navy, had to withdraw from the Continent after a grueling winter retreat.

For the veterans of the campaign, the voyage home was another horror. "In their retreat, the troops suffered extremely from hunger, fatigue, and all the privations incident to war," lamented McGrigor, "while the seeds of contagious fever made their appearance; and by the time they disembarked typhus fever had spread widely among them."[11] The authority on Moore's expedition to Spain, Christopher Hibbert, describes the passage to England in a more gruesome fashion:

The small transports were crammed to the bulwarks with filthy, blood-smeared soldiers; the terrified horses that stamped and kicked viciously on holds so tight that they could only move their legs; with guns and baggage and rows of wounded men with maggots crawling in their wounds beneath slimy bandages.... Between 29 and 31 January, at nearly every port along the coast from Falmouth and Dover, the creaking vessels came into land their shocking cargoes. Ragged, bearded, caked in dirt and covered with lice, the soldiers tumbled upon the quay sides....[12]

One of the first ships to arrive from Coruña carried Sir David Baird, McGrigor's old friend from the Red Sea expedition, now a wounded warrior writhing in agony from a shipboard amputation to his arm. While assisting in his comrade's removal from the vessel, the sight of emaciated and verminous hordes of men disgorged by ship after ship landing at Portsmouth stunned McGrigor. The mauled army "appeared more the victims of disease than of the sword of the enemy," he remembered.[13] "The sick and healthy mixed together indiscriminately it was no wonder that the great number of cases of fever landed in the last stage of typhus was great," he continued. "In fact it was enormous, and it excited great alarm in Portsmouth, and in the neighboring country when an account of the mortality came to be noised abroad."[14] At Portsmouth, McGrigor again demonstrated his administrative ability during a crisis by winning a reputation for his efficiency and humanitarianism in the handling of the sick. In a cogent account, McGrigor described how he found more medical personnel and how he acquired additional hospitals:

The number of sick and wounded were overwhelming for the accommodation which Portsmouth could afford. I had all my energies at work in framing arrangements. In order to provide medical attendance, Mr. [Francis] Knight sent down the medical officers of the household troops, and those of the militia who were disposable; and I was further empowered to engage the services of such of the civil practitioners as I could obtain in and about Portsmouth; and the whole of these found ample employment. After occupying all the ordinary hospital accommodations in and about Portsmouth and converting some barracks into hospitals, on application to the admiralty, the large naval hospital at Haslar . . . was given up to use. . . . Still the number of typhus fever cases continued to accumulate, and we were obliged to have recourse to floating hospitals, such as transports, prison ships, etc; and these were the very worst description of hospitals. . . . The number of sick landed at Portsmouth was great, and that number was increased considerably. Typhus fever spread to all the militia and other corps in and near Portsmouth, and the militia suffered most. These corps furnished orderlies and attendants for the sick and further, all their medical officers gave their professional attendance to the sick and wounded at Portsmouth.[15]

Commenting on the Coruña crisis, McGrigor explained that the typhus among the rank and file placed an enormous strain on overcrowded military hospital facilities. By July, 1809, regardless of heroic efforts of his diligent medical staff, another 400 soldiers died of the disease. "It is probable that the whole of the misfortunes of this brave and ill-fated army," he noted, "were induced by causes which no human ability could have foreseen or averted. . . ." Anxious to raise the prestige of the army doctor, and to praise those brave surgeons who risked their lives on the battlefield, in the dank holds of ships, and in pestilent hospital wards, McGrigor made a novel and forthright plea for the dignity of the medical professions:

What could be done by the gentlemen of the Medical Department in Spain, under circumstances the most arduous, I firmly believe was done. I willingly bear public testimony to the great zeal and humanity of these gentlemen on landing at Portsmouth, as well as of the other medical gentlemen employed to attend a sick army here. Theirs was a service of a real danger as any that had occurred to military officers in Spain, and it is much to be lamented that so many of them fell a sacrifice to the zealous and unwearied discharge of their duty here.[16]

McGrigor's handling of the sick after Coruña won praise from the Horse Guards and, on August 25, 1809, a promotion from the Army Medical Board to the rank of inspector of hospitals.

Sir Lucas Pepys, the physician general, Thomas Keate, the surgeon general, and Francis Knight, the inspector general of hospitals, were criticized for inept administration by surgeons who had served in Spain. These charges publicized the inability of the quarreling board members to agree on policies, the wretched handling of the sick at Salamanca, the miserable hospital diet of the sick, and the board's zeal for economy in hospital accounts compared to their neglect of proper medical care. Furious at the treatment of the wounded in Spain, the lack of medical supplies, and at the brutal handling of the incapacitated men in Portsmouth, where men were "left to pine in the harbours of their native country for several days...," Dr. Adam Neale complained bitterly to the physician general that the board was "imposing a Task upon Medical Officers, much beyond the abilities of a single man to execute—by which I mean the preposterous system of requiring one man to prescribe for a considerable number of sick, while at the same time he acts as purveyor, keeping a most intricate set of stoppages accounts and besides called upon daily to furnish daily returns." In a similar vein, Charles Tice, physician to the forces, cited the lack of hospital facilities at Portsmouth, where, as a consequence, many medical cases "proved fatal and the exertions of the medical officers on many occasions are entirely frustrated." Shocked by the callous treatment of the troops, Tice explained "that my obligations toward the sick soldiers are the sole motives in calling for reforms of the medical department." Supporting his colleagues in these accusations was Dr. Arthur Brooke Faulkner, who protested bitterly about the hospital diet for the Coruña sick: "The pernicious effects of Salt rations and Rum upon Invalids suffering from a complaint so peculiarly liable to relapse as Dysentery requires no commentary."[17]

Now, for the first time since its formation, the Medical Board's administration was subject to protracted and publicized debates. Yet, compared to the state of military medicine in 1793 when the board was formed, the members had initiated some improvements. Since 1794, the board advised on the location in construction of barracks, on quarantine measures for troops returning from the Indies, and upon sanitary precautions to safeguard troops sailing from British ports. Furthermore, the board had standardized the type and amounts of drugs and medicines for a regimental pharmacopoeia and the instruments and supplies for a surgeon's kit. By 1798, more rigid medical inspections of recruits were under way, regulations were promulgated for general and regimental hospitals, and by 1801, rules for the administration of smallpox vaccination were issued. For a decade the board had attempted to convince the authorities that a specific number of hospital ships should accompany each military expedition, a suggestion that Abercrombie had heeded on his Egyptian invasion. In addition to the establishment of special hospitals (York, Ealing, Wight, Chichester), the board had tried to better the standard hospital diet for patients. The board had also improved the pay, pension, and promotion policies for medical personnel.[18]

Nevertheless, the board was frequently charged with corruption, favoritism, inequitous personnel policies, with inexplicable lethargy in providing medical staff for campaigns and in handling casualties. When the board was established in 1793, the three members were supposed to work in unison, but because their duties and responsibilities were never coherently defined, each member acted independently. A Royal Warrant (March 12, 1798) inadvertently splintered the board's authority, as the members became virtually autonomous over specific areas of medical administration.[19] As long as no Parliamentary inquiry or public outcry over the inadequacies of army medical care occurred, the board continued to direct the medical affairs of the service in this devisive manner. Due to their incessant quarrels, however, the board members achieved notoriety as Pepys and Keate, usually on one side, feuded with Knight on the other. They bickered about respective areas of jurisdiction and responsibility in many aspects of military medicine: patronage, appointments, the purchase and distribution of supplies and medicine, the respective merits of Oxford and Cambridge degrees in medicine compared to degrees from northern universities, and the relative advantages of general hospitals compared to regimental establishments.

The endless squabbling remained submerged from public view until 1808, but the members' particular views on these subjects were familiar to the medical staff. Supervisory personnel like McGrigor, who usually supported Knight, found themselves involved in the board's disagreements. Knight had military experience at home as a surgeon with the Coldstream Guards, where he won the praise of the Duke of York for his accounting procedures, and he had served in the Helder campaign. But Pepys and Keate, who still maintained their civilian practices in London, were unfamiliar with the actual practice of medicine in the army, and neither had served on overseas expeditions. The physician general, claimed a surgeon, had made only one brief visit to an army hospital during his entire tenure of office.[20] It is apparent that the board was incapable of providing proper leadership to the medical department, that the members themselves were inept representatives of the medical profession, that morale of the medical officers was low, and that a drastic reorganization of the leadership of the medical department was long overdue.

Even during the Coruña crisis, the Medical Board quarreled. Declining any blame for the mismanagement of hospitals, Knight wrote to the war secretary that the surgeon general had the responsibility for the medical department overseas and that he himself was innocent of any charges. For his part, Keate denied the accusations of negligence and blamed Knight for incompetence.[21]

The scandalous feuding of the Medical Board merely confirmed the outspoken views of McGrigor's friend, Robert Jackson. The temperamental Jackson had criticized the board for a decade because of its corruption, inefficiency, and for its neglect of the rank and file. Through Jackson's books and articles, which attracted a wide following, the Medical Board was often castigated by the angry doctor. When Jackson was nominated in 1808 for an administrative post in Spain the vindictive physician general and surgeon general vetoed the appointment. Soon after, the embittered Jackson encountered Pepys on a London street, and thrashed his enemy with a cane. Charged with assault, Jackson offered no defense and served six months in King's Bench Prison. Jackson was not the only capable medical man who earned the board's enmity, but the example of Jackson's difficulties with his immediate superiors aptly demonstrated the viciousness of the board to subordinates who dared to criticize its administration of military medicine.[22]

The supervision of the army medical department had heretofore not been scrutinized by Parliament. In January, 1808, however, the Fifth Report of the Commissioners of Military Inquiry, a Parliamentary committee that was part of a broad investigation of the handling of naval, military, and financial matters by the Portland government, was published. It was very critical of the Medical Board. After citing the need to improve personnel policies, and the elimination of superfluous offices, the commissioners severely indicted the methods by which the Medical Board purchased, inspected, and distributed drugs and hospital equipment from the apothecary general who held the monopoly of medical supplies for the army. Critical of the vast patronage held by the board members, their ill-defined functions and their overlapping, uncoordinated responsibilities, the report urged "an undivided and more efficient management." The M.P.s on the committee sympathized with numerous complaints from surgeons about the board's mania for conformity to its budgetary regulations, and they urged "a less interfering control" by hospital inspectors who enforced the board's decrees on financial matters.[23]

But more significant was the report's opinion on the controversy over the administration of army hospitals. The commissioners indicated their preference for the regimental hospital system advocated by Jackson and by McGrigor, both of whom had testified to the committee. Citing Jackson's books as exemplary commentaries on the need for army hospital reforms, the commissioners stated that general hospitals have "been attended with most destructive consequences to sick soldiers . . . and that Hospitals, both at home and Abroad . . . should be managed Regimentally."[24]

Furthermore, the commissioners recommended improvements in the training of army surgeons to match the navy and ordnance medical departments. For example, the M.P.s noted that prior to the appointment of ordnance hospital mates to engineer or artillery battalions, candidates were required to attend a course of military medicine at Woolwich where they learned "a knowledge of the discipline and economy of a Military Hospital, and of the habits and peculiar diseases of Soldiers. . . ." Agreeing with Jackson, who had long called for an army medical college, the commissioners proposed "that a school should be established expressly for the education of surgeons from the British army, where they might learn similar management and economy." Most important, the report recommended that the existing Medical Board "should be discontinued, and that the superintendence of the Medical Department of the Army should be placed in a Board of Commissioners, consisting of a Chairman, and of two junior members." The report stated that "it is requisite that the Chairman should be well acquainted with the details of the Military Service, both at home and Abroad, and the two Junior members should be medical officers, who have served in the capacities of Regimental and Staff Surgeons in different climates, and on active service. The Existence of a Board so constituted would, we think, provide much beneficial improvement in the medical System of the Army."[25]

In numerous letters to the Ministry, each board member proclaimed that the commissioners had conducted a partisan inquiry and that his own professional integrity had been damaged. Joining the acrimonious debate as a defender of Pepys and Keate was the surgeon general's deputy—Dr. Edward Nathaniel Bancroft, a Cambridge graduate, and physician at St. George's Hospital. A staunch advocate of the prerogatives of the Royal College of Physicians, Bancroft claimed that physicians had traditionally supervised the medical affairs of the army and that regimental surgeons were not qualified by training and experience to administer army hospitals. Denouncing the arguments in favor of regimental hospitals, Bancroft claimed that he had refuted McGrigor's testimony by demonstrating that general hospitals supervised by physicians were superior to regimental hospitals in economy, discipline, and in checking contagion.[26]

Drawn into the quarrel, McGrigor countered with a pamphlet entitled *A Letter to the Commissioners of Military Inquiry in Reply to Some Animadversions of Dr. E. Nathaniel Bancroft*. McGrigor indignantly denied Bancroft's charges about his own supposed lack of experience with general hospitals and stoutly insisted that regimental hospitals were superior:

But independently of all fact, is it now known that many diseases acquire a malignant form, and some are even generated by crowding a number of sick into one partment, or under one roof . . . . We do not say, that in regimental hospitals, patients are absolutely not subject to contagion, but we affirm, without fear of contradiction, that contagion is much less frequent in regimental hospitals than in general hospitals.[27]

Thus, the debate revealed information long concealed from the public about the machinations of the Medical Board. If the recommendations of the Fifth Report were followed, a reform of the army medical department was inevitable. Dundas, for example, wrote to Viscount Castlereagh, secretary of war and colonies, on June 23, 1809, that members of Parliament had complained "that due attention was not paid to the Medical System of the Army during the late campaign [Coruña], and that the Sick on their return were not properly accommodated."[28] As a result of such criticism, Dundas requested a board of general officers to investigate the charges of negligence on the part of the Medical Board. Although the five generals on the board mildly criticized the hospital administration in Spain, they stated that "we are convinced that upon an examination of the whole system you will see much to praise and nothing to repudiate in the arrangement of the sick at Coruna." The military board added: "It appears to us that all possible dispatch was used in making arrangements to provide efficient accommodations for [the troops] at the ports at which it was probable or even possible that they should be landed." There were adequate medical supplies at Portsmouth, they stated, and no sick man was kept on board a ship in the harbor more than a day. Praising the efforts of the army, navy, and civilian surgeons who assisted during the emergency, the generals reflected, in a rare tribute by the military to the medical world, that "in justice to the Medical Officers of the Army . . . we must add that their zeal, activity, and intelligence appeared to have been most distinguished."[29]

While the politicians pondered reforms of the Medical Board, Mc-Grigor continued to supervise army hospitals, to provision transports destined for the Peninsula with medical supplies, and to oversee the passage of medical personnel to the British army in Portugal. Busy with his duties, McGrigor explained to his aunt that he was "overwhelmed with public business. . ." and that he was "entirely engaged in the expeditions which of late have gone to Spain, which inclination as well as public duty prompts me to do anything in my department to forward." Anticipating that his term of duty at Portsmouth would soon terminate, McGrigor added that "I am no means stationary, but am subject to being sent to Spain or any quarter of the world where the Service may require me."[30] And the army did require him for a new task—as inspector of hospitals in Portugal.

The former commander of the 88th, Sir William Carr Beresford, had requested that McGrigor join him at Lisbon. After commanding a division in Spain, Beresford was appointed a marshal in the Portugese army in 1809 and was authorized to reform the Braganza regiments. While Beresford tried to improve the Portuguese army, he sought British officers to aid him. "Desirous to organize the medical department after the British fashion," McGrigor explained, Beresford, "obtained from the Duke of York . . . that I should be sent to Portugal, as chief of the Portuguese medical staff, with the rank of Inspector of Hospitals."[31] But while McGrigor's appointment was being considered, the Duke of York resigned from office, and the new commander in chief delayed approving McGrigor's transfer to Lisbon. In September, 1809, McGrigor received his new assignment. It was not to Portugal as he had anticipated, but to Holland where the mysterious "Walcheren Fever" was destroying an entire British army.

# VI

## THE EXPEDITION TO
## THE SCHELDT

Wellesley's victories in Portugal and Spain in 1809 provided the British with the opportunity to impede the French conquest of the Iberian Peninsula. Instead of reinforcing Wellesley, however, the Portland Ministry opened "a second front" against Napoleon in northern Europe. The target was the coast of Holland.

Encouraged by an Austrian victory over Napoleon (May, 1809), the British invaded the Scheldt in August, 1809. The objectives of the expedition were to destroy shipping facilities along the Scheldt, to sink enemy vessels at Flushing and Antwerp, and to demolish the naval base on Walcheren.[1] But, by the time the armada sailed, national uprisings in Prussia and Bavaria had failed, and the Hapsburgs, defeated by Napoleon in July, had signed an armistice. Thus, without the military support of any continental ally, the largest armada ever assembled in Britain departed for the Lowlands.

In command of the expedition were Lord Chatham (the Second Earl) and Sir Richard Strachan. Chatham, the eldest son of William Pitt, had an undistinguished military record. Due to his influence, however, he had even been considered as commander of the Peninsular army; the invasion of Holland was considered as a means to enhance his ministerial potentialities. Strachan was a fine "deep-water" sailor, but he was unfamiliar with the sinuous twisting and the treacherous shoals of the Scheldt that could make navigation an admiral's nightmare.

There was great confidence as the fleet sailed from the Downs. The vessels were "one mass of white canvas, one forest of masts," exclaimed Lieutenant Colonel Thomas St. Clair. "I counted thirty-eight ships of the line, thirty frigates, with numerous small ships of war, gunboats, and transports, mounting in all to upward of nearly 40,000 troops equipped for any uncertainty."[2]

But the generals and admirals encountered unexpected obstacles.

Alerted by the activity in English ports, the French prepared for the enemy assault. They strengthened their garrisons and prepared to cut the sea-dykes. Even if the British captured the islands of Walcheren, North Beveland, and South Beveland, they faced a 40-mile passage to Antwerp of ominous fogs, shifting sandbanks, and unpredictable tides. To protect their vessels at Antwerp, the French built additional fortresses and stretched a chair boom across the Scheldt.

In addition, there was the added danger of disease. The entire Scheldt area was historically one of the unhealthiest places in western Europe, and its inhabitants among the sickliest. Most of the fighting would occur on Walcheren, a flat plain reclaimed from the ocean that was below sea-level at high tide and that was intersected with dykes, resulting in pools of stagnant water. The greatest amount of sickness from the strange "Walcheren Fever" traditionally occurred in hot, steamy August, exactly when the English landed on the island amid morning mists, daily thunderstorms, and polluted polder water swarming with mosquitoes.

A graphic commentary on the unwholesome Walcheren environment was reported by John Webb, inspector of hospitals:

Independent of the existing Records of the Unhealthiness of Zealand every object around us depicts it in the most forceful Manner; the Bottom of every Canal that has communication with the Sea is thickly covered with an Ooze, which when the Tide is out omits a most offensive and Noisome Effluvia; every Ditch is filled with Water, which is loaded with animal and vegetable Substances in a state of Putrefaction; and the whole island is so Flat, and so near the Level of the Sea that a large Proportion of it is little better than a Swamp, and there is scarcely a place where Water of a tolerably good Quality can be procured. The Effect of all these Causes of Disease is strongly marked in the appearance of the Inhabitants, the greater Part of whom are pale and listless. Scrophula is a very General Complaint among them. The Children are sickly, and many of the grown Persons are deformed. The Endemic Diseases of the Country, remittent and Intermittent Fevers begin to appear about the middle of August, and continue to prevail until the commencement of Frosty Weather checks the Exhalations of the Earth, gives Tone to the debilitated Frames of the People, and stops thereby the further Progress of the Complaints. It is computed that nearly a third of the Inhabitants are attacked with Fever every sickly Season.[3]

Pringle described the unhealthiness of Zealand in his account of the Lowlands campaign in 1747 during which four fifths of the British army was sick. Fatalities in Dutch garrisons on Walcheren were enormous; one Scot regiment serving the House of Orange had been destroyed by fever within three years. The French, too, had suffered, losing one third of their troops on Walcheren within seven years. Yet the British political and military authorities seemed unperturbed by the enormous risks they incurred with thousands of lives. Nor did the Medical Board even offer advice about the potential danger of the Scheldt. With the assurance that pestilence would obliterate the invading army, Napoleon stated: "We must stop the British with nothing but fever, which will soon devour them all. In a month the English will be obliged to take to their ships."[4]

The initial British landings on Walcheren were successful. Troops led by Lieutenant General Sir Eyre Coote captured Middleburgh and then marched on to beseige Flushing. Other regiments landed on South Beveland, from where they could see, 15 miles up the Scheldt, the French warships anchored at Antwerp.

After Flushing fell to the British on August 15, French resistance on the island ended. But now that Chatham held Walcheren, what could he do with it? The French had made Antwerp impregnable, and the movement of British troops on vessels up the Scheldt was dangerous. Chatham's only gain was the demolished city of Flushing, which proved to be a lethal trap. A plague struck the invaders and practically terminated the campaign.

The "Walcheren Fever" hit British troops on South Beveland and on Walcheren. Soon 1,200 men were sick from the pestilence. On August 27, the returns listed 3,400 ailing men in Chatham's army. By September 17, the fever incapacitated 8,200 soldiers, and 250 men were dying weekly.[5] The malady cut through the entire army—men dropped to the ground while on guard duty, whole regiments reported unfit for action, and wagons piled high with the dead became a familiar sight.

The medical department was helpless. Regimental surgeons distributed Peruvian Bark and antimonial powder to their patients; they warned the healthy not to sleep in the open air, to avoid wading in the ditches, to wear flannel clothing, and to shun unripened fruit. Troops were given extra rations of rum and were urged to smoke cigars in order to purify the air. Chatham's army, huddling and shivering in damp hovels without heat, adequate clothing, or sufficient food, became a terrified body of men, desperate to be evacuated from this horrible land. After he realized that an assault on Antwerp was impossible,

Chatham relinquished his command to Coote and sailed home leaving his army to its fate.

What was this fatal disease that so baffled the learned physicians? The medical officers accepted Pringle's opinion that the malady was a combination of typhus and dysentery. Yet the pestilence had other puzzling characteristics.[6]

George Hargrove, an assistant surgeon serving on Beveland, wrote the best published account of the Walcheren fever. "It was about the 18th of August," Hargrove stated, "that I was first alarmed by the accession of disease among the troops." Examining his patient, Hargrove commented that "I found this poor man writhing in agony, who told me he felt his brain was burning and his bowels were twisting around.... On examination I found his skin hot, and covered with a clammy moisture, his tongue white, his pulse full, and his breathing quick and accompanied with ... frequent sighing." Soon after, Hargrove was transferred to Flushing. There he claimed that he saw a different disease. "I was deeply concerned on my entrance to the hospitals, that the intermittent and remittent fevers frequently assumed the character of a low, malignant and contagious disease, such as occur in confined and crowded gaols..." Accepting the current climatological explanation of the origins of disease, Hargrove explained:

These provinces then, lower than the surface of the sea . . . abound with stagnant marshes, and the summer and autumnal months are so intensely hot, that as to account at once for the miasmata continually evaporating from the surface. It is to this circumstance, that of being surrounded by a humid atmosphere, with the frequency of rain in the climate, that I almost exclusively attribute the prevalence of the disease, which caused the devastation in our army during the campaign.

In an unintentionally ironic passage, Hargrove added that "during the hot weather, we were much annoyed by a description of Moschetos, who attacked us in immense swarms . . . the buzzing noise they make is more alarming than any harm they inflict."[7]

Writing to the commander in chief from Middleburgh on September 11, Webb emphasized that uncontrollable environmental forces caused the disease which periodically struck the Dutch burghers on the island:

If Individuals who have lived in this Island from their Infancy, who observe a degree of Cleanliness that can scarcely be surpassed, and who live in spa-

cious apartments, cannot obviate the Effects of the Climate; it may natu-
rally be concluded what a Foreign Army must suffer by being exposed, in
the first Instance, to excessive Fatigue, and to the Inclemency of the Weather,
and afterwards by being crowded into Barracks, where under the most favorable circumstances, the sudden transition must have produced a severe
and extended Disease. . . .

The Rapidity with which the Disease has extended itself . . . is almost un-
exampled in the History of any Military Operations. . . . A very considerable Number of [Cases] . . . have . . . assumed a more Serious Form, and
have degenerated into that Species of low Fever which often prevails in
Gaols and other ill-ventilated Places in England . . . .[8]

As these commentaries about the Walcheren fever indicate, it is
apparent that army surgeons were unprepared to cope with this disease. A recent description (1968) of the Walcheren fever by Dr. Richard Feibel, who studied the contemporary medical accounts, provides
a succinct summary of the dilemmas confronting the bewildered medical staff on the expedition. "What types of fevers decimated this army?" he inquired.

The clinical and pathological evidence adduced from the texts studied does not
indicate that any one disease was the primary cause of the morbidity and mortality. In view of the periodicity of the fever, the splenomegaly, the frequent
relapses, and the value of bark in simple cases, it seems clear that endemic
malaria formed a substantial substrate of disease. Several modern medico-
historical studies state or imply that malaria was the sole cause of this disaster. However, only falciparum malaria can cause such severe constitutional symptoms or death, and there is no evidence that this species of
plasmodium was ever present in Holland; nor are the pathological findings
consistent with a diagnosis of falciparum malaria. Further, it is unlikely on
epidemiologic grounds that malaria could infect so many soldiers in such a
short time. The common findings of ulcerated intestines indicate typhoid
fever or dysentery. The over crowding of the sick in transport ships and the
barracks especially at Flushing, where the housing of the ill was abominable
and the filth consequent upon the lack of medical attention would predispose
to typhoid and dysentery as well as to typhus. All these diseases seem to have
been present in some degree and to have contributed to the Walcheren
fever.[9]

Although the Army Medical Board cannot be blamed for their ignorance of bacteriology, nevertheless, the members were negligent in
provisioning and staffing the expedition. As a result, they inadvertently enlarged the scope of the Walcheren tragedy. Even though the
army was destined for a notoriously febrile area, the board failed to

warn the Ministry. If they can be believed, the members claimed ignorance of the expedition's destination. As a result of constant feuding, the
recent inquiries conducted by military officers and members of Parliament, the board members so distrusted each other that their official
actions were nearly paralysed. They failed to create a reserve of medical personnel, nor did they prepare for sufficient hospital ships or for
an efficient distribution of supplies to the Lowlands. The Medical
Board had assembled a medical staff for only 30,000 troops, and some
regiments were still without surgeons and hospital mates after they
landed on Walcheren.

Keate at least displayed some initiative, and repeatedly requested
Viscount Castlereagh, secretary for war and colonies, to provide additional hospital ships. Castlereagh replied that, considering the short-
ness of the voyage from England and the demands for shipping to
Spain, no more transports could be spared for the medical department. After the troops were landed, wrote Castlereagh confidently,
"any use may be made of the empty Storeships for the accommodation of the sick and the wounded."[10] Even on September 24, when
Coote begged for additional medical staff, the Medical Board was unable to comply. Castlereagh, who gradually awoke to the tragedy on
Walcheren, answered that day to an earlier complaint from Coote for
the board members: "When you consider the number of Medical
Assistants already sent to Walcheren, and reflect upon the precious Necessity of succouring to the demand for aid to the wounded in Spain,
you must feel how extremely difficult if not impossible it must be to
provide an adequate number for a calamity so sudden and so extensive."[11]

The board's feeble efforts to supervise and to coordinate organization for the Walcheren operation, and the government's negligence in
preparing emergency facilities, increased the scope of the tragedy. The
Walcheren hospitals were teeming with feverish patients, begging for
relief and pleading for evacuation. Even the transportation arrangements were bungled. After waiting hours for conveyance to vessels,
the sick men were merely dumped on the open decks of the ships, giv-
en pails of Peruvian Bark, and were unattended for the passage home.
Even when the poor wretches arrived in England, they were inhumane-
ly treated. Attending physicians at the ports were stunned at the emaciated condition of the scarecrow army as it crawled off the ships.[12]

On Walcheren, in his medical report to Coote on September 18,

Francis Burrows, deputy inspector of hospitals, stressed the deplorable condition of the men and cited the sick returns:

You will there perceive the lamentable fact, that already more than half the Army under your Command are in Hospitals; and, from the numerous Additions daily; nay almost hourly, swelling the Sick . . . you will be enabled to form a Judgement . . . of what we have to look forward to, nor need to explain to you who have so lately visited all the Hospitals in this Island, the distressing Embarrassments we experience from Medical Officers, Orderlies daily falling ill, and the Impossibility of procuring adequate Accommodation and Attendance for the numerous Sick. The wretched State of the Hospitals is greatly to be deplored, more especially at Flushing, where, in consequence of the late Bombardment, the Very best Buildings that can be procured as Hospitals are not Weatherproof. . . .

Under such circumstances, I am of Opinion that we have but little grounds to calculate on the Efficiency [of the army] in this Climate for the next Six Months. . . . Probably not less than Two-Thirds of the Army may become ineffective for that Period . . . .[13]

Anticipating a French counterattack on Walcheren, Coote wrote to Castlereagh on September 17 that although he needed 20,000 men to defend the island, he had only 7,800 fit for duty out of 14,000. The Royal Navy, he believed, would "not be able to keep the Sea, or the Surrounding Channels, during the Winter." The worried general warned of the "present defective, and . . . untenable State" of Walcheren. Commenting on the breakdown of the medical department, he added:

I can assure your Lordship, without any Fear of Exaggeration . . . that the Situation in this Island is deplorable: and it grieves me to say, that none of the Medical Assistance (One Staff Surgeon and Three Hospitals Mates excepted), or any of the promised Comforts, have yet arrived. On the contrary, our Medical Corps is daily diminished, either from Sickness or from the Necessity of sending some of the Staff with sick Men to England.[14]

Meanwhile, the embittered Medical Board seemed inert. When the war secretary and the commander in chief requested that a member of the board and two "able" physicians nominated by the board visit Walcheren, Knight replied "that it is the opinion of the Surgeon General, as well as myself, that the duties required are purely Medical, and as such, belong to the province of the Physician-General. Sir Lucas Pepys will probably make his own representation on this subject to the War Department and name two able Physicians who are to be selected for that service. . . ."[15] Keate also begged off from the task and claimed that he was overwhelmed with "arduous and complicated duties" in providing for the returning sick from Holland and Portugal. As the duty in question, he stated, was "entirely Medical, and unfit for a Surgeon by profession, I cannot but consider the Physician General as the only proper member of the Board to undertake such a duty...."[16]

But the physician general insisted that the inspector general of hospitals was the proper individual to be sent to Walcheren. Pepys claimed that he himself was completely occupied visiting local army hospitals. Recommending that Dr. Gilbert Blane and other physicians be sent, Pepys tried to clear himself of any responsibility for the tragedy by stating that "by this means [sending the others], the business will be effectually done, the Surgeon General and I will be able to attend to concerns at home of that Army as they arrive and require assistance." Pepys pleaded that he was processing sick leave requests from officers and was giving qualification examinations to potential hospital mates. "I cannot indeed be spared at present,"[17] he stated.

In a second letter on this subject, Pepys wrote indignantly that he was "much concerned to find the Secretary at War and the Commander-in-Chief have conceived it possible that a man of near seventy with infirmities, would be capable of undertaking such a duty as must require proper age and proper health as well as knowledge to perform it. I hereby solemnly declare myself incapable of performing it." Dr. Pepys, president of the Royal College of Physicians (1804–10), concluded his tirade by admitting his unfamiliarity with military medicine and by stating that "whereas if I was able to go, who know nothing of the investigation of Camps and Contagious Disease, it [the duty] would be merely performed, and no possible good could arise from it."[18] The War Office then informed the board members that three other physicians would be sent to Walcheren.[19]

The medical commissioners, Sir Gilbert Blane, now a prominent London physician, Dr. James Borland, an inspector of army hospitals, and Dr. William Lempriere, physician to the forces, departed in late September. Blane, who arrived before his colleagues, wrote to Pepys on October 3, from Middleburgh "that near two-thirds of the whole numerical strength of the army is incapable of duty. The mortality during the last four weeks has been about a thousand." Claiming that typhus and dysentery, which ordinarily would have been prevalent in the Low Countries, were not present in the army, Blane found that "so great a proportion on these cases to consist of those inter-mitting and remitting fevers, so peculiar to marshy countries, that there can be no doubt that the sickness of the army has been owing to this cause." Pointing out that the disease was caused by "the contamina-tion of the air from a soil the most productive of deleterious exhalations of any, perhaps, in producing an endemic fever . . . ," Blane noted that "you will clearly perceive how much these causes are out of the reach of human control." He urged that the men be given hot break-fasts, and that their barracks be heated with stoves. Blane also sugges-ted that the convalescents be transported "to the purer air of Eng-land."[20] The three commissioners supplemented this report with a joint communication. Assuming that the army would continue to oc-cupy Walcheren, they recommended that troops shipped to the Low-lands be "seasoned" to the climate, that better barracks be construc-ted, and that the soldiers be provided with better clothing and food.[21] But beyond these suggestions, the physicians did little and soon de-parted for Portsmouth.

While the Walcheren expedition was underway, McGrigor was pre-paring to sail for Lisbon. However, the situation on Walcheren was critical. To replace the fever-stricken John Webb, the Medical Board ordered McGrigor on September 2 to assume direction of the medi-cal department at Middleburgh. "The letter which I received ordered me to embark with all possible speed . . . . I accordingly left Ports-mouth on the evening of the day on which I received my orders, and, as directed, went to London on my way for instructions."[22] After being appraised of his new responsibilities by the Medical Board, McGrigor hurried to Deal and embarked with a dozen medical assistants on the H.M.S. *Venerable*.

As the vessel approached the Dutch coast, it "gave a tremendous lurch," reported McGrigor. "We had struck a sand bank, and the ves-sel on swinging on round from this, struck upon another. An anchor was let go, which we lost. Another was thrown out, and with consterna-tion it was found we had gone into a quarter where we ought not to have been. We were in fact surrounded by sand banks." By nightfall after hours of continual thumping on the shoals, the rudder was smashed, and water poured into the hull. To prevent the ship from sinking, the crew threw the cannon overboard, cut the masts and rig-gings, and pumped water out of the hold. "But after a long trial the men were found to be so much exhausted, as not to be able to accomplish this, and we gained little upon the leaks. At this time our situation became truly awful; the vessel appeared at each thump to take in more water . . . ." McGrigor hoped that the distressed *Venerable*, only four leagues from Walcheren, would be sighted from the shore, "but in truth, the situation was very appalling."

As day broke upon us, the spectacle of the wreck was frightful. The whole deck was a mass of ruin, and the sides were all out, torn away in part by the guns in throwing them overboard; one mast, the mizen only, was standing. We were at this time firing signal guns of distress, every five minutes. We had about eight women on board, mostly Irish, the wives of soldiers going to their husbands at Walcheren. After every signal from the guns, a general scream and yell followed from the women, who were most troublesome, running about below and above.

Finally, a small brig approached the *Venerable* to rescue the screeching women, and later, other vessels rescued the rest of the passengers and crew. Exhausted from the ordeal, McGrigor was treated ashore by a surgeon. That night, McGrigor had a troubled sleep. He dreamed that he was "at the bottom of the sea, where I was attacked by all sorts of horrible fish which were about to devour me."[23]

McGrigor reported to headquarters at Middleburgh on September 9 just as his predecessor, Webb, delirious with fever, was being carried off to a ship. Throughout his career, McGrigor had continually sought opportunities to enlarge what he termed his "sphere of observation" in medicine. Yet after a rapid inspection of the Walcheren hospitals, he was shocked. Never before had he encountered such a mass of dying men. "The number of sick was immense, that of the wounded officers and men, who could not be conveyed thither was considerable, and both together, most unhappily, nearly equalled that of the men in health." Due to his recent experiences at Portsmouth in handling casualties, he continued, "by the greatly extended sphere of action in which I was there placed, I had added much to my plan of organization. But the amount of sickness at Walcheren was great beyond all comparisons with that which I had hitherto witnessed."[24] Forwarding his sick returns to Coote on September 18, McGrigor explained: "You will thus perceive the lamentable fact that already more than half the Army under your command are Sick. . . . The wretched state of the Hospitals is a subject deeply to be deplored; more especially at Flushing, where from the effect of the late Bombardment, the best buildings that could be procured, are in many instances not Weather proof."[25]

Anticipating that over two thirds of the army would soon be ineffective, McGrigor realized that he needed additional medicine and staff. He was particularly worried about the shortage of Peruvian Bark, and he begged the Medical Board to send him additional supplies. But the shipment of the bark from England was delayed. Fortunately, an American vessel, selling wines and champagne to the commissary on Walcheren, docked at Flushing, and it carried some chests of the precious bark. Without waiting for an authorization from London, McGrigor ordered his purveyor "to make a purchase of whatever stock of bark the American might have; and the supply lasted till the quantities forwarded by the mailcoaches [from London] to Deal, and then by the packet to Walcheren, arrived."[26]

Anxious to staff the undermanned hospitals, McGrigor tried to utilize the services of captured French medical officers. He requested that the navy send him some surgeons[27] and suggested the Dutch civilians work in the hospitals as orderlies,[28] along with British army pensioners from home to "do the Duties of Fatigue about the respective hospitals and barracks where they are most urgently required."[29] Reiterating his suggestions to the surgeon general, McGrigor wrote that "such being the State of many Corps that they report themselves unable to either furnish Men for duty or attendance on the Sick."[30] This display of energy and initiative prompted Coote to report to Castlereagh on October 23 that "amidst all these difficulties, it will be a Consolation to your Lordship to learn . . . that the Attention of the medical officers, under the able and zealous Superintendance [sic] of doctor McGrigor, Inspector of Hospitals, has been most unremitting and praiseworthy."[31]

For the first time in his reports to the Medical Board, McGrigor now began to assert himself to his superiors. When the surgeon general insisted that McGrigor keep the sick on Walcheren until additional medical staff arrived, McGrigor, determined to evacuate the men, angrily replied: "From possessing local knowledge on the subject, I unfortunately cannot give in to your opinions. . . . The inhumanity in this business . . . if there has been any, clearly, does not lie on this side of the water."[32] Embittered over the inexplicable delay in shipping him supplies and personnel, and indignant that Keate repeatedly doubted or contradicted his reports on the crisis, McGrigor complained to Lieutenant General Sir George Don (the new commander who replaced the exhausted Coote on October 2) that "unless protected by you in the execution of my duty here, I will not be able to go on with it to the advantage of the service."[33]

The sickness and mortality toll continued to mount. Don reported to Lord Liverpool, the home secretary, on October 27, that his garrison was so depleted that if the enemy attacked, he could barely defend Flushing. "There is not a Chance of a single Man now in the Hospitals . . . recovering sufficiently to undergo the duties of a soldier in the field unless he be removed from this Island in a short time." Of his so-called "fit men," he warned, only one third were capable of duty.[34]

By early November, as the Cabinet realized that the expedition was a catastrophe, Don was ordered to evacuate his force. Throughout the following weeks, the British prepared to leave, and on December 25, after demolishing the guns, docks, and harbor facilities of Flushing, the last contingent of troops departed. "On the night of the day on which we embarked," commented McGrigor, who supervised the evacuation of the sick on the hospital ship *Asia*, "the dockyard of Flushing was set on fire, and from our anchorage we had a full view of an awfully grand sight. From the numerous explosions and the violence of the fire, fed by barrels of tar and every kind of combustible, not only everything in the dockyard was doomed to destruction, but also several men-of-war in the stocks."[35] The devastation of the city aptly symbolized an end to the most disastrous campaign of the British army during the Napoleonic era. Disease, not the bullets or bayonets of the enemy, had destroyed an entire army.

Another invasion of Bonaparte's Europe had ended in defeat. Only 106 men were combat fatalities on the expedition, but over 4,000 men died from pestilence, and another 11,500 troops were confined to hospitals for weeks in England.[36] Even months after their recuperation, the Walcheren veterans sent to Wellesley's army in Spain were usually the weakest troops in the field and were often the first to succumb to the rigours of a tough campaign. As the epitome of administrative bungling, the failure of a joint army-navy command, the inertia and negligence of politicians and generals during a crisis, the Walcheren fiasco is a classic example of how disease became a virtual epidemic and how it led to a national disaster.

The ill-fated Walcheren expedition delayed the reinforcement of the Peninsula army, it led to a protracted political debate about the Ministry's conduct of the war, and it caused the dismissal of Pepys, Knight and Keate from the Medical Board, and to a reform of the army medi-

cal department. So intense was the public indignation about the failure of the Scheldt expedition that a committee of the whole House of
Commons conducted an investigation, from January 23 to June 21,
1810, that involved scores of key figures in the tragic enterprise.

Along with Chatham, Strachan, Castlereagh, and the Medical
Board members, McGrigor was a witness. Aware that he would have
to appear at the bar of the House of Commons to testify, McGrigor
waited nervously for weeks before he was finally called. At last the
dreaded day came. Just as McGrigor was about to enter the chamber,
the previous witness, Sir Richard Strachan, known for his daring and
courage at sea, emerged shaken and pallid from his own examination
by opposition M.P.s who were anxious to acquire political leverage
from the inquiry. McGrigor, now even more apprehensive about the
pending ordeal, stepped into the Speaker's Chamber. "Examination
on both sides of the house was a very long one," he recalled. "I kept
full possession of myself for a considerable time, but at last, from the
extreme heat of the house, my position, and the length of my examination, I became somewhat confused, and I completely stuck at one
place relative to the supply of medicine to the sick." When Samuel
Whitbread, M.P., asked him about the bark that was purchased on
Walcheren, McGrigor replied that he had bought it from "adventurers," meaning an American vessel. Whitbread quickly responded,
"What adventurers?" "For the life of me I could not explain the
meaning of the word adventurer," confessed McGrigor. "He several
times repeated the word, but I could not go on, and felt most confused." Fortunately for McGrigor, to assist him out of his tongue-tied
embarrassment, Lord Spencer Perceval, first lord of the treasury,
helped him with the question, and McGrigor was able to resume his
testimony with composure. After being "questioned and cross-exam-
ined on both sides of the house . . ." McGrigor was delighted to retire from the inquiry.[37]

McGrigor's testimony was not inspiring, nor was it particularly in-
formative. More crucial was the fact that the entire investigation
showed generals and admirals contradicting each other and politicians
demonstrating an incredible lack of foresight in planning the Walcheren expedition. Moreover, it revealed that the Medical Board was an
incompetent, despicable triumvirate that had been careless with the
lives of troops. The government was nearly defeated in a vote which
was, in effect, a Parliamentary censure of the tragic expedition to the

Scheldt. Throughout the inquiry, the Medical Board members insisted that they had been tardily informed about the expedition and that they had not been required to consult with the government. Weary of their bickering, the Perceval Ministry dismissed them from office in January, 1810, and appointed three army doctors to a new board.[38]

The administration of the medical department was entrusted to a director general and two principal inspectors who had overseas military experience. John Weir, the director general, held a degree from Aberdeen and had served as purveyor on Abercrombie's West Indian expedition. Dr Charles Ker, one of the principal inspectors, was a graduate of Edinburgh who had risen through the ranks as an inspector of hospitals. The other principal inspector, Dr. Theodore Gordon, was also an Aberdeen graduate who had served in the Americas. Mc-Grigor stated that Gordon "was one of the most judicious and talented officers in the department of the army."[39] The reorganization of the board was based upon revisions suggested by the Fifth Military Inquiry. As a result, the definitions of responsibilities and the assignment of duties to the members, along with a clarification of policies about rank, promotion, and hospitals, signified a reform of an archaic department.

The new Medical Board had little immediate effect on McGrigor's career. He resumed his duties in Portsmouth where he supervised the shipments of medicines, surgical instruments, and hospital personnel to Spain, and prepared for the sick and wounded from Wellesley's army. Although the new board was an improvement compared to its predecessor, the members plagued their inspectors in the field with directives and admonitions. They displayed a zeal for strict accounting of medical supplies. Correspondence from the board to McGrigor is full of references for detailed explanations from him about expenses for drugs and equipment.[40]

A major change in McGrigor's life occurred in June, 1810, when he married his aunt's niece, Mary Grant. In September, 1811, he was boasting to his relatives about his new-born son, "a fine thriving fellow," as McGrigor put it, named after his brother Charles.[41] In Lisbon, Beresford still wanted McGrigor at his side. But McGrigor, now a happy family man, stated in his *Autobiography*:

But my recent marriage had rendered the situation of chief of the medical department of the Portuguese army less desirable than it would have been when I was a bachelor; and, after some exertion, I was mainly instrumental in getting my friend Dr. [William] Ferguson appointed inspector of hospitals with the Portuguese army . . . and he proceeded forthwith to Portugal.[42]

Yet McGrigor was destined for the Peninsular War. Wellesley (the Viscount of Wellington since Talavera) was handicapped in his campaign by poor medical services. When his chief inspector of hospitals, Dr. James Franck, became sick, Wellington requested a replacement. The Medical Board informed McGrigor on November 22, 1811 that "the Commander-in-Chief [has] directed that you do proceed to Portugal to take charge of the Medical Department of Lord Wellington, vice Dr. Franck, who is about to return to England."[43] McGrigor's response to the promotion was a mixture of pride and sorrow; sorrow at the thought of leaving his family and pride over the appointment with Britain's foremost soldier:

At any other time this appointment would have gratified me to the full extent of my ambition; but the happiness I had enjoyed in the married state, made it now a sad and painful change to me. The announcement was a sad blow to my beloved wife, who at once determined to be my companion [in Spain]: I had however seen enough of ladies on service in the field, to decide me against that step, and I knew well, that with the care of my wife and child, I could not do my duty in the way I had determined it should be done, while I remained in the service.[44]

McGrigor embarked in late December for Lisbon where he would encounter problems to tax his ingenuity. It was in the Peninsula that McGrigor, Wellington's surgeon general, would win his fame.

SIR JAMES McGRIGOR, BART.
1771-1858

Sir James McGrigor. Unfinished portrait by Thomas Heaphy, about 1814.
(By permission of the National Gallery of Art)

The Duke of Wellington. Portrait by Sir Thomas Lawrence, 1814. (By permission of the Victoria and Albert Museum)

George James Guthrie. Stipple engraving by J. Cochran after a portrait by H. Room. (By permission of the Wellcome Institute of the History of Medicine)

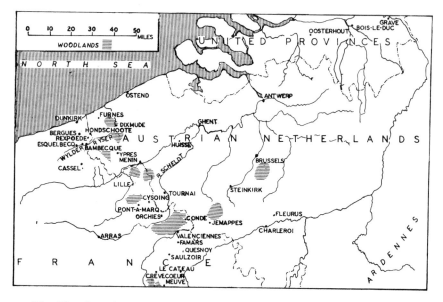

The Flanders Campaign, 1793–94. (By courtesy of R. H. Thoumine)

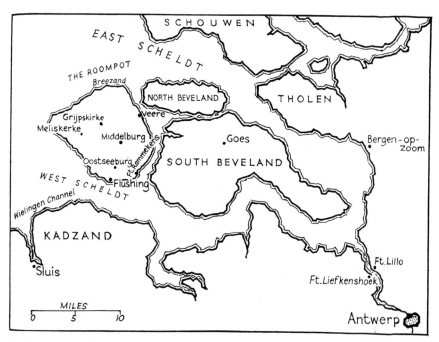

Walcheren and the estuaries of the River Scheldt. (By courtesy of the editors of *History Today*)

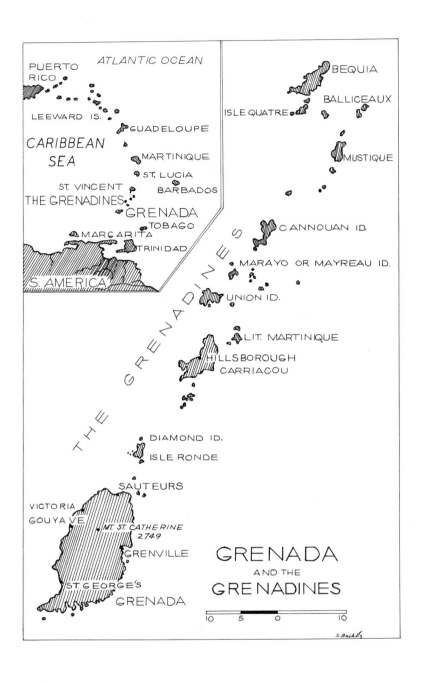

ATLANTIC OCEAN

PUERTO
RICO

LEEWARD IS.

CARIBBEAN
SEA

GUADELOUPE

MARTINIQUE

ST. LUCIA

ST. VINCENT
THE GRENADINES
GRENADA

BARBADOS

MARGARITA
TRINIDAD
TOBAGO

S. AMERICA

BEQUIA

BALLICEAUX

ISLE QUATRE

MUSTIQUE

THE GRENADINES

CANNOUAN ID.

MARAYO OR MAYREAU ID.

UNION ID.

LIT. MARTINIQUE

HILLSBOROUGH
CARRIACOU

DIAMOND ID.

ISLE RONDE

SAUTEURS

VICTORIA
GOUYAVE

MT. ST. CATHERINE
2749

GRENVILLE

ST. GEORGE'S

GRENADA

GRENADA
AND THE
GRENADINES

10   5   0   10

S. Buchölz

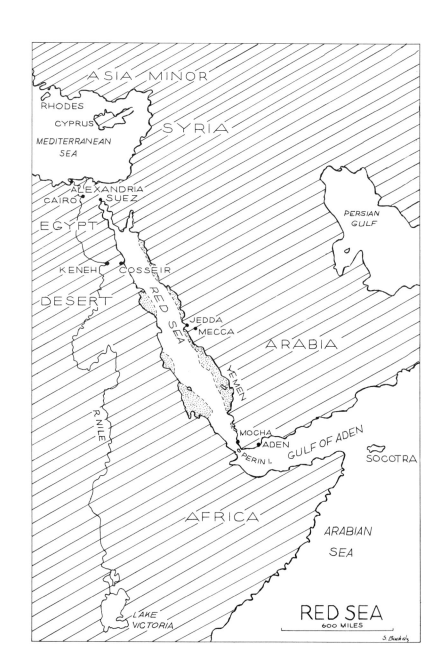

ASIA MINOR

RHODES

CYPRUS

SYRIA

MEDITERRANEAN
SEA

ALEXANDRIA
CAIRO    SUEZ

EGYPT

PERSIAN
GULF

KENEH    COSSEIR

DESERT

RED SEA

JEDDA
MECCA

ARABIA

YEMEN

R. NILE

MOCHA
PERIN I.    ADEN

GULF OF ADEN

SOCOTRA

AFRICA

ARABIAN
SEA

LAKE
VICTORIA

RED SEA
600 MILES

S. Buchols

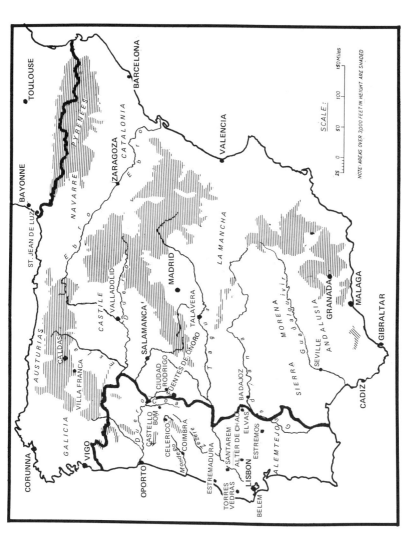

Spain and Portugal. (By permission of Macmillan, London and Basingstoke; from Anthony Brett-James, *Wellington at War, 1793–1814*, Saint Martin's Press, 1961)

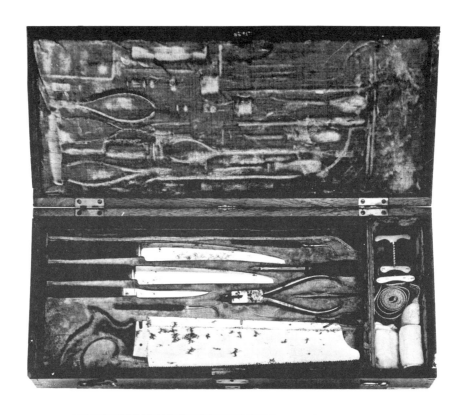

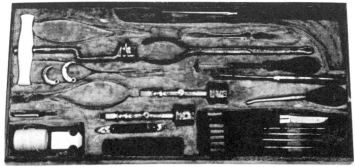

Military surgeon's chest which belonged to Assistant Surgeon Richard Spencer (1778–1869) of the Twenty-first Light Dragoons. (By courtesy of the Royal Army Medical College)

# VII

## WITH WELLINGTON IN
## THE PENINSULA

What was the state of medical services in Wellington's army? Since the Flanders campaign, few improvements had transpired in the training of surgeons, the evacuation of casualties, or in the supervision of hospitals. The medical department functioned as ineffectively in the field as in 1794, for it still lacked an ambulance system, medical corpsmen, and an efficient regimental hospital organization. Nor was there on Wellington's staff, until McGrigor arrived, a surgeon capable of promoting improvements in medical care.

The French ambulance system, for example, inspired by Dominique-Jean Larrey, was far superior to the British treatment of casualties. During his first combat experience in 1792, Larrey realized the need for a more efficient method to transport the wounded. While serving on the Rhine, he began to experiment with what he termed his "flying ambulance":

I now first discovered the inconvenience to which we were subjected in moving our *ambulances*, or military hospitals. The military regulations required that they should always be one league distant from the army. The wounded were left on the field, and were collected at a convenient spot, to which the *ambulances* [meaning mobile hospitals as well as the conveyances for the transport of the wounded] repaired as speedily as possible; but the number of [supply and munitions] wagons interposed between them and the army, and many other difficulties so retarded their progress, that they never arrived in less than twenty-four or thirty-six hours, so that most of the wounded died for want of assistance. . . . This suggested to me the idea of constructing an ambulance in such a manner that it might afford a ready conveyance for the wounded during the battle. . . . My proposition was accepted, and I was authorized to construct a carriage, which I called the flying ambulance.[1]

By 1801, Larrey had improved his ambulance wagons and had attached a cadre of surgeons, medical corpsmen, and a complement of wheeled vehicles to each army corps. For troops fighting in Spain, Poland, and Russia, the flying ambulance that accompanied them into battle was a heartening symbol of French skill and vision applied to alleviating the miseries of warfare. The perfected flying ambulance consisted of a convoy of light and heavy spring wagons enclosed to protect patients from the weather and provided with movable floors for rapid transfer of the wounded. Teams of mules and horses bearing medical supplies, and a corps of surgeons, assistants, and litter-bearers, accompanied the ambulance. It was this system, designed for an efficient movement of the wounded, that symbolized a rare element of humanitarianism in the Napoleonic wars. Reversing the traditional practice of removing the wounded far behind the line of fire to the surgeons, Larrey tried to bring the surgeons to the wounded, thereby adding a new dimension to military medicine on the battlefield that matched the increased speed and mobility of army operations characteristic of Napoleonic warfare. The French method of transporting their wounded, stated William Fergusson, McGrigor's associate, "contained much that we might copy with great advantage. . . ."[2]

Yet the British military neglected to copy this model. The transportation of the sick and wounded to general hospitals far behind the British lines in the Peninsular must have been a nightmare. Due to chronic shortage of wheeled vehicles, some of the casualties had to ride on mules, or they were packed into small, clumsy Portuguese ox-carts. The constant lurching of these vehicles, the incessant noise from their fixed axles, and the slow movement over rocky roads inevitably increased the torment of incapacitated victims who lay unprotected from rain and snow. With constant exposure to the weather, and without any intermediate aid station on the routes, the distress and misery of the helpless victims, McGrigor recorded in his journal, "may easily be imagined without much stretch of the imagination."[3] So great was the suffering of the wounded after one retreat, recalled surgeon James Elkington, that some of them requested to be shot, rather than continue the horrible journey to Lisbon.[4] On some occasions, Portuguese peasants tending the oxen strayed off to plunder, or they deserted their charges by stealing the animals, leaving the wounded by the wayside. As an anonymous British officer who guided such convoys wrote:

There is no duty so vexatious as the detachment of wounded to the rear. The eternal screeching of the ungreased wheels of the Portuguese bullock carts . . . the breaking down of the carts, or the escape of the drivers . . . the upsetting of the wagon train from the badness of the rocky road, the assembly of the sick in the morning, the only novelty being some new misery . . . are daily occurrences.[5]

No training in military medicine existed, and newly commissioned surgeons and hospital mates were dispatched to Iberia after only a very casual examination by the Medical Board. As the scope of the war expanded, and the demands for surgeons and mates mounted, the board even lowered its lenient standards to attract more candidates. Warning Dr. James Franck, Wellington's inspector of hospitals since 1809, of this problem, the board explained in February, 1811, that "many of the mates lately ordered to Portugal, are persons of inferior qualifications, and, as such, are merely appointed by warrant, nor can they be held eligible for promotion, until they have given evidence of further professional studies. . . ."[6] A few months later, the board admitted to Franck, "It becomes necessary to state that the urgent demands lately made for hospital assistance have compelled us to receive into the Service, several, who under other circumstances would not have been admitted. . . ."[7]

A surgeon and a soldier both commented about such medical personnel. With his certificate from Surgeon's Hall, Walter Henry appeared before the board in 1811. "The wise men on the medical bench there," he remarked, "having examined me, and reported that I could feel a pulse and physic [sic], as well as bleed, I was in due course gazetted Hospital Mate for general service to His Majesty's Forces."[8] A caustic commentary about hospital mates came from Sergeant John Donaldson, a Peninsular veteran. "Apothecary's Boys, who having studied a session or two, were then thrown into the army as a huge dissecting room, where they might mangle with impunity, until they were drilled into an orderly knowledge of the business . . . they generally did much mischief." He continued:

The extent of their medical practice was to blister, bleed, and purge again . . . . In the field they did more mischief, being but partially acquainted with anatomy . . . . In cutting down a ball for the purpose of extracting it, ten chances to one, they severed an artery they know not how to stem; but this gave no concern to these enterprising fellows, for after clapping a piece of lint and a bandage, or a piece of adhesive plaster on the wound they would walk off very composedly to mangle some other poor wretch, leaving the former to his fate. . . .[9]

In the field, the medical personnel and equipment for a regiment consisted of a surgeon, two assistant surgeons, one cart, 12 sets of hospital bedding, and a mule to carry panniers for drugs and surgical in-struments. When the toll of casualties mounted or the numbers of sick suddenly increased, there was no organized method of shifting medical teams from one regiment to another. Although there are references in contemporary documents to "dressing stations" and "field hospitals" near the scene of action, the usual practice in the Peninsula was to es-tablish a central depot close to the lines as a regimental dumping ground for incapacitated men. A temporary depot sometimes became a provisional division hospital or sometimes a permanent general hos-pital, depending upon the exigencies of the war.

Surgery performed in such hospitals was done hastily on tables or planks. Amputated limbs were tossed onto grisly piles near the doors or out the windows, often in sight of wounded men waiting for their own operations. After the battle of Fuentes de Onoro, for example, the casualties were transported to Villa Formosa, where Lieutenant Grat-tan of the 88th found men lying in a courtyard awaiting surgery. "It would be difficult to convey an idea of the frightful appearance of these men," he lamented. "They had been wounded on the 5th [May, 1811] and this was the 7th; their limbs were swollen to an enormous size, and the smell from gunshot wounds was dreadful."[10] George James Guth-rie, the most famous British army surgeon of the era, recalled that he had to supervise surgery after the battle of Albuera, one of the blood-iest battles of the Peninsular War, with hardly any trained personnel. He and his few assistants toiled eighteen hours a day for three weeks to alleviate the misery of 3,000 wounded. The Spanish convent that he converted into an operating ward, said Guthrie, was like "a slaughter house."[11]

Some distance behind the lines were the general hospitals, located at larger towns or villages in which churches, convents, monasteries, schools, and other municipal buildings were utilized as hospital wards. Such make-shift establishments were usually equipped for 300 pa-tients, but during an emergency they could care for 500 men. Principal medical officers who supervised the functions of their staff—a staff sur-geon, a physician, surgeons and assistant surgeons, hospital mates, wardmaster, and orderlies—administered general hospitals. During the course of the war, permanent general hospitals were maintained at Lisbon, Belem, Coimbra, Celerico, Abrantes, Elvas, and at other Por-tuguese towns. As the scope of the war expanded over the border, various Spanish cities, recaptured by the Allies, became hospital sites for the military.

Although Dr. Franck preferred general hospitals to regimental hospitals, by 1811 the criticism from army surgeons about medical administration was increasing. General hospitals were blamed for a high incidence of sickness and mortality, for their unsanitary conditions and the consequent spread of contagion, and for the numerous relapses of former patients discharged for active duty. Furthermore, critics lamented the continual depletion of regimental surgeons to man these rear-line hospitals, and that whatever the type of disease, the seriousness of the wound, or the degree of recovery, patients were indiscriminately mixed in the same wards. And there were even more objections. These hospitals were also criticized for their lax discipline, for inefficiency in treating the sick, and for neglecting injured men from the front.

Wellington labored to improve the efficiency of the British regiments and considered means to improve their health. The sick and wounded men in the British army, numbering, at various times, from one tenth to one third of his command, inhibited the scope of his campaigns. True, Wellington is sometimes remembered as the angry general who blurted out that his men were "the scum of the earth." Yet this stern soldier was deeply concerned about the condition of the rank and file, less from humanitarian reasons than from the pragmatic necessity of maintaining his outnumbered army in fighting trim. From the "morning state of the Forces" reports which he scanned daily, he knew that each Peninsular veteran was worth two recruits and was too valuable to lose to hunger and disease. Heavily outnumbered until 1813, Wellington knew that his army could not sustain a single major defeat. He realized that his men should be exposed to the hazards of battle and of sickness as seldom as possible. Wellington demanded that officers consider the welfare of their men. He berated regimental commanders who carelessly selected unhealthy campsites or who neglected to supply their troops with shoes, blankets, "greatcoats," or breakfast. Repeatedly, he urged Whitehall to exclude from the British recruits destined for Iberia the weak and sickly unable to withstand the rigorous Peninsular campaigning.

In November, 1809, Wellington wrote to Lord Liverpool, secretary for war and colonies, that "one of the reasons which induced me to

cross the Tagus on the 4th August [after Talavera], instead of attacking
. . . was the want of surgeons with the army . . . and if we had had an
action, we should not have been able to dress our wounded."[12] He
pointed out in October, 1810, to General Robert Craufurd of his command, the continual discrepancies in the medical department's sick
returns. "This is one glaring fact which the gentlemen of the hospitals
can not get rid of, that the military returns of sick absent is double that
of the number returned by them in hospitals."[13] The worried Wellington lamented to Liverpool in December: "You can have no idea of the
difficulties to which I am reduced in moving the army from its present
quarters, for want of medical assistance; and if unfortunately the
troops should be sickly on their march, I do not know what is to become of them."[14] The hard-pressed commander stated in February,
1811, to Charles Stuart, the British ambassador in Portugal, that "It
is obvious, however, if this [medical] system continues much longer,
the whole army will be sick or must disband; I hope some efficient
measures will be adopted to apply some remedy to it."[15] And in September, 1811, after the mauling summer's fighting in Spain, Wellington confided to Liverpool that "we are almost an army of convalescents . . . I never saw an army capable of bearing so little [sic] nearly
one-half of all those recently arrived from England have gone into hospitals."[16] Furthermore, Wellington's pattern of waging mobile warfare in Spain—involving long thrusts into enemy territory and occasional pitched battles, followed by a retirement to winter sanctuary in
Portugal—required an efficient regimental hospital system rather than
the base hospitals preferred by his medical chief.

Wellington's first inspector of hospitals, Dr. Franck, a veteran of the
Corsican and Egyptian campaigns, tried to supply headquarters with
information and to improve regimental medical services. But he rarely
demonstrated initiative or decisiveness in his work, and for these reasons, McGrigor completely overshadows his predecessor. It is apparent
that Franck's management of the medical service was unimaginative,
and that he possessed neither the energy nor dedication necessary to
convince Wellington that reforms of casualty evacuation procedures
and of hospital administration were necessary.

One looks in vain at Franck's tenure of office for a single major improvement. Sensitive to hints of criticism, Franck feuded with his subordinates and with his superiors. He complained to the Medical Board
about his low pay, the vagueness of his title, and about his requests for

drugs and equipment. On the other hand, the board was shocked at the callous treatment of convalescents shipped from Lisbon to England in December, 1810, a voyage on which 64 men perished from lack of medical attention. But Franck stoutly disclaimed any responsibility for the tragedy.[17] Furthermore, he was unable to provide Wellington or the board with regular and accurate data about sickness and mortality rates. "This want of due and indispensable information," warned the board to Franck in February, 1811, have [sic] long been felt in this office."[18]

A pathetic picture of the harassed Dr. Franck emerges from Guthrie, who was trudging to the Coa River in September, 1811, with 300 men in his care. Guthrie encountered Franck sitting in a dazed condition by the roadside with a party of sick. Guthrie asked his medical chief for instructions, but he was merely told by Franck to do as he liked, "as long as you do not disobey orders."[19] When Franck was invalided home in October, 1811, Wellington sent him a courteous note of appreciation, but undoubtedly, Wellington wanted a more vigorous man for the post. "It will be necessary," Wellington wrote the Duke of York, restored as commander in chief in May, 1811, "that we should have the most capable and the most experienced person that can be found to fill this station."[20] For the task of reforming the medical department in the Peninsula, York selected McGrigor, who sailed in December for Portugal.

After repelling a French offensive to capture Lisbon in 1810, Wellington had again driven the enemy out of Portugal by March, 1811. While thwarted in Portugal, however, Napoleon's marshals were still masters of Spain. The French held the citadels of Ciudad Rodrigo in the north and Badajoz in the south which dominated the routes into western Spain from the Portuguese border. Until Wellington captured these bastions, he was unable to manuever his army beyond the Estremadura. Although Wellington and Beresford won battles against the enemy in the spring, the Allies were unable to capitalize upon these victories and they retreated to winter quarters. Yet Wellington, who normally avoided campaigning during Peninsular winters, surprised the French in December by attacking Ciudad Rodrigo. On January 10, 1812, the old medieval fortress fell to the British, and soon after Wellington prepared to besiege Badajoz.

In the meantime, McGrigor landed in early January at Lisbon, where he encountered many problems. There was a shortage of medical staff for the line, "the army was sickly,"[21] as he put it, and there were numerous officers and men at Belem, recuperated from their injuries, who were reluctant to rejoin their regiments. Furthermore, McGrigor discovered that the records of the purveyors and apothecaries were in disarray and that medical supplies were scattered in warehouses all over Lisbon.

First, McGrigor reorganized the storage and accounting procedures. Then he expedited the flow of medical supplies and soon reported to the Medical Board that the material was moving to the front. McGrigor then wrote Wellington requesting authorization for measures designed to expedite the movement of the sick to the rear and to prod the reluctant "Belem Rangers" into returning to duty. He also urged the transfer of some medical personnel from Lisbon to the line, the establishment of local medical boards to determine the degree of illness claimed by convalescing officers and men, procedures by which his staff would determine the degree of a soldier's injury before dispatching him to the rear, and the immediate embarkation to England of the permanently invalided and other serious medical cases who could not recuperate in the Peninsula. Wellington agreed to these suggestions and requested McGrigor to inspect hospitals en route to Ciudad Rodrigo where he waited for his new medical chief.[22]

McGrigor traveled on horseback through incessant rain in late January over "a bleak country which every town bore marks of having been ravaged by the French," he recorded in his journal.[23] He rode through the lines of Torres Vedras, outside of Lisbon, and the towns of Caldas and Villa Franca. Exhausted from the journey, he finally reached Coimbra. McGrigor discovered that "we occupied the best buildings in it as hospitals. The situation was good, and they were large and airy with lofty rooms and abundantly ventilated."[24] Yet there was a distressing record of high mortality at Coimbra from typhus, gangrene, and various fevers. McGrigor's examination of the medical registers revealed that many former patients, discharged for military duty, had relapses and returned for additional care. He thereby initiated a significant reform in hospital administration, a method that was duplicated throughout the Peninsular army. In an attempt to check the contagion at Coimbra, he classified the sick by type of disease and degree of recovery and placed them into separate wards and buildings. To accelerate the rate of recovery for convalescents, he instituted recuperation depots in outlying villages.[25]

Receiving an urgent message from Wellington ordering him to hasten his inspection, McGrigor left Coimbra on February 12 for Celerico. As he traveled to the front, he noted that there were few intermediate aid stations for convoys of invalids between the major towns:

The suffering of the sick and wounded on this route was very great. . . . As the sick and wounded were conveyed on this route almost only on bullock carts, a journey of ——— miles, meeting little cover on the route, and often without the means of having any vituals cooked, and not infrequently without comforts, their distress and misery may be easily imagined . . . The loss on the road was as might ——— immense, but the loss was not only that of those who died on the road. They suffered so much by the transport, the weather, and the privation on that ———, many particularly of the wounded and those ill of dysentery arrived in so bad a state as only to survive a few days—after their reception in the hospitals at either Celeri[c]o or Coimbra. In truth the medical officers at these stations had not fair play with them. They received these patients in that state when it was impossible to do anything with them.[26]

McGrigor found that Celerico was an unhealthy location for a hospital and that a high mortality rate of patients and hospital staff prevailed there. Yet the army needed a station at this junction to receive casualties from the line. So alarming were the hospital reports about Celerico, said McGrigor, that Wellington himself had visited the town the previous December and had promptly ordered 400 men transferred to Coimbra's healthier environment.[27]

On February 19, McGrigor arrived at Wellington's camp at Castello Bom. While journeying to the front, McGrigor had pondered means of bettering his department, and he related: "Immediately on joining headquarters a number of things pressed upon my mind, which I thought would be improvements in the medical department of the army . . . ."[28] Wellington had supported McGrigor's measures thus far to rectify the administrative confusion in Lisbon. But would he support his medical chief's requests for additional spring wagons to transport the wounded? Would he agree to the closure of some unsanitary and inefficient hospitals and agree to McGrigor's cherished plan of regimental hospitals?

Although McGrigor was seldom awed by ranking military officers, he was reticent with Wellington. Describing his first meeting with the general since his own service in India, McGrigor remembered that "he received me most kindly, and he recollected our having met in Bombay . . . ." Then in front of the entire staff, Wellington inquired if Mc-

Grigor had yet encountered the 88th in Portugal. When the doctor replied that he had not, Wellington retorted in jest:

"I hope from your long living with them, you have not contracted any of their propensities; for I hang and shoot more of your old friends for murder, robbery, etc. than I do of all the rest of the army." The laughter of the whole party was loud. At this I felt somewhat abashed; which Lord Wellington observing, he continued,—"One thing I will tell you, however; whenever anything very gallant or desperate is to be done, there is not a corps in the army, I would sooner rely than your old friends, the Connaught Rangers."[29]

Ordered to report the following day for a conference with Wellington, McGrigor withdrew to set up his own headquarters in nearby Castello Bom. To his dismay, he discovered that Dr. Franck had departed with virtually all the medical records. Both Wellington and McGrigor complained to London about this absurd situation, and within a few months the Medical Board supplied McGrigor with copies of its correspondence with the erratic Dr. Franck. Another difficulty in conducting a systematic administration of his department was that hospital and divisional medical reports sent to headquarters for McGrigor's consideration contained little information about disease and casualties. "Reports of sickness having never been regularly established," McGrigor claimed, "I immediately set about establishing certain returns and records. . . ."[30]

At his first discussion on administrative matters with Wellington, McGrigor was delighted to find that the general endorsed his endeavors to reform the supply depots and the hospitals.[31] Wellington intimated to his new medical chief that he desired someone who understood "the habits of soldiers and who would prevent the malingering propensities of both officers and men at the hospital stations . . . and he promised me his utmost support which from that moment I fully experienced."[32] Thereafter, whenever McGrigor was at Wellington's headquarters, every morning he personally presented the general with his report. "But I soon discovered that he disliked my coming with a written paper. He was fidgety, and evidently displeased when I referred to my notes."[33] Thereafter, McGrigor committed his reports to memory and pleased Wellington with detailed accounts about the health of the army.

Wellington supported McGrigor's efforts to terminate the depots of "malingerers" in Lisbon, to embark invalids to England, and to establish local medical boards at the divisional level. These measures provided the medical department with more systematic control over the flow of sick and wounded from the lines, prevented an overcrowding at stations in the rear, and supplied McGrigor with precise information about the numbers of sick men absent from duty. "Lord Wellington at once saw the great advantage that would accrue to the army from this part of my plan," boasted McGrigor, "in the considerable addition which it would give to his force in the field; and he immediately gave his unqualified assent to the regulations which I had laid before him, ordering General Stewart, the adjutant-general, to issue them in orders to the whole army."[34]

But when McGrigor proposed the establishment of regimental hospitals and an ambulance service with ox-carts and spring wagons under medical department supervision, Wellington "at once exclaimed against it, and said he would have no interruption to the movements of the army which my plans would clog. On my further explaining, he warily said he would have no vehicle with the army but for the conveyance of the guns; so that for the time I was obliged to give up my plan, I saw that he was strongly opposed to it." Yet McGrigor's suggestions for expediting the transfer of the wounded intrigued Wellington. Soon after, he told McGrigor that "my views were excellent if they had been practicable." Thus, McGrigor admitted ruefully that, "for the time the matter was dropped."[35] Nevertheless, the medical chief was still determined to press his views upon the general.

In March, Wellington prepared to besiege Badajoz. In preparation for the anticipated casualties, McGrigor established supply depots and additional hospitals (at Elvas, Estremos, Alter de Chao, and Santarem). Arriving on March 11 at Elvas, McGrigor noted that regardless of his arrangements, "I found an inundation of complaints of the inadequacy of the means which the medical department had for opening the campaign." Furious to learn that the Commissary had delayed shipments of medical stores and hospital bedding to Elvas and that his surgeons were still short of equipment, McGrigor stated that "I was further mortified to find that medical and purveying officers arrived very ——— slowly at their destination . . . and that . . . there was not a single spring wagon in the Alentejo."[36] McGrigor tried to rectify these deficiencies as the investment of Badajoz continued during April. He even attempted to provide every regiment with vehicles for casualties, for he discovered that military commanders wanted "some kind of conveyance . . . but having no authority, they fear to incur censure by carrying slight cases with them." However, disregarding Wellington's injunctions, McGrigor managed to acquire transportation for each regiment. As he explained:

This practice . . . gradually crept in; few corps were to be seen without a cart to carry their slight cases with them when they marched, and the commanding officers, wishing to have as many effective men as possible with their regiments, were anxiously desirous to carry with them, men, who in a few days could carry their firelock and appear in the ranks.[37]

Reporting at Badajoz on April 4, McGrigor established a field hospital there and sent to Elvas only the severely wounded who could be moved with safety. "It rained heavily during the whole of the siege," he recalled, "which with the severity of the duties . . . induced a good deal of disease."[38]

After his artillery bombarded Badajoz day after day, Wellington, usually extremely cautious about risking the lives of his troops, ordered waves of assault teams to penetrate breeches in the enemy ramparts. But these attacks were repulsed with heavy losses. Then came the news that a French army, marching from Seville, was advancing closer and closer. Wellington now began to despair of ever capturing the seemingly impregnable bastion. On the night of April 6, when an officer reported that the latest assault had been beaten off by the French with great loss of life, Wellington was aghast. McGrigor was in the general's tent at this critical moment as Wellington pondered whether to withdraw from the bloody siege: "At this moment, I cast my eyes on the countenance of Lord Wellington lit up by the glare of the torch . . . I never shall forget it to the last moment of my existence . . . . The jaw had fallen, and the face was of unusual length, while the torchlight gave to his countenance a lurid aspect; but still the expression of the face was firm."[39]

The outcome of this horrible battle now depended upon the ability of some troops to storm the city walls. Waiting for news about their attempted escalade of a castle defense and wondering whether he would have to withdraw in defeat from Badajoz, Wellington was suddenly startled by a voice from the darkness. An excited horseman appeared, shouting for the duke and proclaiming: "My Lord, the castle is your own."[40]

Wellington's men had stormed a castle wall and opened the city gates for their comrades, who triumphantly poured in to have their revenge on the enemy. Following the victorious soldiers into the citadel, McGrigor was appalled at the destruction, the casualties, and at the orgy of pillaging committed by Wellington's heretofore well disciplined troops. "In a little time the whole of the soldiers appeared to be in a state of drunkenness," reported the startled doctor. "In every street, and in every corner we met them forcing their way like furies into houses. . . . In passing some houses . . . we heard the shrieks of females, and sometimes the groans of those whom [the soldiery] were no doubt butchering."[41]

The French governor of the city, General Armand Phillipon, was searching for a sanctuary for his two daughters while Badajoz was being sacked. He was suddenly accosted in the street by some drunken Rangers of the 88th. Encountering the frightened Frenchman and his charges cowering before these troops, McGrigor immediately came to Phillipon's defense. Indignant that these men had disgraced his own old regiment by threatening a French officer and his family, McGrigor awed the men with a withering criticism of their disgraceful conduct and then aided the governor and the females to safety.

Describing to his brother-in-law, Lieutenant Colonel Lewis Grant, "this horrible scene of carnage" at Badajoz, McGrigor stated:

Being with His Lordship the whole time the business went on I saw everything and heard everything, and most interesting it was. . . . My duty has been extremely harassing. . . . During the time the thing [the final assault] lasted, about five hours, Lord Wellington was extremely anxious to know the numbers of men that came wounded to the different posts, and I went from one to the other and occasionally informed him. When the thing was won, and I told him what I believed the actual number he really cried.[42]

There is no mention in McGrigor's *Autobiography* of this very rare display of grief by the usually stern and composed Wellington. In his published version, McGrigor related that when he entered the Duke's headquarters after his inspection of Badajoz, Wellington was writing an account of his victory to be dispatched to Britain. Sensing that this was the opportunity to press a favor, McGrigor carefully chose his words:

"I trust, my Lord, you are satisfied that the medical officers during last night did their duty, as well as the military officers, and that you will receive my testimony that they discharged their arduous and laborious duties most zealously, and often under circumstances of personal danger . . ." He replied that he himself had witnessed it. I then added, "Nothing could more gratify those officers, nothing could be a greater incentive to their exertions on future occasion, than . . . noticing them in [the] public dispatches." He asked "Is that usual?" My reply was "It would be of the most essential service;" and I ventured to add, that "really their extraordinary exertions gave them justice and a claim to this." He rejoined, "I have finished my dispatch,—but very well, I will add something about the doctors." When the [London] Gazette appeared, the medical officers of the army in England saw with delight that the merits of their brethren had been publicly acknowledged, in the same manner, as those of the military officers. This was the *first time* that their merits had been thus publicly recognized; and the example of Lord Wellington has been followed after every action that has since been fought . . . .[43]

As McGrigor contended, although the army surgeon was often cheered during the course of battle for bravery, and "that by officers in particular, he is caressed, flattered, most idolized," too often his heroism was later forgotten, his courage under fire ignored, and his efforts to combat disease overlooked.[44] Until the siege of Badajoz, army surgeons had never been publicly cited for gallantry in action, nor would they, for another forty years, be candidates for military honors from their sovereign. It was at Badajoz, where 25 percent of the British troops were casualties, that this military testimony to the skill and bravery of the doctor was recognized. Wellington's dispatch enhanced the surgeon's prestige in both the medical and military worlds. His commendation of McGrigor's staff was a landmark in the evolution of British military medicine in the nineteenth century climaxed in 1898 by the creation of the Royal Army Medical Corps.

McGrigor related in his *Autobiography* that upon returning to headquarters at Frenada, "nothing remarkable occurred, till the movement of the army commenced in the beginning of June."[45] Yet while Wellington was preparing to strike deep into Castile during the summer of 1812, McGrigor was extending his own control over the medical department. He chastised irresponsible regimental surgeons who neglected to supervise the movements of invalids to the rear, he berated careless staff surgeons for failing to provide him with comprehensive reports on their patients, warning his negligent subordinates that such incompetence, if continued, would be reported to the commander of the forces. Moreover, he promulgated regulations to enforce strict hygienic standards in general hospitals, requiring that wards be cleansed daily by orderlies and be inspected weekly by principal medical officers. A rigid schedule for the care of the sick would be maintained, he declared: "Every hospital to be cleaned out by 7 o'clock in the morning, the patient to be given breakfast at 8, dinner at 1, and supper by 6 o'clock. Every medical officer must be in his ward by 9 o'clock in the morning and 7 in the evening."[46]

McGrigor required that Portuguese muleteers, conveying the wounded from one station to another, show documented proof that they had completed their assignments before receiving payment. To his credit, McGrigor ordered that newly arrived surgeons and mates, fresh from medical schools and civilian life, be first introduced to military medicine at Lisbon hospitals before assignment to a regiment. The medical chief also established aid stations along routes from the line to hospitals in order to provide some comfort and protection for casualties en route. To eliminate the horrors of a voyage home for incapacitated men, McGrigor instigated measures for thorough cleansing of the ships, adequate staffing to care for the sick, proper provisioning, and a rigid inspection by ranking medical officers before the vessels sailed from Portugal.[47]

McGrigor was a stern taskmaster. He constantly prodded his ranking medical officers for explanations about the prevalence of a particular disease and deluged them with questions about the reasons for a high mortality rate. The sting of a McGrigor letter to a subordinate is evident in this example to a deputy inspector concerning an inept surgeon: "I beg you will express to Staff Surgeon Hussie my dissatisfaction with the slovenly and incorrect manner in which he exerts his duties and that if he is not more attentive I will recommend to the Medical Board to remove him to the West Indies or any other station where inefficiency may be attended to with less public service."[48]

Letter after letter to his staff in the Peninsula indicates McGrigor's compulsion for precise and regular statistical information so that he could provide Wellington with correct information about the numbers of men returning to their corps, a calculation that could make the difference between defeat or victory. Beyond the necessity of this data for purely military reasons, however, McGrigor pointed out to his principal medical officers that the compilation of medical returns was essential in medical practice. As he explained: "In the hands of an Officer of observation and research they ought to be turned to the purpose of science, and ought not to be considered as mere official documents or tasks."[49]

In preparation for the campaign, McGrigor repeatedly reminded his staff that troops had to be properly fed, clothed and sheltered in order to curtail the incidence of disease on the march. In a letter di-

rected to staff surgeons of divisions on June 12, McGrigor requested
their help in maintaining the health of the army:

In the season which is approaching and which is now to bring so much sickness with it, in most parts of the country, I have to request that you direct
the attention of the Medical Officers of your Divisions to the modes of prevention disease [sic], with which you are so well acquainted. In your superintendence, it will not ——— you to notice the clothing of the men, their
regular ———, their having a portion of vegetables whenever possible they
can be had, their getting their breakfast in every possible situation, the soldier having a blanket or Greatcoat and the cleaning out of whatever quarter
they come to.[50]

McGrigor advised Wellington about his men and pointed out
means to eliminate sickness in the ranks:

I beg leave to draw your Lordship's attention to some points which may
materially affect the health of the Troops on this Service of which may not
be undeserving of the attention of the Government. During the short time
I have been in this country the diseases of which are so much akin to those
of other countries where I have served, have ——— and devoted a good deal
of attention to the Corps which I have found have been ——— particularly
unhealthy with a view of discovering the causes of their unhealthiness. I find
that sickness falls most on regiments when they first arrive in this country,
or the recruits sent out to them. This appears to be invariably the case; but
I shall adduce it only in the instance of the two Regiments, the 7th and 40th
as particularly good. [Then, after some statistical evidence to support his
statements, McGrigor listed his suggestions.]

1st—I beg leave to submit to your Lordship that for the Service when the
duties are so active, and when there is not garrison duty, neither recruits
under age, nor those who are incapable of performing the various duties of
a soldier in the field should be sent out; and that if possible, men should be
selected who have for some time ——— to the life of a Soldier.

2nd—That the men for this Service be embarked in December or after the
Autumnal Equinox, so as to be gradually inured to the climate, and to the
Country before the warm and unhealthy months come on . . .

3rd—Tho' it be an object of some consequence, that in the summer and
autumn months, the soldier should march as light and disencumbered as
possible; yet in October when dysentery begins to appear, and thereafter,
inflammatory diseases, warmth is necessary and the issue of blanket and
great coats are essential to health.

4th—The period of payment of the accumulated balance of pay due to the
soldier, is in every country a period of disease. If the balance could gradually
paid to him, and material for breakfast provided out of it, it would tend to
the prevention of disease.

5th—If it were possible to issue the rations to the soldiers daily, it would be
greatly conducive to the preservation of his health, when three days rations

are issued to him, he very frequently consumes or destroys the whole on the first day, being two days without food, unless he has an opportunity to plunder.

6th—I am aware that when I recommend any change in the mode of conveyance of sick to the rear, I risk the recommendations of what may be unpopular, but it is my duty to state, that if any steady and regular mode could be secured to each brigade, it would greatly diminish the mortality, which has sometimes been very great.[51]

Wellington endorsed some of these proposals by enclosing McGrigor's recommendations to Lord Liverpool on June 12: "I concur with Dr. McGrigor in deeming it desirable that the troops and recruits destined for this army should be sent out in the winter, before the spring equinox gales, these should leave England, if possible with the first easterly wind in December."[52]

However, Wellington informed McGrigor that he objected to the other suggestions. The general insisted that because of transportation shortage, he could not provide the soldiers with seasonal clothing changes. Furthermore, he could do little to change the method of feeding men, nor would he modify the system of providing his troops with their usual allotment of three days of rations. If he followed McGrigor's suggestions, stated Wellington, "the army would be incapable of all movement, if I were to order that the soldier carry no provisions. The British soldiers on such occasion," he continued, "carry three days bread, the Portuguese soldiers, six days bread, and the French soldiers fifteen days bread." And, on the crucial issue of transport for the wounded, Wellington insisted that he had already authorized the maximum number of vehicles that he could spare for casualties. Blaming the high sickness and death rates in the army on other factors, Wellington concluded: "But the causes of mortality, you have noticed and among them the irregularities of the soldiers themselves, it is impossible for me to remedy, till the Mutiny Law and the whole system of the service is altered."[53] Thus, Wellington supported some of McGrigor's suggestions, but he refused to tamper with his own dependable supply system.

With the capture of Ciudad Rodrigo and Badajoz, the tide of war turned gradually in Wellington's favor, and he could now boldly penetrate into Castile. The Allied army marched from the Agueda River in June, then along the Duero to encounter a French force at Salamanca. Here at Salamanca in July, Wellington had one of his greatest victories, but the casualties were enormous.

"After this great battle," McGrigor commented, "my own labours, as well as those of all the medical officers, were very arduous."[54] Writing to Wellington on July 24, the medical chief explained that he had placed over 5,000 wounded British and French soldiers in Salamanca and "into those villages near the field of Action 600—there are still a few on the field which we are collecting. I am glad to say that there are many of the wounded slight." McGrigor's plan of removing the casualties further back along the line to Portugal was working, and he informed Wellington that "if you do not disagree, I mean to commence sending some of the cases to Ciudad [Rodrigo], having a week ago given orders to remove 700 sick from there to Celerico."[55] To this communication, Wellington replied: "I think you do well to send to Ciudad Rodrigo only those whose wounds are not likely even to recover and movement of whom will not be prejudicial to them, as we must get the men to their regiments again as soon as we can."[56]

Wellington still faced four other French armies. But three of these commands were suppressing attacks in eastern and southern Spain by guerrillas, the Spanish army, and British troops landed from Sicily. With control of the Tagus and Duero rivers, Wellington decided that, for a few months at least, he could continue his offensive without fear of being trapped. The prize was now Madrid, which was occupied by the Allies in August.

In the meantime, McGrigor traveled slowly to Madrid, for he was supervising the care of numerous casualties which he encountered along the route from Salamanca. Appalled by the suffering he witnessed, and discovering that there were few facilities available to assist the stragglers, McGrigor took the initiative. Aware of an emergency, he ordered that stragglers be collected at village depots, and even though he did not have Wellington's authorization, he requisitioned commissary carts and commissary personnel to assist in the evacuation of the incapacitated men.

The relationship between Wellington and "Mac," as the duke called him, was one of mutual respect. One incident, however, nearly marred their understanding. When McGrigor arrived in Madrid, he immediately reported to Wellington, who was then sitting for a portrait by the famed Goya. Wellington listened patiently to his inspector's account of the handling of casualties en route from Salamanca. "But when I came to inform him that for their relief I had ordered up purveying and commissary officers, he started up," McGrigor re-

marked, "and in a violent manner reprobated what I had done." Mc-
Grigor noted that the numbers of neglected sick and wounded were
great, and that there had been severe criticism in England after the retreat from Talavera when many casualties were left behind to the
French. "But all was in vain. His Lordship was in a passion, and the
Spanish artist, ignorant of the English language, looked aghast, and at
a loss to know what I had done to enrage his Lordship so much. 'I
shall be glad to know,' exclaimed his Lordship, 'who is to command
the army? I or you? I establish one route for the army, you establish
another, and order the commissariat and the supplies by that line. As
long as you live, sir, never do so again; never do anything without my
orders.' "[57]

Yet after this outburst, Wellington soon relented and invited Mc-
Grigor to dine that evening with the rest of his staff. One of the hon-
ored guests at the banquet was the famed Spanish guerrilla leader "El
Medico." Wellington amused himself by jesting that McGrigor and
the ferocious mountain chieftain were "brothers of the profession of
medicine. . . ."[58] Later in the year, when McGrigor was sick and unable to move, Wellington provided the Scot with his own carriage, the
only one attached to the entire army, and thereafter he always treated
McGrigor with great consideration.

Wellington realized that he could hold Madrid only briefly, for the
French had regrouped their armies and were advancing toward the
capital. Leaving General Rowland Hill in September to delay the
French offensive, Wellington besieged Burgos, the enemy's major supply link to the Pyrenees. When McGrigor arrived in early October at
the ancient Moorish citadel, the siege was proceeding badly—casualties were heavy, morale was low, and the fortress was ably defended.
Wellington had outdistanced his supply train, he had insufficient cannon and sappers, and he knew that Hill, holding Madrid, was in danger. McGrigor related how day after day, when Wellington's staff
presented unfavorable reports about the progress of the investment,
"Lord Wellington was often in bad humour, for everything went
wrong for him. . . . This, therefore, was the period of his life when fortune seemed to turn her back upon him." Wellington became more
sullen and more critical of his staff, and at one point, he blurted out a
caustic indictment of the medical department that McGrigor believed
was unfair. That evening, Wellington sent McGrigor a note requesting
his presence. But the indignant Scot explained:

I felt unwell; so much so that I had applied a few leeches to my head, which relieved me by the time the note arrived. I could have then gone, and waited upon him; but my pride had been wounded by him in the morning. I felt that I, personally, and the medical officers, had made extraordinary exertions; that no part of the army was more warmly animated by zeal for the service than the medical officers. I therefore wrote an apology for not calling on him that evening.[59]

When McGrigor awoke on October 20, he was informed that the army was preparing to withdraw from Burgos. Despairing of capturing the bastion, conscious of large French armies advancing toward him, and fearful of losing Badajoz or Ciudad Rodrigo to the enemy, Wellington had ordered a retreat to Salamanca, to be coordinated with Hill's withdrawal from Madrid. McGrigor quickly caught up to Wellington in the field while the general was observing the movement of the French by telescope. Wellington informed McGrigor that:

We cannot keep Madrid. Hill is obliged by an overwhelming force to quit his position; he is in fact on the march toward us, and must leave this place this very night. But what is to become of our sick and wounded? I feel that they are numerous; and of the wounded there are many who cannot be moved. What do you propose to do?

McGrigor replied that he had foreseen such an emergency, that he had already sent many incapacitated men by mules and carts to Valladolid, and that he was leaving at Burgos only 60 patients in charge of six surgeons in the expectation that the French, who usually exchanged such courtesies in the war with the British, would care for them. "Admirable," Wellington exclaimed, "I shall be off tonight; make your own arrangements; quietly and quickly; but be most careful not to let a syllable of my moving escape you."[60]

In spite of his numerical troop inferiority, Wellington skillfully withdrew his command from Burgos and checked the pursuing French on numerous occasions during the long retreat. As he moved onto Salamanca for a juncture with Hill, the duke passed through Valladolid. Here, McGrigor tried to coordinate the evacuation of casualties without impeding the movements of the retreating army. Finding Wellington in a nearly demolished observation post in the bombarded city, McGrigor noted that "on my entering, he came quickly from a window with a glass [telescope] in his hand, and early inquired about the hospital in Valladolid, saying: 'I fear our numbers are very great. What is to be done, for, you see, we must be off from this place, and

conveyance there is none?' " McGrigor replied that he had already established a chain of hospitals to Ciudad Rodrigo and to Oporto, and
that the flow of wounded to the rear would not impede Wellington's
retreat. "This is excellent," replied Wellington, as he prepared to evacuate the town. But McGrigor could not resist the temptation to re-
mind Wellington that he had proposed similar measures in the past
without receiving his approval:

My Lord, you recollect how much you blamed me at Madrid for the steps
which I took on coming to the army, when I could not consult your Lordship, and acted for myself as I had done. Now, if, I had not, what would the
consequences have been? He added, "It is all right, as it has turned out; but
I recommend you still have my orders for what you do." This was a singular
feature in the character of Lord Wellington.[61]

McGrigor then rode all night through a torrential rain. In the darkness, he lost his way and nearly stumbled into an enemy camp. But
fortunately McGrigor found some British stragglers who directed him
to safety. The constant rainfall, the lack of provision, the degree of
looting and drunkenness on the route, and the disintegration of discipline marked this retreat as a tragic episode for the Peninsular army.
McGrigor reported: "great was the disorder, the insubordination, and
intemperance; I never witnessed the like. One day I am sure, I saw
five hundred men at least in a state of intoxication. . . . Had the enemy
come upon us at the time, we should have been easy prey for him."[62]

When the retreat ended at Ciudad Rodrigo in late November,
Wellington realized that he has lost another 3,000 men, even though
the French had not pursued closely, nor had the enemy inflicted a
defeat on his army. The daily marches had not been excessive, and
there were periods when the regiments rested from their ordeal. Yet
the months of constant campaigning, the shortage of food, and typhus
in the ranks all severely weakened the army as it crawled to its sanctuary. Writing on November 19, to Earl Bathurst, the secretary for
war and colonies, Wellington lamented: "The constitution of the soldier of the British army are [sic] so much shaken by disorders acquired
by their Service, Walcheren, or by their irregularities, that the British
army is almost a moving hospital, there being generally, almost one
third of the men sick in hospitals or attending upon the sick."[63] And
in December, McGrigor answered the Medical Board's inquiry about
the health of the army with a graphic passage:

Here the whole army is constantly in face of the enemy for the last eleven months. The Army has been incessantly marching, the soldiers suffering the utmost fatigue and every privation which the human frame is capable of supporting, his pay irregular and in scanty portions, his clothing very bad while he frequently is without covering from the inclemency of a very variable and frequently cold climate. The Hospitals, here are filled with sick and men wounded to the verge of the Grave by excessive discharge of their wounds. All of these requiring and deserving every comfort and support which this country can afford.[64]

Yet the retreat, in the face of overwhelming odds, was a success. The Allied army was safe in winter cantonments, Castile was no longer under French control, and the enemy had withdrawn from Spain's southern provinces. Furthermore, a related military campaign far from Iberia was Napoleon's own tortuous retreat from Moscow in the winter of 1812 with the decimated remnants of a once mighty army. At both ends of Europe, in Russia and in Spain, the deteriorating French legions were being challenged by a resurgence of nationalism as Allied armies massed to contest the Napoleonic hegemony over the continent.

The aftermath of the retreat from Burgos was a test of McGrigor's ingenuity. "As soon as the army halted," he stated, "Lord Wellington issued the strictest orders, and everything was done to re-clothe the men, to provide them with blankets, to procure an abundance of provisions, and to restore order and discipline."[65] Gangrene, dysentery, pneumonia, and typhus spread rapidly through the regiments. Short of medical personnel as usual, McGrigor pleaded with the Medical Board for additional staff. But as weeks would pass before replacements would arrive from England, McGrigor characteristically sought another solution:

I proposed taking into our pay all the Spanish medical officers I could find, with such of the French medical officers, our prisoners of war, as would take employment; and I recommended the English pay instead of their own. This bait took, for I do not think one of those gentlemen refused, and I posted them [the French] to the hospitals in the rear that they might be out of temptation of deserting to their countrymen.[66]

With these French and Spanish doctors, the shortage of personnel was temporarily filled. "But I found many of them ignorant and inefficient," complained McGrigor, "and they by no means made up for the want of British physicians and surgeons."[67]

In December, McGrigor finally received Wellington's sanction for a procedure which he had quietly instigated on his own initiative months before—the establishment of regimental hospitals. McGrigor informed the Medical Board that "His Excellency the Commander of the Forces [has] been pleased to assent to my proposition that division and regimental hospitals be established in the Peninsula immediately. . . ."[68] McGrigor was delighted to observe the rapid development of his system. "Everywhere was to be seen a comfortable hospital for the sick, surgeons and commanding officers vying with each other who would construct the best and most comfortable hospital for his corps. . . . In a short time, the march of the sick from regiments to the established hospitals to the rear was stopped; and it was high time, for the number that died on the way . . . was very great."[69]

In January, 1813, McGrigor went on a lengthy tour of the hospitals, for he was particularly distressed about a strange fever at Celerico, and he wanted first hand information about his staff. Explaining to the board that he had divided his administrative area into districts under the local supervision of deputy inspectors, McGrigor commented that "as often as it has to be done, I intend to round the whole myself; by my last visit I have acquired a knowledge their characters and merits which I could not other ways have obtained."[70] Wellington also visited some of the hospitals and McGrigor reported that "he had been pleased to express his perfect satisfaction with the whole of them, and with the medical officers doing duty at them."[71] What particularly delighted Wellington was the recovery of more men than he expected, a factor which the medical chief attributed to the exertions of his staff and to the benefits derived from regimental hospitals. "These destructive diseases, typhus and gangrene, soon disappeared in every regiment," he wrote, "and in four months, the army was effective and in perfect condition to take the field again."[72]

In the meantime, McGrigor pondered the problem of providing shelters for his patients and for casualties during the forthcoming campaign. The army would pass through devastated country in northern Spain and many towns had been demolished. McGrigor explained to Wellington that while in the West Indies he had witnessed the use of portable wooden shelters, whose parts had been transported from England, utilized as temporary hospitals. He pointed out that such mobile structures could provide additional hospital space and could provide cover for the wounded after a battle:

In this Country I am of opinion; that the Portable Hospitals would be highly useful if the present circumstances of the Service, did not render something of the kind absolutely necessary. Having these Portable Hospitals Marquees I think accommodation might be easily provided in advance for a body of sick and wounded, and that the necessity of sending them to Hospitals at a great distance in the Rear might be obviated, a measure always fraught with great inconvenience and most serious injury to the Service.[73]

Wellington considered the suggestion and then wrote to Lord Bathurst on February 13, pointing out the difficulties in accommodating casualties. He enclosed McGrigor's letter on the subject and requested that when the material was shipped from England some carpenters accompany the timber so that the buildings could be quickly erected.[74] Happy with Wellington's support, McGrigor selected a location close to the Duero as a convalescent center. By the spring, clusters of new, white cottages for the sick had been erected, buildings that were dismantled and were transported with the army on its march.

In the spring of 1813, many patients had recovered and were rejoining their regiments. Wellington was pleased with the numbers of men returning to their divisions, explained McGrigor, "as the number sent from the hospital fit for duty was so much greater by some thousands than he expected."[75] Wellington himself wrote to Bathurst on May 25 that "in general, the troops are more healthy than I have known them to be."[76] Due to the success of the medical department in curing soldiers during the winter of 1812–13, another 4,000 or 5,000 men were added to the army, a factor which may have helped turn the course of battle in Wellington's favor.

As McGrigor increased the efficiency of his department, he relied increasingly on Wellington's support in various disagreements with the Medical Board, of which Wellington had a low regard. On two issues in particular, Wellington and McGrigor were again in accord— the continual need for additional medical staff, which the board had consistently underestimated, and the necessity of promoting surgeons already with the Peninsula army to supervisory positions rather than acquiesce in the appointment of candidates selected by the board.

The board repeatedly questioned McGrigor's urgent request for drugs, equipment, mates, and surgeons, and it often inquired why the material and personnel in his command were not adequate. Through his gradual rise through the ranks from a regimental surgeon with the 88th to inspector of hospitals with Wellington, McGrigor had rarely disagreed with his superiors. His dispute with Keate during the Walcheren expedition was the one exception in the cautiously worded reports to the board that fill his journals. The picture of McGrigor is that of an earnest, uncomplaining, ambitious medical officer, performing his duties without question, an obedient army doctor trying to please the board. Only on the issue of regimental hospitals had McGrigor debated with his superiors in the past, and his arguments were cautious and controlled; even his testimony in Parliament over his part in the Scheldt enterprise indicated a reticence to criticize his medical chiefs. But, now, weary of the board's continual pettiness which demonstrated little appreciation about the enormous problems confronting him, the embittered McGrigor responded on July 28 from Salamanca:

It is painful to me, that in the execution of my duty, I should have merited your disapprobation or displeasure, because from the moment of my arrival in this country, I have steadily been anxious to act in strict conformity of your orders . . . I have even flattered myself that I was entitled to the same approbation from you, that His Excellency of Commander of the Forces had on more than one occasion been pleased to bestow on my arrangements and exertions. I would hope that with the local knowledge as His Lordship possesses, you would not disapprove of any proceedings of mine.[77]

In November, when the board again questioned his request for additional staff and intimated that he was not fully utilizing his personnel, McGrigor caustically replied that his staff was overworked, that there were few "idlers" among them, and that he made such pleas for reinforcements due to "the peculiar nature of this service, and from circumstances with which those only who are on the spot can be acquainted . . ."[78]

The board again questioned McGrigor in December about why the sickness and mortality rates for the Peninsular army were far greater than for the British in Sicily, and why the prices of foodstuffs and necessaries were higher in Iberia than in Italy. Irked by these remarks, McGrigor explained that any comparison between armies fighting in different areas was difficult to assess, that the British army in Sicily was on garrison duty and not marching on campaigns.[79] These letters are not the communications of an awed subordinate cowering before superiors, but those of a man confident of Wellington's support.

Furthermore, when McGrigor recommended that two surgeons on his staff, George Guthrie and Charles Tice, be promoted to the rank of deputy inspector, he again encountered the board's opposition. Dismayed that the board was sending him deputy inspectors from home who were unfamiliar with the Peninsular army, McGrigor sought Wellington's assistance:

I do earnestly intreat [sic] your Lordship's protection for the Staff, and interposition to prevent a most serious injury, not to Messrs Tice and Guthrie alone, but the body of Officers on this Service, who animated by your Lordship's approbation have displayed an extraordinary degree of zeal.

Then, explaining his selection of Tice and Guthrie for their meritorious service McGrigor pointed out that:

Dr. Tice has with diligence and admirable system regulated the hospitals at Celerico, Coimbra, and the intermediate stations; he has introduced order where none existed before, and brought stations which produced the greatest mortality to be among the most healthy.

Mr. Guthrie is one of the ablest surgeons and best medical officers in the service; his exertions during the siege of Badajoz and after the battle of 22nd July, and his arrangements at Salamanca did him the greatest credit and really are beyond praise.

Adding that he had no intention of questioning the merits of the other two appointees in England, McGrigor concluded:

It really has been my most anxious wish and highest ambition to obtain your Lordship's confidence, and your approbation of the Medical Department. Flattered as I have been by your notice of them, and seeing the officers of the Department animated to fresh exertions of this notice, I would deeply deplore the occurrence of anything that could dampen their zeal, or slacken their exertions, and I much fear that this threatened act and intrusion would have this evil tendency.

I feel an affection for the Service and my own Department noticed as it has been by your Lordship, I am therefore earnestly to entreat that you will kindly interfere to those who look to your Lordship as their protector.[80]

Wellington himself had complained to Bathurst on September 27 that his army was perennially short of medical staff:

This want arises entirely from the practice of waiting till the last moment to send out the officers required. . . . The returns go to them [the board] regularly, but for what purpose it is difficult to say, and the deficiency is not supplied til the demand is made, and three of four months elapse before medical officers arrive. . . . I beg likewise to draw your Lordship's attention to the practice of the Medical Board in promoting to vacancies in this army, instead of promoting the officers on the spot, who deserve promotion highly for their merits and services, officers are selected in England, the Mediterranean, or elsewhere to be promoted. The consequence is, increased delay in their arrival to perform their duties, and all who do arrive are sick in the first instance. It would be but justice to promote those on the spot, who are performing their duty; and we should enjoy the advantages and the seniors of the department at least would have experience in the disorders of the climate, and of the troops serving in this country; to which climate they would have become accustomed.[81]

Then on December 20, Wellington forwarded McGrigor's commentary on the promotion policy of the board to Colonel Henry Torrens, the military secretary to the commander in chief, and added:

I entirely agree with Dr. McGrigor in opinion, that it is no encouragement to those who are performing their duty with the army in this country to see that when by their merits and exertions they have attracted the notice of their immediate superiors . . . others have been preferred to them. . . .[82]

There is insufficient evidence to indicate the outcome of this policy debate, which illustrates McGrigor's determination to control promotions within his own command and demonstrates another aspect of his relationship to Wellington. Both Tice and Guthrie, however, were promoted to the rank of deputy inspector in the Peninsular army in 1813.[83]

In early 1813, Wellington prepared his army for the thrust into northern Spain. As commander of all the Spanish, Portuguese, and British forces in the Peninsula, he now had the manpower available for an offensive long and sustained enough to throw the French back over the Pyrenees.

For his part, McGrigor labored to improve regimental medical services. "Every corps was . . . complete in its ———— of medical officers," he recorded, "but extra officers were added, and each division had likewise Inspectoral Officers, Physicians, or additional Staff Surgeons attached to it. Besides the Spring wagons, I recommended that each battalion according to its strength should start provided with one or two carts or . . . wagons."[84] When the troops marched in April, he remarked, "the divisions of the army were set out as complete in medical means, and in ———— proved to meet the occurrences of disease." And, as another improvement, McGrigor reported to the board that:

Before the army took the field this Campaign, I made every surgeon in charge of a corps provide himself with a tray, to fit into the top of one of the panniers. The tray had compartments into which fitted boxes, which always contain a month's supply of the necessary medicines made up into pills,

powders, etc., and with ————. The medicine in doses, are made up comfortably to a field Pharmacopiae of the army here, and in prescription only.
The articles in the tray can be got out in the field or on the march without
unloading the mules.[85]

Describing the operation of his regimental hospital system on the
campaign, McGrigor stated:

However, short a time a battalion or corps rested in one place, a regimental
hospital was established. It was frequently established in the face of an enemy
and nearly within reach of his guns. By making every corps constantly keep
up an establishment for itself, we could prevent the general hospitals from
being crowded. Much severe and acute disease was treated in its early and
curable stage, and no slight wounds or ailments were ever sent off from the
regiments; by which means the effective force of the army was kept up, or
perhaps increased by several thousand men, and this was effected by the
joint exertions of medical officers who served in the Peninsula, the result of
medical science and their experience of soldiers, their habits, and their apti-
tude to particular diseases.[86]

The key battle during the march into northern Spain was at Vitoria.
Wellington's decisive victory here in June threw the French to the
Pyrenees and it broke Napoleon's grip on the Peninsula. The news in
northern capitals about Vitoria helped to strengthen an already tot-
tering Allied coalition, for Napoleon had defeated the Prussians and
Russians in the spring of 1813. However, as Wellington marched toward the Pyrenees after Vitoria, the alliance against France hardened,
and even long-hesitant Austria joined the coalition. As the Peninsular
War merged with the Wars of Liberation in the north, Napoleon's
empire began to disintegrate. Even his mighty victory in August at
Dresden did not stem the tide of defeat. After the battle of Leipzig in
October, the French armies retreated to the Rhineland, while from the
south, Wellington's command penetrated the Pyrenees. Pushing
through the passes of Maya and Roncesvalles, Wellington led his
troops in early October into France. In February, 1814, Bordeaux
toppled to the British. The last battle of the Peninsular War, in which
Wellington's army suffered the greatest number of casualties in the
entire war, occurred in April at Toulouse. However, Paris had already
capitulated to the allies on March 31, and on April 6, Napoleon ab-
dicated.

Although McGrigor omitted a clear reference to Vitoria in his
journals, there is some evidence of his activity there. According to the
judge advocate general, F. S. Larpent, he and McGrigor watched the

battle from a hillside, and after the action McGrigor entered the town to supervise the casualties.[87] Walter Henry, a surgeon on the scene, explained that he himself had set up a regimental hospital and that "spring wagons were in attendance, in which were placed the worst patients and [he] sent them to Puebla, where Dr. McGrigor had, earlier in the day, made the most judicious arrangements for their accommodation."[88]

During the last year of the war, as the army fought a series of bitter battles in the Pyrenees, many troops succumbed from the severe duty, and from the biting cold. The hospitals from Bordeaux to St. Andero were filled with the victims of typhus, gangrene, and pneumonia. The medical department was very efficient, McGrigor claimed, as he wrote to a general in London: "We never had so many able surgeons as we have at this moment in the Peninsula."[89] Reporting to the board from St. Jean de Luz on July 13, McGrigor commented:

I have just returned from a tour of the regimental hospitals in all the divisions of the Army, and I have much satisfaction in being able to report favourable of them, almost without an exception. . . . The measures of keeping up the establishment of regimental hospitals has so greatly tended to render the forces of the army effective that, it has now the fullest sanction of his Excellency the Commander-in-Chief of the Forces. No other measure so effectively kept down the prevalence of ———, fever, or Hospital Gangrene. It is really delightful to see several of the regimental hospitals in readiness and in everything conducive to the comfort of the sick soldier, several of them do not yield to any establishment at home. To their establishment and to the ability and zeal with which all medical officers discharged their duty, I ascribe the extremely small mortality which has occurred of late.[90]

And the great Guthrie noted that after the last battle, Toulouse, where McGrigor made speedy arrangement to house 5,000 casualties:

Nearly all the wounded had every possible assistance, the hospitals were well supplied with bedsteads, the medicines and materials were in profusion . . . and the whole [medical staff] worked from morning to evening with assiduity. The surgery of the army was at its highest peak of perfection attained during the war. . . .[91]

The reformed medical department in the Peninsula and the gradual improvement in the care of the troops were vital factors in explaining Wellington's many victories. Writing to his brother, Sir Henry Wellesley, in January, 1814, Wellington remarked, "I can only say that, during the five years that I have commanded the army, I have never known it so healthy as it is, and has been since of the month of May last;

that there is little sickness and the men in the hospitals are generally wounded."[92] Although the death toll of British troops in the Peninsular War from 1812 to 1814 was far greater from disease than from combat fatalities (8,889 men died from injuries received in battle and 24,930 from sickness out of 61,511 troops),[93] under the diligent supervision of McGrigor there was seldom a chronic shortage of surgeons or medicines in the 1813–14 campaign, nor was there another Walcheren.

In a tribute to his principal medical officers, as the hospitals in France and Spain were being closed and as regiments were embarking for England, Ireland, and the war in North America, McGrigor wrote from Toulouse on May 19, 1814:

The Service on which the Army has so ――― long been engaged is now fast drawing to a close, but I cannot silently let the tie which had existed between the officers of the hospital staff and myself dissolve. The medical service has been ―――, and the medical officers have frequently been under difficult and trying circumstances and where the ――― utmost zeal and highest professional talent were required. Whenever complaint was preferred or when I have seen the appearance of error, I have never hesitated to question the conduct of any Englishman, and it is ――― honorable to the department which comprises so great a number to find that the exceptional cases have been so few, fewer perhaps than in any other body of the same number.

I have more than once felt it my duty to express to yourselves, and to the officers under you, my highest satisfaction with the zeal, and action [that] have been so beneficial to the public service. . . . I will always point with pride and satisfaction to the ――― which I have had the honor of directing the medical department of the Army.[94]

The Peninsular War was an impetus to improvements in military medicine. In surgery, there were new techniques such as the use of the tourniquet, the extraction of foreign bodies through a counteropening, in addition to the lessons of speed, efficiency, better instruments, and superior medications in surgical operations.[95] Although surgeons were unable to stem communicable diseases, they now had sanitary codes, a more humane casualty evacuation system, and superior hospital organization. Furthermore, surgeons had acquired experience in protecting large bodies of men from pestilence, and they had collected data about many diseases. Yet regardless of his unique relationship to Wellington, McGrigor was unable to establish a corps of medical technicians, nor was he permitted to duplicate Larrey's ambulance. Although McGrigor insisted that British army hospitals were superior to the French, he admitted his frustrations in copying Larrey's field service: "I once proposed our adoption of it in Spain to Lord Wellington; but he would not hear of it; nor would he give the credit of humanity to Napoleon, as the motive for his introduction of it into the army."[96]

However, McGrigor had raised the prestige of the army doctor, and he had installed a sense of pride and professionalism in the medical department that had heretofore not existed. Historians have tended to immortalize generals like Wellington, and they have overlooked dedicated army surgeons like McGrigor who also displayed skill, courage and imagination in war. Although military medicine in 1814 was relatively crude by modern standards and had not achieved any significant "breakthroughs," McGrigor, by his solicitude for patients and by his accomplishments in hospitals, emerged from the smoke of battle symbolizing a humanitarianism that contrasted sharply with the increasing savagery of modern warfare.

# VIII

## WATERLOO

After the armistice in April, 1814, McGrigor had an opportunity to visit enemy military hospitals in southern France. While riding through enemy lines dressed in a British uniform, he became conscious of French hostility, and at the infirmaries that he visited—Narbonne, Montpellier, Carcassonne—the military commanders devised excuses to prevent his inspection. Montpellier's civilian doctors treated Mc-Grigor with greater courtesy and permitted him to inspect the city's medical facilities. Returning to Toulouse, McGrigor supervised the evacuation of casualties to Britain and then took a leave in Paris. There he met Baron Larrey, whom he had encountered in Egypt, and his colleagues in military medicine, Baron Pierre François Percy and Baron Rene Nicholas Desgenettes, who arranged for McGrigor to visit army hospitals in the capital.[1]

Returning to London, McGrigor called upon Wellington. Wellington needed him to assist with hospital accounts, and for some weeks McGrigor worked on the medical records. One morning, Wellington casually commented to McGrigor:

Mac, we are now winding up all the arrangements with the government; I have asked them how you are to be disposed of, and I am told you are to be placed on half pay; but I consider your peculiar services will entitle you to a specific retirement. Before I enter on this subject with Lord Castlereagh [the foreign secretary], I wish to know your own sentiments.[2]

McGrigor stated that he would be satisfied with a small pension. Wellington replied: "To that they can have no possible objection; the demand is moderate." Supporting McGrigor's request, Wellington wrote on July 30, 1814, to the Duke of York's military secretary: "I have every reason to be satisfied with the manner in which Mr. Mc-Grigor conducted the department under his direction; and I consider him one of the most industrious, able and successful public servants I have ever met with."[3]

Wellington, made a duke in May, soon informed his medical chief that the government would award him a pension and a knighthood. Anxious to share in the grander titles and honors lavished upon Wellington's military commanders, McGrigor now requested a greater reward. "On a service of such magnitude and importance as that in which I have been employed," McGrigor informed the duke, "and after having been repeatedly honoured with your Grace's approbation . . . I did hope that if they conferred any honour upon me, it would be the permanent one of the baronetage." Wellington merely replied: "You are the best judge of what you will take; but I would recommend your taking the knighthood in the mean time."[4]

Summoned to receive his accolade from the prince regent at Carlton House in late July, McGrigor ordinarily would have been presented at court by his sponsor, Wellington. But the duke, traveling to Castlereagh's estate in Kent, had asked Lord Bathurst to assist McGrigor at the ceremony. Always embarrassed by formal affairs, McGrigor waited patiently in an antechamber to introduce himself to his substitute sponsor. Then suddenly, Wellington in riding dress strode into the room; he spied McGrigor, introduced him to Bathurst and said to McGrigor: "I thought it was well to place you under Lord Bathurst; you are a shy fellow, and might not have found him out."[5] Flattered by Wellington's thoughtfulness in delaying his own journey in order to assist an old colleague, McGrigor was duly presented to the prince and was knighted.

After vacationing in Scotland, Sir James McGrigor returned in October to London. Like other service doctors who had been long absent from lecture halls and who needed additional medical training, McGrigor enrolled, at the age of 43, in chemistry and anatomy courses at the "Windmill Street Academy." He also pondered the prospects of his career, for on October 25 he was placed on half-pay, a salary that he considered insufficient to support his family. Tempted to leave the army for private practice in London, he remarked: "It then appeared that I could do this with every prospect of success, known as I was to the whole body of officers who had been in the Peninsula, and through them to their relatives in London, many of them of the aristocracy, or most opulent individuals."[6]

Fortunately for McGrigor, the incumbent director general, John Weir, gave notice of his retirement due to ill-health, and immediately, McGrigor's name was mentioned for membership to the Medical Board. To his surprise, McGrigor learned that the Duke of York was overlooking the claims of the other board members (Sir Charles Ker and Sir William Franklin) to the directorship and was appointing him to the post. Although Sir James realized that claims for his patronage would be tedious, and that he would be financially handicapped in the administration of the medical department, he was ambitious and was anxious to initiate reforms in military medicine. His appointment as director general commenced on June 13, 1815, only five days before the battle of Waterloo.

Before McGrigor assumed his post, the Napoleonic wars had erupted again, and preparations were underway for a campaign in northern Europe. Bonaparte had escaped from Elba, and on March 1, 1815, he landed in southern France. Marching onto Paris to the acclaim of his veterans, Napoleon toppled the inept Bourbon regime of Louis XVIII and rallied the nation to renew the struggle against the Allies. Awed by the dramatic resurgence of France, the Allies hastened to reorganize their armies. Postponing his diplomatic role at the Congress of Vienna, Wellington hurried to Belgium to assume his role as defender of the Restoration. Arriving in Brussels on April 5, the duke began to concentrate his force (British, King's German Legion, Hanoverians) along with Allied troops under his command (Dutch, Belgians, Nassauers, Brunswickers) near the northeastern border of France, and to coordinate his strategy with Field Marshal Gebhard von Blucher, who was massing Prussian troops at Namur.

When the British army mobilized for the campaign, many regiments were still unprepared for combat. Some battalions had been disbanded in 1814, many veteran infantrymen from the Peninsula had been shipped to North America, and most regiments in Wellington's force were filled with recruits. Furthermore, only one third of the duke's heterogeneous command were British troops. Worried about the quality of his divisions, the duke grumbled in May: "I have got an infamous army, very weak, and ill-equipped, and a very inexperienced staff."[7] Determined to have Peninsular generals at his side, by June, Wellington had many of his trusted commanders from previous campaigns in Brussels. While uncertain about the dependability of his 100,000 man army, a force much larger than he had ever led before, Wellington surmised that the Allies would heavily outnumber the French, for at Ligny were 120,000 Prussians preparing to invade France.

Probably McGrigor would have been with Wellington in Brussels, but during the spring of 1815 he was preparing to assume his new duties in London. Yet on April 12, McGrigor had offered to serve the duke in the field:

By an arrangement which has been for some time in agitation, it is intended to place me as Director-General of the Medical Board, and I have reason to think that this arrangement is now in a state of forwardness. When in that situation, I hope to be able to obviate many of the inconveniences felt on the late Peninsular service, and to meet your wishes and wants of the hospital department of the army.

I beg to add, that if, after being appointed Director-General, it be at all agreeable to your Grace, I will be proud to go out for some months to know your wishes, and put into execution arrangements in regard to the hospitals and health concerns of the army. [8]

Traditionally, the director general remained in Britain to administer the department, and as a consequence, Sir James, who only assumed his post on the eve of battle, did not supervise the medical preparations for the campaign. In fact, on June 19 he was in London presenting a scholarly paper to a medical society, and neither in his *Autobiography*, nor in his journal (which both terminate in early 1815) is there a mention of the fighting. Unfortunately, many of the lessons supposedly learned in Spain about the handling of casualties were forgotten at Quatre-Bras and at Waterloo.

Yet the medical staff assembled at Brussels was competent. The principal medical officer, a respected veteran of the Flanders and Walcheren expeditions, was McGrigor's brother-in-law, James Grant. Among the deputy inspectors of hospitals were capable men like William Taylor, John Gunning, and Stephan Woolriche; posted to Wellington's headquarters was John Hume, who had served as the duke's personal physician in the Peninsula. Similarly, the general hospitals and divisional headquarters were staffed with experienced surgeons and physicians. Although it is difficult to determine the number of medical personnel attached to Wellington's Allied troops, his own British-Hanoverian force had 273 medical officers, a number considered adequate for his large army. Nor was there laxity in providing general hospitals, for Grant established accommodations for casualties in Antwerp, Bruges, Brussels, Ghent, and Ostend. Furthermore, the evacuation procedures devised by McGrigor were repeated in the general orders. The fault, then, was not in the planning of medical arrangements, but in their execution. Due to the fact that Bonaparte initiated combat in Belgium some weeks before Wellington was ready, and because great bodies of troops participated in the fighting, the medical services were unprepared for the speed and scope of the warfare. Consequently, army surgeons were inundated with unexpected numbers of casualties.

What went wrong with the planning of medical care? Although McGrigor's predecessors had ample supervisory personnel at hospitals in the rear, apparently the Medical Board could not provide sufficient surgeons for the line. Many veteran surgeons from the Peninsular war were on half-pay or could not be located; others had entered civilian practice. Therefore, in order to staff the regiments the board had to recruit medical students or civilian surgeons who had never witnessed the carnage of battle. Some personnel were still traveling to their posts in mid-June when Napoleon's offensive began, and as a result, some battalions lacked medical services. As their regiments marched to battle, some surgeons were still without medical supplies and conveyances for the wounded; apparently many even were uncertain about the location of field hospitals and about casualty evacuation routes. As Guthrie aptly commented about the hurried preparations for the campaign: "The army was not the Peninsular army, neither were all its doctors."[9]

Regardless of the expressed admiration by leading British army doctors during the Peninsular war for the French system of casualty removal, Wellington's army was still without medical corpsmen, stretcher-bearers, or adequate casualty transportation. Each regiment had three surgeons, and each surgeon had a mule or pack-horse to carry his instruments and a cart to transport bedding and supplies. Moreover, each division was equipped with two or three spring-carts, labeled "ambulances," that each carried eight men, but these rudimentary provisions were woefully inadequate when thousands were incapacitated. The technical lag in handling the wounded, compared to the attention devoted by the military on weapons and tactics in the 1790s, was still apparent at Waterloo. The medical services needed time to organize for the campaign, but Napoleon, aware that he had to strike quickly, did not intend to give Wellington time.

Bonaparte knew that the Russian and Austrian armies in the east could not march against him until August. Before those forces could concentrate, Napoleon planned to eliminate the nearest threat—the Prussian and Anglo-Dutch divisions on his border. He knew that the forces of Wellington and Blucher were spread over a hundred mile front, that the duke drew his supplies from Antwerp and Ostend, and that the Prussian line of communications stretched out in the opposite direction to Liège and Coblenz. If either army retreated, Napoleon reasoned, it would have to retire toward its supply base and hence away from its ally. To separate the armies confronting him, Napoleon selected the town of Charleroi as his target. Here he could drive a wedge between Wellington and Blucher; then he could proceed to pin down one opposing force with his wing and could utilize his other wing and reserve to destroy the other enemy. With his army of 124,000, Napoleon calculated that he could push the Prussians to the Rhine, march on to Brussels while driving the Anglo-Dutch before him, cut Wellington off from the Channel, and then force Britain and Prussia to accept his peace.

With his customary strategic skill, the emperor screened his forces near the Belgium frontier, concealed his objectives by numerous feints, and duped his enemies about the disposition of his corps. Then, to the bewilderment of the Allies, Napoleon opened his offensive on June 14 when his army crossed the Sambre at Charleroi and threw the Prussians back to Fleurus. Simultaneously, Napoleon's left wing under Marshal Michel Ney attacked the junction of Quatre-Bras, 20 miles south of Brussels, where a hard-pressed Dutch division awaited reinforcements from Wellington.

Until June 15, Wellington had only contradictory information about Napoleon's intentions. Uncertain of the emperor's strategy, the duke believed that his adversary would thrust at Mons, 23 miles west of Charleroi. Not until midnight did Wellington learn that Bonaparte had tricked him. "Napoleon has humbugged me, by God!" he exclaimed. "He has gained twenty four hours on me." Hurrying reinforcements to Quatre-Bras, Wellington doubted if Napoleon could be defeated there, and "if so, I must fight him there," he declared, indicating on a map the village of Waterloo.[10]

On June 16 Napoleon encountered unexpected difficulties in his offensive. Due to faulty staff work and the tardy arrival in battle of the reserve, Marshal Emmanuel Grouchy, who attacked the Prussians at Ligny, was unable to destroy the enemy. Blucher led his battered army to Wavre, only 13 miles from Wellington's defenses. In the meantime, Ney, who at first greatly outnumbered the Allies at Quatre-Bras, delayed his attack until noon. By then, Wellington was on the scene with additional troops and was able to repel the assault. Yet with 4,800 casualties it was a costly and indecisive engagement for the duke. Aware of the deteriorating Prussian position and certain that Napoleon would renew the attack on Quatre-Bras, Wellington ordered a retreat on June 17 to the more defensible postion at Mont-Saint-Jean, near Waterloo, where his men bivouacked that night and awaited the French attack.

The furious fighting at Quatre-Bras was the first test in the field of the medical department. Regimental aid stations were not ready, medical supplies were miles away, and there was a shortage of medical men. Sergeant Edward Costello of the 95th, who lost his trigger-finger by a musket ball, was unable to find aid at a farm house which was crammed with wounded pleading for help.[11] Sergeant Thomas Morris of the 73rd also commented about the inadequacies of medical treatment. Pitying an armless soldier he encountered, Morris doubted if the man would even receive treatment that day, "as there were so many wounded awaiting their turn to be tended to."[12] For James Vansittart, an assistant surgeon with the Life Guards, it was depressing to watch helplessly as scores of injured men crawled from the battlefield: "I was unable to do anything for these wounds as I had no sort of medical supply with me, and could only watch their painful progress with useless pity."[13] Stunned by his first combat experience, William Gibney, a surgeon with the 15th Hussars, remembered that on the retreat to Mont-Saint-Jean:

Nothing could exceed the misery exhibited on this road. . . . Here a man with an arm suspended only by a single muscle, another with his head horribly mangled by a sabre cut, or one with half his face shot away . . . but what made the scene more depressing [was] . . . the conviction that for very many, their cases being utterly hopeless, time could not be spared on their behalf. . . . It was a cruel task to be obliged to tell a dying soldier who had served his king and country well that day, that his cause was hopeless. . . .[14]

At Waterloo on June 18, Wellington had 63,000 troops to confront Napoleon's 70,000, and he expected to receive reinforcements from Blucher even though the Prussian was fending off Grouchy's attacks. For Napoleon, victory depended upon his ability to smash Wellington's line before the Prussians arrived. His plan of attack was simple, and it nearly succeeded. First, he ordered a heavy bombardment of the enemy's center. Then with divisional artillery fire and cavalry feints on Wellington's flanks to draw off his reserves, Napoleon hurled a massive charge at the Allied center. But the French assault was deflected by the fanatical defense of the château at Hougoumont. Another French attack on the center faltered and the British cavalry threw the French back from the slopes of Mont-Saint-Jean. Still, Napoleon's veterans tried again. Leading a ferocious charge, Ney captured the outpost of La Haye Sainte, and there he began to crack the Allied line. At this crucial point in the battle, Ney pleaded for reinforcements. The emperor tardily ordered his Imperial Guard to support Ney, but by then the Prussians had reinforced Wellington's flank and were attacking French positions. The Guard was repulsed with enormous losses. Its failure to penetrate Wellington's line signalled the doom of Napoleon's army. The entire French line faltered, and Napoleon's demoralized army began to retreat. While the defeated French fled in disorder to be pursued by Prussian horsemen throughout the night, Wellington's army, decimated by casualties and stunned at the sheer butchery of the struggle, seemed paralysed.

Thousands of dead, maimed, and mutilated men lay over the battlefield. Within a two-mile area were 47,000 casualties—7,000 Prussians, 15,000 Anglo-Dutch, 25,000 French. Almost the entire 27th regiment had been obliterated. "The immediate neighbourhood of Hougoumont," wrote Captain Cavalié Mercer, "was more thickly strewn with corpses than most other parts of the field—the very ditches were full of them."[15] Some regiments, reduced to a few companies, lost most of their officers. Over one half the infantry and one third of the cavalry officers were casualties. Out of 63 commanders, 11 were killed and 24 wounded. In his dispatch to London, Wellington reported: ". . . such an action could not be gained without a great loss; and I am sorry to say that ours has been immense. . . ." The duke related to his old friend Beresford that "never did I see such a pounding match . . . . Napoleon did not maneuvre at all. He just moved forward in the old style . . . ." Writing to his brother that he had nearly lost the struggle, Wellington admitted: "for I must confess that I have never been so close to defeat."[16] In the bloodiest battle of his career, Wellington lost twenty-nine percent of his army.

Everywhere were layers of bodies, piles of corpses, and mounds of dead. From over the fields came the maddening sobs, moans, and screams of men who had been cut, shot, burned, hacked, pierced, fractured, twisted, and crushed during the battle. Although hundreds of infantrymen had assisted their wounded comrades to safety during the fighting (whether from friendship or from fear of remaining in combat, it is impossible to say), nevertheless, troops had been ordered to remain fighting on the line, regardless of casualties. After the battle, many survivors moved to the deserted French bivouacs at La Belle Alliance where they built fires, quenched their thirst, and tried to rest. Other units, like Captain Mercer's battery, remained where they had fought, and hence, Mercer's description of the eerie moonlit scene is particularly graphic:

Here and there some poor wretch, sitting up amidst the countless dead, busied himself in endeavours to staunch the flowing stream with which his life was fast ebbing away. Many whom I saw so employed that night were, when morning dawned, lying stiff and tranquil as those who had departed earlier. From time to time a figure would half raise itself from the ground, and then, with a despairing groan, fall back again. Others, slowly and painfully rising . . . would stagger away with uncertain steps across the field in search of succour.[17]

Regardless of the cries of pain throughout the night, the able-bodied generally did little to help, partly because of their own fear and exhaustion, but mainly because the care of casualties was not a soldier's responsibility. The next day, the army began to move off to Paris, taking with it many of the 156 surgeons and their assistants who had been at Waterloo, and leaving behind a depleted and exhausted medical staff.

    For days after Waterloo, surgeons labored at Mont-Saint-Jean with the wounded. The medical men were extremely fatigued, noted Captain William Hay of the 5th Dragoons on June 19, "and still there appeared not an end to their toil."[18] Every shelter within miles—barns, stables, cottages, châteaux, courtyards—was choked full of casualties. The arrangements, said Gibney, were "hideous, each house was packed to overflowing, every room was full . . . and little relief was given, often none." Amputating for hours in a barn, he lamented that no one had expected "so prolonged and bloody a battle."[19] Isaac James, a hospital assistant, wrote that he operated continually for three days and nights: "We had lots of arms and legs to chop off."[20] Vansittart complained that "we had no time to make arrangements" and wrote a gruesome commentary about his task at Waterloo:

Our work behind the lines was grim in the extreme, and continued far into the night. It was all too horrible to commit to pages, but this I will say, that the silent horror of the greater part of the sufferers was a thing I shall not forget. When one considers the hasty surgery performed on such an occasion, the awful sight the men are witness to, knowing that their turn on that bloody-soaked operating table is next, seeing the agony of amputation . . . then one realizes of what our soldiers are made.[21]

The casualties kept on coming, and the medical department was swamped. Hundreds of men, fearful of being killed by cruel peasants who searched corpses for loot, and maddened by pain, thirst, and hunger crawled to the roadsides. Farmhouses, hamlets, and villages throughout the countryside were packed with the wounded. At Malines, an English civilian remembered that after the local hospital was filled, "barracks, churches, convents were converted into temporary hospitals . . . . Tents were pitched . . . but nothing could contain the multitude of wounded who continually entered the town."[22] Days after the fighting, search parties were still finding casualties in the fields. Four days after Waterloo, wounded men were discovered at Quatre-Bras, where they had lain hidden in the tall fields of rye. On June 21, Surgeon James Elkington at Mont-Saint-Jean "rode over the field to report on the number of French wounded still to be removed."[23] And incredibly enough, there were wounded survivors discovered who had lain on the ground exposed to the elements for nearly two weeks after Waterloo. Some of these poor wretches were conveyed to Brussels where the famed anatomist, Charles Bell, who had treated wounded soldiers after Coruña, tried to save their lives. Bell, who established the existence of the sensory and motor nerves in 1811, wrote a gruesome account of his experiences amputating on French casualties:

I found that the best cases, that is, the most horrid wounds left totally without assistance, were to be found in the hospital of the French wounded. This hospital was only forming; they were even then bringing these poor creatures in from the woods. It is impossible to convey to you the picture of human misery continually before my eyes . . . . At six o'clock [in the morning] I took the knife in my hand, and continued incessantly at work till seven in the evening; and so the next day, and again on the third.

All the decencies of performing surgical operations were soon neglected; while I amputated one man's thigh, there lay at one time thirteen, all beseeching to be taken next; one full of entreaty, one calling upon me to remember my promise to take him, another execrating. It was a strange thing to feel my clothes stiff with blood, and my arms powerless with the exertion of using the knife; and more extraordinary still, to find my mind calm amidst such a variety of suffering.[24]

One of the major obstacles in providing prompt medical care was the lack of transportation. No regiment had enough vehicles for the task, and troops had to scour the countryside for carts and wagons. Furthermore, there were no aid stations en route to Brussels, hence, the wounded had to ride in open wagons, without relief, on a bumpy, rutted road over eight miles to the city. Sergeant Costello was horrified at the agony inflicted on his comrades by "that long jolting ride (on which) . . . many carts broke down being overloaded and through their haste to go forward."[25]

What emerged as a rudimentary medical corps was the unexpected assistance of the Belgian rural population. True, some peasants preferred the French to the British; some peasants were scavengers who robbed the dead; and others resented being pressed into service as gravediggers for the thousands of corpses that were strewn over the landscape. Yet, many Belgians helped the wounded. They guided casualties to shelters, opened their barns, stables, and even their homes to the sick, and they transported the wounded to Brussels. Belgian nuns helped sufferers, and priests used their churches for hospitals. The owner of a lace factory utilized his building for the wounded and ordered his employees to care for the soldiers. How many casualties were helped by this extraordinary display of humanitarianism (which seems to be unmatched in the campaigns of the British army in this era) is difficult to estimate, but certainly, many lives were saved by the generous actions of the Belgian people.

Brussels became the major casualty depot for the Allied forces, and here too, the Belgians donated their services. Urging his fellow citizens to assist the wounded during the emergency, the mayor of the city suggested that countrymen supply clothing and blankets. He sternly added: "this warning to well-to-do-people: he will feel himself obliged to billet the wounded or sick soldiers on them if they do not respond to his appeal."[26] Nevertheless, inhabitants of all classes willingly assisted during the crisis. Virtually every commentator who wrote about Brussels after Waterloo praised the spontaneous and generous efforts of the population. The inhabitants, stated Captain Hay, made bandages, provided blankets and opened their homes to the injured.[27] "Even the churches were turned into hospitals," declared Fanny Burney, the famous author, "and every house in Brussels, was ordered to receive or find asylum for some of the sick . . ."[28] Costello, still searching for someone in Brussels to treat his injured hand four days after Quatre-Bras, was amazed at the willingness of the women to assist:

... thousands of wounded French, Belgians, Prussians, and English (arrived); carts, wagons, and every other obtainable vehicle were continually arriving heaped with sufferers. The wounded were laid, friend and foes indiscriminately, on straw, with avenues between them, in every part of the city, and nearly destitute of surgical attendance. The humane and indefatigable exertions of the fair ladies of Brussels, however, greatly made up for this deficiency; numbers were busily employed—some strapping and bandaging wounds, others serving out tea, coffee, soups, and other soothing nourishments; while many occupied themselves stripping sufferers of their gory and saturated garments, and dressing them in clean shirts and other habiliments; indeed, altogether careless of fashionable scruples, many of the fairest and wealthiest of the ladies of that city now ventured to assert their pre-eminence on the occasion.[29]

More important in saving lives was the presence in Brussels of many civilian surgeons who hurried to offer their services. From Britain came anatomists like Charles Bell, George James Guthrie, and John Thomson; from the Lowlands came an undetermined number of practitioners who volunteered for the crisis; and there were captured French army surgeons on hand to treat their wounded. Noting this remarkable display of cooperation by the medical profession during the emergency, James Simpson, a London barrister on the scene, remarked: "Something, if possible, beyond the average care for the sick and hurt, appeared to me to animate all the medical men for the wounded of Waterloo; and their zeal made no distinction on whether their countrymen or the enemy."[30] Even "the great Larrey" was in Brussels, but there under unique circumstances.

During the battle of Waterloo, Larrey was on the French line. According to one account, through the turmoil of battle Wellington observed the courageous surgeon at work. Informed that the famous Larrey was on the scene, the duke ordered: "Tell them not to fire at him. Give the brave fellow time to pick up his wounded." After raising his hat in a distant greeting to the Frenchman, Wellington was asked whom he was saluting. "This honour and loyalty you see yonder," he responded.[31]

Wounded during the French retreat, Larrey was captured by Prussian cavalry. Instead of being humanely treated, Larrey was insulted and robbed. To his dismay, Larrey was unable to convince his excited captors that he was not the notorious Napoleon. "My build, a grey coat I was wearing, gave me a certain resemblance to the Emperor . . . " he explained. Without providing Larrey with the opportunity to identify himself, the Prussians hastily proceeded to march the Frenchman off for execution. Fortunately, a surgeon recognized Larrey, convinced the commander, General Friedrich Wilhelm Bulow, of the mistake, and arranged for Larrey to be presented to Blucher. The old marshal, grateful to Larrey for having once saved his own son's life, treated his distinguished prisoner with respect. After Larrey had recuperated from the ordeal, Blucher utilized the Frenchman's talents in healing the wounded. Larrey was sent to Louvain where he advised on amputations of French casualties. He was then taken to Brussels where he found "almost all of our own [medical] men in the town's military hospital, in charge of one of my former colleagues . . . . Together we performed a considerable number of major operations such as an amputation of the arm at the shoulder joint [a remarkable achievement for the day] and others equally difficult, which were generally successful." Larrey departed soon after for Paris praising the generous treatment of his countrymen; "never was there greater and more disinterested hospitality," he remarked.[32]

Larrey's counterpart in the British army was George James Guthrie, then a prominent London surgeon, often called "the English Larrey" because of his unmatched experience with combat injuries during the Peninsular campaign and because of his pioneering techniques in wound surgery.[33] Soon after Waterloo, Guthrie volunteered again for the army, but only for a few months. Due to regulations on short-term appointments, McGrigor was unable to accept the offer. Undaunted by "red tape," Guthrie hurried to Belgium and worked as an unpaid civilian adviser. Caustic about the inadequate medical preparations, Guthrie complained that "the arrangements were not, however, made at first, on the extensive scale that circumstances required . . . ."[34] Regardless of the difficulties Guthrie managed to demonstrate surgical techniques in Brussels that confirmed his leadership in British military surgery.

For surgeons in Guthrie's era, the amputation was the most important surgical operation. Wounds of bodily cavities were considered too dangerous for a surgeon to explore, and therefore, penetrations of the thorax and abdomen were regarded as inevitably fatal. Hence, there remained the limbs, and on these Guthrie performed some outstanding feats. At Albuera in 1812, he introduced the practice of tying both ends of a wounded artery at the seat of the injury, a method which was contrary to John Hunter's advice to tie the artery above the injury. At Lisbon in 1813, Guthrie demonstrated the use of a long splint for fractures of the leg and thigh. Then in Brussels, he won praise for some novel operations. He removed a musket ball from the bladder of an Englishman; for a German soldier he divided the muscles of the calf in order to tie the main artery; and he amputated the leg of a Frenchman at the hip joint, a formidable task which he performed without exerting any pressure upon the main artery except by the fingers.

Perhaps Guthrie's greatest contribution in wound surgery was to teach the importance of primary, or early amputation, for gunshot injuries, again in contrast to Hunter who had advocated delaying amputation. What may now seem like a virtual mania for chopping off arms and legs may be appreciated when one considers that primary amputation was then considered the surest method to save a victim with a compound fracture. The possibility of saving a limb shattered by missiles such as musket balls, grapeshot, or cannon balls was poor, and early amputation offered a chance. Such wounds were particularly dangerous, because the bones usually splintered, local tissue traumatized, and pieces of clothing became imbedded in the wound. Thus, writes Dr. Henry Dible, the injury became "an ideal breeding-ground for the microbic invasion which constitutes sepsis," and gangrene or tetanus often resulted.[35] Furthermore, the main veins, arteries, and nerves were often severed by the impact of the missile, resulting in gangrene, hemorrhaging, and paralysis.

Military surgeons viewed quick amputation as necessary, an attitude which prevailed until the Listerian era of the late nineteenth century which brought the antisepsis that dramatically revolutionized surgical procedures. Amputation also had the advantage of completely removing the damaged limb, and of leaving the patient with a relatively simple wound instead of a complicated one. Although the wound usually became infected, and invariably, suppuration (known as "laudable pus") followed, the incision was made through healthy tissue, and as a consequence, the patient could survive. Even though no sterilization of the saw or knife occurred, when "a series of amputations was performed in quick succession, the mere mechanical cleansing of the instrument by wiping, coupled with the bactericidal property of blood," Dible explains, "probably gave a rough degree of antisepsis."[36] Furthermore, even the unhealthy conditions of the typical field hospital were probably more favorable for avoiding sepsis than the infected wards of rear line hospitals.

Unfortunately, a victim's chances were often ruined by the contemporary panacea of copious bloodletting. Yet, Lieutenant Colonel Frederick Ponsomby, of the 12th Light Dragoons, injured at Waterloo believed in that remedy: "I had received several wounds; a surgeon slept in my room and I was saved by excessive bleeding."[37] Perhaps more typical was Colonel Sir William De Lancy, Wellington's quarter-master general, whose side was smashed by a ricocheting cannon ball at Quatre-Bras. His wife, on hand during his few remaining days, stated that before her husband died, the surgeons bled him constantly, "wishing also thereby to make the recovery more complete."[38]

Like Larrey, Guthrie advised early amputation, when amputation was necessary. Although he failed to appreciate the nature of shock,[39] and he lacked modern pathological knowledge, his clinical experience convinced him that operations on war wounds should be within four hours of the injury. While evidence about the relative success of Guthrie and his colleagues at Waterloo and at Brussels is limited there is some information. Bell stated that there were 147 primary amputations at Waterloo from which 40 deaths occurred, and that "within the next three months," there were 225 secondary amputations and 106 deaths.[40] Without making a distinction between primary and secondary amputations, Guthrie wrote that from June 16 to July 31, out of 374 amputations in Brussels, 146 died.[41] Praising Guthrie's *On Gunshot Wounds of the Extremities* (1816), the *Edinburgh Medical and Surgical Journal* declared that the proper time to amputate "seems now finally decided by the experience of military surgeons in favour of early and immediate amputations when the limb can not be saved."[42] Yet this prevailing attitude of "when in doubt, amputate," had unfortunate consequences, for under the stress of battle, many arms and legs were sacrificed that might have been saved. One lucky officer related that while being conveyed from Mont-Saint-Jean, his wounded leg was actually saved by enemy fire on three successive occasions just as surgeons prepared to saw it off. Fortunately, he inadvertently escaped the overzealous surgeons, made his way to the rear, and preserved his leg intact.[43]

Along with such tales are the ghastly and macabre descriptions of brave men who calmly and stoically observed their own limbs being severed. There is the story of the amazing Frenchman who gaily picked up his sawed-off leg, threw it into the air, crying "Vive l'Empereur."[44] Courage in such situations was common with the British. After watching his leg amputated, a British officer at Mont-Saint-Jean, refused any more help, immediately crawled off the operating table, managed to hop across the room and outside to a cart.[45]

One of the most famous accounts of the incredible bravado of the British aristocracy under such circumstances was related by Captain Thomas Wildman of the 7th Hussars, aide-de-camp to Lord Henry Paget, the Earl of Oxbridge, Wellington's cavalry commander. Paget's knee was shattered by grape-shot, and he was amputated upon at Mont-Saint-Jean:

He never moved or complained; no one even held his hand. He said once perfectly calmly that he thought the instrument was not very sharp. When it was over, his nerves did not appear the least shaken. He said smiling: "I have had a pretty long run, I have been a beau there forty-seven years, and it would not be fair to cut the young men out any longer. . . ."[46]

A similar patrician indifference about the loss of his limb, severed at La Haye Sainte, was demonstrated by Wellington's aide, Lord Fitzroy Somerset, who was married to the duke's niece. After his operation, Somerset called out to his surgeons: "Hallo! Don't carry that arm away till I've taken off my ring."[47] And finally, there is the gruesome story related by Sergeant Costello, who waited patiently in a hospital for someone to treat his hand. He witnessed the amputation of a tough Royal Dragoon veteran who actually held on to his arm as it was being cut, while spitting out a steady stream of tobacco juice on the floor. Nearby was a wounded Frenchman screaming with pain as a surgeon probed the man's shoulder for a bullet. "This seemed to annoy the Englishman more than anything else," remarked Costello. "He struck the Frenchman a smart blow across the breast with the severed limb, holding it at the wrist. 'Here take that, and stuff it down your throat and stop your damned bellowing.' "[48]

How well were the sick and wounded treated in the hospital during the recovery? Guthrie related that McGrigor visited Waterloo, inspected the overcrowded hospitals in Brussels, and moved some cases to coastal cities for evacuation to Britain.[49] The only satisfactory account of hospital conditions was written by John Thomson, Professor of Military Surgery at the University of Edinburgh. Arriving in Belgium on July 8, he noted that although some casualties had lain in fields for days, few seemed to have suffered from exposure. He related that accommodations in the hospitals for the French were excellent, that Brussels had six hospitals for 2,500 Allied patients and that Antwerp, which handled the overflow of casualties, had another 2,500 sick and wounded troops. Although Thomson encountered cases of gangrene, dysentery, and "the bilious remittent fever of the Country," he found few traces of "contagious fever" at either city. He claimed that "the great attention which we saw everywhere given to cleanliness and to ventilation in the British hospitals, must undoubtedly have had a powerful influence in preventing the occurrence of contagious diseases." The men were well treated, he remarked. The wards were spacious and clean; the beds were spaced properly, and careful attention was paid to diet, comforts, and clothing changes. While some cases of remittent and intermittent fevers occurred among the wounded, the rate of recovery of the British sick and wounded, Thomson claimed, was rapid.[50] In August, nearly one half the hospitals were closed and many patients were transported to Ostend for shipment home; and in August another large shipment of casualties took place, leaving behind a small contingent of patients who remained until 1816. Some of the most interesting surgical cases were sent to York General Hospital where Guthrie had his own ward, and where he lectured for two years. Other incapacitated soldiers recuperated at Colchester General Hospital, where McGrigor's staff officer from the Peninsula, James Forbes, supervised their recovery.

After Waterloo, Napoleon was exiled to St. Helena, Europe had a lasting peace, and Wellington, virtually immortalized as Britain's savior, reached the pinnacle of his military career. The duke's sheer delight in defeating Bonaparte at Waterloo is evident in his famous comment that the victory was "so nice a thing—so neatly run a thing."[51] Yet this triumphant general, who rarely demonstrated grief over losses in war, must have pondered the cost in manpower after witnessing the massive butchery at Waterloo. Visiting the dying De Lancey on June 19, Wellington openly remarked that he "never wished to see another battle. This [was] so shocking," he admitted to Lady De Lancey, "to see brave men equally matched cutting each other to pieces as they did."[52] At Badajoz, McGrigor had witnessed Wellington quietly sobbing over the fearsome casualty rates. At Waterloo, another doctor, John Hume, also reported the toll of dead and wounded to Wellington the morning after the victory. The duke grasped Hume's hand, the doctor related, and unashamedly began to cry. Brushing the tears away from his cheeks, Wellington whispered to him with emotion, "Well, thank God, I don't know what it is to lose a battle; but certainly nothing can be more painful than to gain one with the loss of so many of one's friends."[53]

Whether McGrigor's skill and experience would have made a discernible difference in medical arrangements if he had been appointed director general some months earlier, or if he had been on the battlefield, is conjectural. However mighty a military triumph for Wellington, Waterloo, a lamentable contrast in the care of the wounded compared to the progress made in Spain under McGrigor's direction, was a medical disaster.

# IX

## McGRIGOR'S POST-WATERLOO
## REFORMS

McGrigor's tenure of office as director general spanned the years from Waterloo almost to the Crimean War (1854–1856). Due to the Crown's control and prerogatives over the army, Parliament's passion for economy in peacetime, the public's apathy toward military affairs, and Wellington's domination over the officers as commander in chief, the army was permitted to corrode. The post-Waterloo desire by society for economy and efficiency in law, commerce, and manufacturing overlooked the army. During the turbulent post-Napoleonic era, with its revolutions or threats of revolutions at home, in Central Europe, and the Mediterranean, the peacetime army encountered numerous difficulties. The army was involved in policing duties at home and abroad, it was weakened by demobilization and by budgetary cuts, and its officers feared that administrative reforms would weaken the force that had defeated the French. Under these circumstances, even with McGrigor's background, experience, personal conservatism, and his influence with Wellington, it was difficult to initiate significant reforms of the medical department.

Yet for the first time in the history of the army medical department, an able officer in the prime of life, trusted by generals and politicians, and one who planned to modernize military medicine, presided over the service. McGrigor, now at the age of 44, began to impose stricter standards for officer candidates and for promotion, helped to establish chairs of military surgery, encouraged studies of preventive medicine, and supported the scientific interests of his men. Furthermore, he improved the status of surgeons in the army and labored to improve the welfare of the rank and file.

McGrigor's efforts to better his department mirrored the changes in medicine underway in civilian society during the Age of Reform. A series of interrelated developments transpired after Waterloo that resulted in a decisive "breakthrough" in the professionalization of medicine. Medical reformers gradually improved medical training by improvements of textbooks, curriculum, and teaching methods. Medical students had opportunities to learn the hospital medicine of the era by practical experience, demonstration, and observation. Similarly, educational standards for the profession were raised by stricter licensing requirements, by the legalization of dissection (the Anatomy Act of 1833), by medical directories which listed qualified practitioners, and by the proliferation of medical societies and scientific periodicals.

From France came influence that elevated the status of surgery. In the eighteenth century, Pierre-Joseph Desault (1744–1795) demonstrated the importance of dissection, the surgical control of aneurysm, and he reintroduced the practice of arterial ligation. Desault also showed the value of a relatively novel teaching device—he often lectured at a patient's bedside rather than in the lecture-hall. His disciple, Xavier Bichat (1771–1802), tried to span the gap between surgery and medicine. He performed anatomical studies and animal experiments on the cadaver and developed concepts of morbid structure; his great contribution to pathology was to point out that tissues were the basic units in the composition of organs. Furthermore, due to the wars of the French Revolution, military service strengthened the surgeon's viewpoint, and army medical schools were established at Paris, Lille, Metz, Toulon, and Strasbourg. One former army doctor, the highly influential François Joseph Broussais (1772–1838), broke with the prevailing nosography (the systematic description of disease) and claimed that examination of the lesions of organs provided explanations about disease.

After the wars, the famed Paris Hospital, "the cradle of the new medicine," became a center of medical and surgical specialization where improved techniques of statistics, autopsy, and physical examination were developed. At this "medical workshop" significant advances occurred not only in diagnostics, but in otology, virology, pediatrics, orthopedics, dermatology, and psychiatry. Reflecting a trend underway since the French Revolution, surgeons and physicians in Paris shared professional rights and privileges. "Strengthening the position of surgeons within medicine," suggests Erwin H. Ackernecht, "meant automatically shifting emphasis toward their bailiwicks—the hospitals—and furthering the study of pathological anatomy. Conversely, giving the hospitals a larger place in medical education meant elevating the position of the surgeons and improving the hospitals."[1] In the stimulating environment of the Paris Hospital numbers of native and foreign students trained; such future doctors as Spencer Wells, Marshall Hall, and Astley Cooper returned to Britain after their studies to disseminate the techniques and discoveries of the new medicine.

In contrast to the general lack of scientific standards in eighteenth century medicine and to the metaphysical concepts of disease that flourished in McGrigor's youth, medicine was emerging with scientific concepts and techniques. The profession, states S. W. F. Holloway, "freed itself from the morass of theories and systems and concentrated upon clinical examination, checked and complemented by extensive and intensive studies of the autopsy table. Clinical examination was transformed into active examination through large-scale application of new and revived methods of physical diagnosis and the symptoms thus delineated were considered in the light of lesions found in post-mortem."[2] The result of this clinical-pathological research was the emergence of theories that classified diseases by symptoms alone, and of demonstrations that lesions could be observed not only in the gross appearance of organs but also within the tissue of which they were composed. With the identification of new diseases, heretofore unsuspected or confused with other maladies, and an awareness that diseases were located in specific organs rather than in the blood alone surgeons assumed new importance in the removal of morbid parts. In this shift from the traditional generalized pathology to the modern localized pathology, technical improvements were highly significant in expanding the knowledge about the human body. The stethoscope was available by 1819. French physicians demonstrated the value of the clinical thermometer in the 1830s. The otoscope for the ear, laryngoscope for the throat, and opthalmoscope for the eye were in use by the 1850s. Eventually enough new instruments were invented to examine every accessible part of the body; and improvements in the microscope even revealed something about the mysterious microbe world. Due to the impact of these technical changes, to the systematic observation of disease, and to a greater utilization of scientific methods, medicine was gradually attaining a level attained earlier by the other natural sciences.[3]

To what degree did the army medical department match these innovations during McGrigor's tenure of office? Unquestionably, he made vigorous efforts to improve medical services by an overhaul of personnel. After Waterloo, he put scores of medical officers on half-pay, and in the process he weeded out some of the aged, infirm, and the incompetent. He suggested to professionally unqualified surgeons that in order to receive future appointments it would be necessary for them to be licensed by the medical colleges. As he phrased it: "Gentlemen already in the service are earnestly recommended to avail themselves of every opportunity to adding to their knowledge, by attending universities or schools; for which purpose, every facility will be afforded by the Director-General." When McGrigor was authorized to fill vacancies, he announced that future appointments would be based upon educational accomplishments and upon demonstrated abilities. To qualify for an appointment as an assistant surgeon, a candidate had to "produce certificates of regular study . . . at an established school of eminence," which testified to twelve months courses in anatomy, the practice of medicine, and chemistry, in addition to six months courses in *materia medica* and botany. He also announced the specific training that he desired of candidates:

The practice of medicine and surgery in a hospital or infirmary at least one year, with a regular apprenticeship, or three years without an apprenticeship; in which case a certificate of his studies in practical pharmacy will be required. Regimental officers should also be acquainted with midwifery. It will be considered an additional recommendation to gentlemen entering the service, to have attended an establishment of diseases of the eyes, and mental derangement.

A liberal education is indispensably requisite; and the greater the attainments of the candidate are in the various branches of science . . . the more eligible will he be deemed for promotion; as selections to fill vacancies will be guided by reference to such acquirements than to seniority.[4]

McGrigor screened the applicants from medical colleges in London, Dublin, Edinburgh, and of course, Aberdeen. William Munro, who entered the service in 1844 and later became surgeon general (1875–1881), remarked that the requirements established by McGrigor "were more extensive and comprehensive than that required by the different universities and schools of medicine and surgery."[5]

There were ample candidates for the few openings in the medical department. With an army commission, an impecunious medical school graduate could acquire experience and a small pension, could see the world, and perhaps participate in some great adventure overseas. With letters of recommendation, the candidate presented himself at the headquarters of the medical department at St. James Place in London. The applicant was given a written examination and was questioned by three senior medical officers. If the candidate passed the requirements, he was sent to Fort Pitt, Chatham, to train for four to nine months in a program devised by McGrigor, and to await posting to a regiment. Training at Fort Pitt had definite advantages, the director general explained to the war secretary. It had a good library, a hospital with a variety of medical cases, and experienced officers lectured on surgery and hygiene. A young surgeon in training, McGrigor stated, when he was 59 years of age:

. . . has an opportunity of seeing disease with their various shades from all parts of the world. He has at Chatham an admirable opportunity of studying . . . the morbid structure, the result of disease to which soldiers are subject . . . and in comparing them with the records of each case to see the causes of a fatal termination.[6]

McGrigor was also successful in helping to establish chairs of military medicine at two universities. Due to his efforts, courses in military surgery and military hygiene were offered to students at Edinburgh and Dublin. Although army surgeons in the 1790s had pleaded that the state sponsor a college of naval and military medicine, the Medical Board neglected to support these memorials for better training. In 1806, however, Lord Grenville, first lord of the treasury, provided a government subsidy for a Chair of Military Surgery at the University of Edinburgh. Here, Dr. John Thomson, an Aberdeen graduate who later served at Waterloo, was the first lecturer on the subject. In 1822, Sir George Ballingall, a former army surgeon and the writer of many works on military medicine, was appointed to the post. By 1844, with McGrigor's enthusiastic support, Ballingall had lectured to 400 medical students on his subject. But not until 1846, when Thomas Joliffe Tufnell, surgeon to the City of Dublin, was made Professor of Military Hygiene at the University of Dublin, again with McGrigor's support, was there another course in military medicine at the university level.[7] Ballingall retired in 1849, and, thereafter, Tufnell offered the only university lectures on the subject in McGrigor's era.

From his office in London, McGrigor presided over the medical department for 36 years. A principal inspector (until 1833 when the position was abolished), a secretary, and six clerks assisted him. Although McGrigor did not control the medical services of the ordnance, the Household Troops, or the East India Company, his responsibility for directing an office with units scattered over the world was enormous. Rising early in the morning, he answered much of his correspondence at home. Arriving early at his office, he gave the clerks his letters, and worked until the evening. Impressed by his zeal and energy, *Lancet*, a spokesman for the medical world, claimed that Sir James had transformed a mere appendage of the army into "an important department of the public service."[8]

Summarizing his duties to the War Office, McGrigor explained that his work encompassed a wide sphere—the examination of officers requesting leave and retirement; the supervision of the medical inspection of recruits and of veterans applying for discharge; the administration of hospitals throughout the empire; and the compilation of medical records. Finding no regimental medical histories when he assumed office, McGrigor established procedures for reports from regimental surgeons. These records were inspected at his headquarters. "All medical men heading overseas," he explained, "are directed to study these . . . the knowledge of this, and the desire of making a respectable appearance in their reports had induced Officers to keep up their knowledge and study all recent improvements."[9]

To assist the families of deceased army medical officers, McGrigor helped to found two benevolent organizations. In 1816, the Society for the Benefit of Widows of Officers of the Hospitals and Regimental Staff was chartered. Another welfare group began in 1820, again at McGrigor's instigation, known as the Army Medical Department Benevolent Society for Orphans. Sir James took great interest in this philanthropic work, and as indicated in the record books of the societies, he regularly attended the meetings.[10] The existence of these charities today for the benefit of the Royal Army Medical Corps is an enduring testimonial to McGrigor's vision and humanitarianism.

Anxious to raise professional standards and to encourage medical research, McGrigor established a science library at Fort Pitt. The library began in 1816 when he donated some of his own medical books. His colleagues supported McGrigor's donation; volumes were sent by officers from York, Albany, Portsmouth, and Edinburgh. In 1833 the library had 2,500 volumes. From all over the globe, medical officers contributed works so that by 1850 the library contained 67,000 books, a remarkable size for a scientific library in the mid-nineteenth century, and one built entirely from voluntary subscriptions. The medical library at Fort Pitt was copied at overseas stations, particularly in Canada and South Africa, where such libraries were valuable as reference centers for surgeons heretofore unable to acquire the latest medical literature.[11]

There were also collections of scientific specimens at Fort Pitt—a museum of pathology and a museum of natural history. McGrigor was again the originator of these displays. At Portsmouth in 1810 he started his own museum, but due to his Peninsular service, he had to disband it. In 1816 he instituted a new museum at Fort Pitt and encouraged his surgeons to send specimens. In 1833 the museum contained over 14,000 preparations in comparative anatomy, natural history, and art objects.[12] By 1850, McGrigor had increased the collection to over 41,000 specimens, an indication, he believed, of the growing scientific interests of his men.

To publicize the collections, McGrigor printed a *Catalog of Preparations in Morbid, Natural, and Comparative Anatomy* (1833), copies of which he presented to physicians, surgeons, and scientists. The Muniment Room of the Library of the Royal Army Medical College contains a scrapbook of 70 letters from individuals who praised McGrigor for setting an example to doctors in the services. There are letters here from museums, service clubs, learned societies, and from members of the medical world like George Ballingall, Charles Bell, William Burnett, and Sir Astley Cooper.[13] Proud of his surgeons for assembling these scientific treasures, McGrigor now presented, at a mellow 67 years of age, the catalogue in 1838 to Lord Howick (Earl Grey), the war secretary: "I trust these . . . will satisfy your Lordship that the Medical Officers have not been sleeping on their hands and that they have fully availed themselves of the opportunities . . . of extending the bounds of science."[14]

In addition to his support of the library and museum, Sir James encouraged the famed Aberdeen Medico-Chirurgical Society. As a loyal Aberdonian, he maintained a lively interest in the progress of the society by encouraging medical graduates of Aberdeen University to seek entrance into the medical department and by contributing money for a new building of the society. In 1847, when he was 76, McGrigor modestly presented the society with his own personal collection of papers relating to his army service from 1797 to 1815:

I send by ship volumes of manuscripts being chiefly cases of diseases which occurred in the Regimental Hospitals of the 88th Regimental and of the

Royal Regiment of Horse when I was Surgeon to these Corps and subsequently when I was on the Medical Staff of the Army which I beg you present in my name to the Medical Society of Aberdeen. In presenting these volumes I do so not on account of their value which I am very sensible is small but as holding out to junior members of the society an instance of persevering industry with which I prosecuted my profession from my first entering into the Army and to which I mainly attribute my success in it. The Medical Cases are generally in my own handwriting sometimes in that of my assistants in the two Regiments in which I served as Surgeon. . . .[15]

The society, proud of its link to Sir James, whose portrait dignifies its meeting room, flourishes and maintains a lively interest in medical developments. And the manuscripts that McGrigor donated to the society, which he shyly regarded as of little value, document the progress of military medicine.

Throughout his career, McGrigor had championed the welfare of the rank and file, and as director general, he urged that soldiers be granted decent medical care. "It is not only in the sense of humanity," he claimed, "but in that of a sound policy and real economy, that the state should provide able medical and surgical advice for the soldier when sick or wounded. I look upon it to be an implied part of the compact of the citizen with the state," he continued, "that whoever enters the service of his country to fight its battles, should be provided with the same type of medical aid . . . which he enjoyed as a citizen."[16]

Although gradual improvements ameliorated the harsh living conditions of the troops in the post-Waterloo era—changes in food, uniform, quarters; revisions in the Penal code; the establishment of libraries, recreational rooms, playing fields, regimental savings banks, and classroom instruction in the rudiments of education; and a shorter period on the ranks under the Limited Enlisted Act of 1847—these reforms were within the jurisdiction of the War Office. The medical department played only a minimal role of advisement.

McGrigor's humanitarian concern for the soldiers and his interest in promoting scientific research were best exemplified by his sponsorship of the publication of military medical returns gathered from army garrisons throughout the empire. These returns provided statistical information about the prevalence of disease, climatic conditions, and measures utilized to preserve health in pestilential areas. "Had such records been always faithfully kept," wrote McGrigor with respect to the plague in Egypt, "many practical points would not, as they are now, be involved in doubt and uncertainty. We should not now be so ignorant of some diseases of the countries where we have so often made campaigns, or of which we had so long been in possession."[17] McGrigor bitterly remembered the Medical Board's mania for economy in hospital supplies, the stress on budgetary matters and the relegation of medical knowledge to relative insignificance. McGrigor, however, demanded regular, meticulous reports from his surgeons about their regiments. The medical returns that had so intrigued him on Jersey, and which later became the basis for more comprehensive studies when he served in Portsmouth and in Spain, became the basis for a systematic tabulation of diseases in a variety of environments.

Yet McGrigor's dream of a comprehensive statistical study did not attract official support for many years, and the tomes of regimental medical records shipped from India, West Africa, North America, the Caribbean, and the Mediterranean merely accumulated at Fort Pitt. By 1836 there were 160 volumes. The records contained some scientific information, but while unclassified, they were relatively useless for a study of medical topography. McGrigor's hopes of publishing this data coincided with the views of Henry Marshall, a retired inspector of hospitals. A prolific writer on many scholarly subjects, Marshall was the foremost advocate of reforms for the enlisted man and was the medical department's authority on the relatively new technique of statistics.[18] In October, 1835, their wishes were realized when Lord Howick requested that Marshall and Lieutenant Alexander Murray Tulloch, an authority on vital statistics, prepare a report on the sanitary history of the West Indian command for publication.

Completed in 1837, *The Statistical Report on the Sickness, Mortality, and Invaliding Among the Troops in the West Indies* traced the medical history, from 1816 to 1836, in the British colonies in the Caribbean—Jamaica, the Bahamas, British Honduras, and the Windward and Leeward Islands. The report graphically evidenced how the environment of the West Indies severely affected the health of troops. Compared to the average annual mortality rate of soldiers stationed in Britain of 17 per 1,000 men for a comparable period, the death rate of soldiers in these isles ranged from 78.5/1,000 in the Windward and Leeward Islands, 103/1,000 in British Honduras, 107/1,000 in the Bahamas, reaching the level of 143/1,000 in Jamaica.[19]

With the evidence, the writers, accustomed to describe disease in terms of miasmatic and climatorial pathology, questioned some traditional assumptions about the physical adaptability of whites to the

tropics. One such belief was that Europeans gradually became acclimatized to warm climates by a process known as "seasoning." It had
been assumed that due to "seasoning," the sickness and mortality rates
of older soldiers, accustomed to the environment, was far lower than
younger men with less service in the West Indies. But, "instead of the
mortality of our troops . . . decreasing with age," stated Marshall and
Tulloch, "as has been the general impression, it increases with greater
rapidity than in this country [Britain] . . ."[20]

Was continual exposure to high temperature somehow related to the
yearly decimation of rank and file? Apparently not, for the report explained that "the range of the thermometer . . . in Antiqua and Barbados, is rather higher than in Dominica, Tobago, Jamaica or the
Bahamas; yet we find that the troops in the latter stations suffer three
times as much as the former." Furthermore, the mortality rate of a
garrison could be twenty times greater than that of another year "without any perceptible difference in the range of temperature."[21]

Was the pestilence of the Caribbean due to excessive rainfall, or to
the "miasma" emanating from the swamps, lagoons, and marshes
near many garrisons? If so, areas inundated during prolonged rainy
seasons presumably would have the greatest amount of sickness. But
Jamaica had annually only one-half of the rainfall of British Guiana,
and yet the mortality rate of troops in Jamaica was double the rate in
Guiana. Thus, concluded the statisticians, "neither heat nor moisture
can be the primary cause which influenced the health of troops in the
West Indies. . . ."[22]

Marshall and Tulloch also doubted some other explanations of disease, such as sickness being caused by the lack of trade winds from July
to October, or by the influence of "miasma" from South American
jungles, or by "the exhalation or emanations from the soil." The writers also inquired whether a garrison's location and its elevation from
sea level were related to its sanitary history. By comparing the records
of 27 Jamaican stations located from the seacoast to the Blue Mountains, the report demonstrated that posts close to the sea, such as
Montego Bay, with a mortality rate of 178.8/1,000 were generally the
most unhealthy compared to the relative salubrity of Maroon Town,
located at a height of 2,000 feet, which had a death rate for troops of
32.7/1,000, and that some stations located on "low sandy tongues of
land or peninsulas jutting into the sea . . ." were comparatively free of
that great killer—yellow fever. Thus, concluded the researchers, "it

must be admitted that it is exceedingly difficult, if not impossible to point out a practical rule to be followed in the choice of a healthy location for the troops."[23]

Shunning pretentious theories about causes of tropical diseases, Marshall and Tulloch concluded their study with recommendations to improve the sanitary condition of the troops. They urged a more frequent rotation of regiments from long service in the Caribbean to the cooler climate of the Mediterranean or British North America, the construction of larger and better ventilated barracks at higher elevations, some restrictions on liquor rations, a more wholesome diet for soldiers, and the use of more black enlisted men (whose sickness and mortality rate was consistently lower at virtually every station).[24]

These deductions and suggestions, commented the *Edinburgh Medical and Surgical Journal*, "some will regard as not remarkable for novelty or originality. They are, however, valuable in eradicating various errors, and clearing the ground, as it were, for the construction of a more substantial theory than any yet adduced."[25] Such reports, announced *Lancet*, "will constitute a most important acquisition to medical science; will furnish data for the solution of innumerable questions in the etiology of disease; and will inevitably lead to the salvation of thousands of lives."[26] The *Times* proclaimed that "the great value of this report is the beneficial influence which it is calculated to exercise over the practical arrangements of reliefs for the regiments doing duty in the West Indies."[27] Perusing the document, along with another statistical study, the *First Annual Report of the Registrar General of Births, Deaths and Marriages* (1839), *The Quarterly Review* claimed that "the Military Reports are the most valuable gifts, as to the effects of climate, which has ever been made to medicine. . . ."[28] The major influence of this study, a landmark in military medicine, was to stimulate the publication of similar reports of the health of troops in the rest of the empire and to focus attention on the need for army reforms. As the *United Services Journal* noted in 1864: "from that investigation . . . may truly be dated all the amelioration of the condition of the soldier that have since been effected."[29] And Beresford, who once had refuted his regimental surgeon's defense of some sick soldiers wrote to McGrigor in 1838 to congratulate him:

Would such a compilation had been made before our time, that we might have had the benefit of it. The subject reminds me indeed of your country's expression of "Auld lang syne," when you and I were often so anxious, and conversed over such subjects for the benefit of those under our care and protection. You have in this shown and continued the same uniform zeal, care, and interest in the cause of humanity, which then so honourably distinguished you.[30]

It is to McGrigor's credit, then, that his fascination with medical returns developed into statistical studies that led to similar reports about the sanitary histories of the other commands, and later inspired medical reports on the army in India. By 1860 the British army medical department issued reports on the health of the troops in virtually every corner of the earth.[31]

Due to advances in medical education, gradual improvements in pay and pensions, and to increasing contributions made to medical literature, "there appeared a new spirit of emulation in the service," boasted McGrigor, "which gained for the department much credit from our [medical] Brethren in civilian life."[32] Yet in contrast to the improved status of the medical profession in civilian society, within the rigid hierarchy of the British army, where traditional military values dominated social relationships, the army surgeons still occupied an inferior and degrading position. The occupational stigma of practicing a demeaning craft rather than a profession, of being the literal descendant of a mere barber, of being a "quack" in an era before there were Medical Registers, or of not being a "gentleman" all severely handicapped the army surgeon when it came to offering advice about hygiene and sanitation to his regimental commander. Granted, generals and colonels listened respectfully to men like McGrigor, Guthrie, and Fergusson. But the typical regimental surgeon was rarely consulted about health and sanitation.

The surgeon's pay and pension were always far below the comparative rates for line officers, his promotion was usually much slower, and in the *Army List*, which provided the rules and regulations for the army, the medical department ranked below all the combat corps. In the civil departments, the medical department ranked in precedence after the commissary, paymaster general, department of accounts and just ahead of the chaplain's department, the judge advocate general department, and the storekeeper. In matters of military discipline, although the humble army surgeon had relative rank, i.e., ranking theoretically as a lieutenant or captain, it was firmly stated in the general orders that the surgeons, like the paymasters, had no "claims whatever to Military Command."[33]

And the petty humiliations were further augmented. The surgeon was denied mess and band privileges provided other officers, and even at his funeral on a military post his body was not accorded the military honors of a formal military salute. Even the privileges given other officers—a servant, horse and a forage allowance for the animal—were not available for the regimental surgeon, who had to make his own arrangements for a mount. Guthrie, the most outspoken critic on this subject, complained bitterly: "I have seen a staff surgeon in charge of many hundred wounded . . . brush his own shoes, clean his own horse, and then go out to do many of the most delicate operations in surgery."[34] Although the inequities in pay and promotion angered army surgeons it was the sheer pettiness and snobbery maintained in the ritual of army precedence and privileges that was particularly galling to the medical department. "The whole service was still treated in a contemptuous and humiliating manner," Guthrie thundered in 1840 to the Royal Commission on Promotion.[35] In contrast to the rising prestige of civilian medical practice, the army doctor was still treated like an inferior, someone to be tolerated, but seldom to be respected. Yet, the surgeon had an education more expensive and longer than the average combat officer, he entered the army at a later age due to his lengthy training, and he possessed a fund of scientific knowledge generally unmatched in the army. The greatest degree of class consciousness occurred not in the technical corps, the artillery and the engineers, but in the "purchase" corps, the infantry and cavalry. In contrast to the dedicated surgeon, who had to master a number of subjects and to pass qualifying exams for his commission and then often wait years for a promotion, the young aristocratic rakes in infantry and cavalry regiments usually purchased their commissions and advanced in rank by buying successive commissions from retiring senior officers.

The continued practice of treating surgeons like inferiors discouraged many surgeons from remaining in the service. Surgeons had difficulty initiating hygienic improvements, enforcing sanitary standards, or imposing authority in a hospital when they were often regarded as social inferiors by line officers. To cap the injustices of this discriminatory system, it was apparent that medical officers could not share in the titles and awards bestowed on combat officers by a grateful sovereign for feats of bravery. Heroism with a sword, and heroism with a scalpel were apparently not compatible in the mentality of the Horse Guards. Courage displayed by a surgeon in treating the wounded under a hail of bullets, courage demonstrated during a siege or in the trenches while healing the sick, and particularly, courage demanded of the brave doctor who toiled in pestilential hospital wards did not merit the coveted Order of the Knight Commander of the Bath.

One of the foremost obstacles confronting McGrigor, then, was the removal of these social inequities, and to this task he tactfully and persistently applied his talents. A significant step in the recognition to the services of army surgeons in the field had already occurred at Badajoz and again at Salamanca when Wellington, upon McGrigor's urging, had praised the medical department in his dispatches for public consideration. Sir James initiated the next step, when armed with his knighthood, he tried to obtain for himself a peerage—the order of Baronet—which he finally achieved on September 30, 1831.[36]

In the 1830s there were no efforts to improve the prestige of medical officers. A chance came in 1840 when McGrigor and Guthrie had the opportunity to testify at the hearings of the Royal Commission on Promotion in the Army and Navy. McGrigor explained that a major complaint in his department was the slowness of promotion. He pointed out that the surgeons who entered at 24 years of age at the rank of assistant surgeon were not promoted to the rank of surgeon for another fifteen or twenty years of service, and that service in the tropics was detrimental to their health:

As to the regimental surgeons, I may be permitted to state that in a period of peace, particularly on foreign stations, as in India or the West Indies, the only severe duty falls on the medical officer. In tropical and unhealthy climates, the duties of medical officers are at all times heavy and unremitting, more particularly so from the requested reduction of this number on every station; and the consequence is that annually numbers of them retire to this country in broken health, and the mortality rate is considerable, yet it is from these classes . . . that the higher ranks of the department are to be filled up.

Observing the significance of honors, titles and promotions to his surgeons, McGrigor continued:

I beg here also to state what has generally been complained of a hardship that at the last occasion of the coronation [Queen Victoria I] when the navy and army obtained promotion in all the higher ranks, the medical officers of the army were passed over [even though commissary officers were promoted] . . . . The exclusion of the medical officers of the army was most mortifying to them as they feel, and I believe justly, that they had not less faithfully and zealously discharged their duties than their brother officers of the other departments of the services.[37]

A more caustic commentary came from Guthrie, now a famed Professor of Medicine in London and four times the president of the Royal College of Surgeons. In a bitter tirade, Guthrie claimed that the army surgeon was "the most neglected officer in the service." The situation was most unjust, he continued, for "it is only to the surgeons of the army that promotions or honours or pension are considered unnecessary and are absolutely refused. Medical Officers are human beings," he continued, "subject to the same influences, feelings, and passions as other men, they should have held out to them at all times, the same or similar inducements to good conduct, to exertion, and to emulation in their profession, if found, or are supposed to be found, necessary and proper for the officers of the army at large."[38] Noting the superior treatment accorded surgeons in the French army, Guthrie told the commission that Larrey had informed him that Napoleon had presented the Legion of Honor to Larrey, Percy, and Desgenettes in 1804 for their achievements. After the battle of Wagram, Guthrie continued, Bonaparte made the three surgeons into Barons of the Empire. Analyzing the reasons for the comparable treatment of British army surgeons, Guthrie suggested that:

It is probable that the peculiarity of not bestowing rewards on military medical men for service in the field, has arisen from their not being considered in battle and called non-combatants; but nothing can be more unreasonable that the classification of medical officers with clergymen and other civilians attached to the army, with reference to their exemption from danger. In every siege, a medical man is sent into the gorge of the trenches, and they have, at all times, marched with the troops. They are, in fact, exposed to a great part of the dangers of the field, and afterwards, to those of their own profession, which crowded hospitals engender, and which often have been most fatal.[39]

Concluding his testimony, in what was the most candid recorded description of the surgeon's plight in the era, Guthrie added that beyond the matters of slow promotion and lack of honors, there was still a more important reason to assert the justified claims of the medical officers—the need to keep good surgeons in the army. "Such men . . . of good administrative knowledge and best professional ability . . . can only be obtained by adequate remuneration, rewards and honors."[40]

Yet the Royal Commision, chaired by Wellington, saw little need to change the military code. It reported "that the general impression produced on our minds by the examination of the evidence . . . was the condition of the army medical officers was not unfavourable . . . ," that the improvements in pay and pension since 1830 "were well calculated to secure a succession of accomplished medical officers for the military service; and that few changes in those regulations would be recommended to place that branch of the service in a satisfactory position in relation to other ranks in the army."[41]

And there the matter of the surgeon's prestige rested until the subject came up in Parliament. On April 4, 1845, in a debate on army estimates, Lieutenant General Sir Howard Douglas pointed out to the House that the pay and pension improvements provided other army officers by the Royal Warrant of October 1, 1840, had been denied the surgeons. But his motion for an inquiry was denied.[42] Douglas returned to the matter two years later when he noted that the quartermasters and veterinary surgeons had recently been granted improved pension benefits, an improvement again denied the army surgeons, a "rather neglected class," he commented, "entitled on every account to the first consideration and distinction." Two other military officers in Commons supported the motion to improve the pensions of medical officers, but the debate occurred in "a thin house" and attracted little attention.[43] On June 21, 1849, the subject was revived when a discussion ensued in Parliament about awarding military titles. An advocate for the surgeons, General Sir De Lacy Evans complained that "it was a matter of reproach that no military distinctions had been conferred on such men as Sir James McGrigor . . . and Mr. Guthrie." Evans's view was supported by Joseph Hume, the famous politician, who stated that he regretted the stigma placed on medicine and claimed that the doctors were responsible for the decline of mortality in the army. The debate terminated when Lord John Russell, the prime minister, promised that he would consider the question of granting a military order to the surgeons.[44]

The question of the eligibility of army surgeons for the Order of the Bath became a subject of lengthy correspondence between Wellington and Earl Grey, the secretary for war and colonies. On December 8, 1849, Wellington explained to Grey that he had consulted with McGrigor on the matter, "but the affair is most arduous and invidious and I cannot now report . . . any satisfactory result. . . ."[45] Grey had difficulty in discovering the means to circumvent the regulations which limited the order to military officers. A candidate, he stated "should have been specifically mentioned . . . as having distinguished himself by his valour and conduct in action against the enemy, or as having by some action . . . contributed to the success of some action." Yet, Grey continued, "medical officers of the army are not called upon to expose themselves or to have taken any part in action with the enemy. . . ."[46]

In the meantime, *Lancet* entered the debate. Thomas Wakley, its editor and champion of medical reform, noted that medical officers had been recently killed during combat in Burma, China, and India. "What then is the propriety," he asked, "nay the decency—of classing such officers as civil staff and debarring them from those military honours?"[47] *Lancet* presented a "Summary of Claims of the Military Officers of the Army and Navy to Military Rewards and Distinctions." Although army surgeons on the Continent received military honors, the editor declared, "from the British sovereign they receive none." Granted, the surgeons' pay was low, but money was not the cause of discontent, the journal continued. It was a question of prestige: "No men are more alive to the fact that honour is the vital principle of armies and navies than the surgeons. . . ."[48]

What may now appear to be an acrimonious discussion on a seemingly trivial question was actually a very serious matter, because the award of a royal honor often represented the pinnacle of an ambitious man's career. Furthermore, the entire question pivoted around the need to demonstrate to recalcitrant military officers that army surgeons, whose colleagues in civilian life were receiving honors, also merited equivalent rewards. Fortunately, the necessary adjustments were made in the statutory regulations for the Military Division of the Order of Bath. When the great day came on August 16, 1850, Mc-Grigor, now 79 years old, along with the heads of the naval and India medical services, was granted the Military Divison of Knight Commander of the Bath. Another 17 surgeons (7 army, 6 navy, 4 Indian) were awarded the Commander of the Bath, and still another 20 service doctors were presented with lesser titles. One of the C.B.s went to Dr. John Hume, who had been the personal physician in the Peninsula to the Duke of Wellington. Delighted with the results of the ceremony honoring the profession, *Lancet* proclaimed:

We believe this a signal triumph—for triumph it is—to be the greatest step ever made by our profession towards obtaining its just recognition by the State. . . . It is the removal of a professional stigma . . . [and surgeons] are no longer to be treated as aliens to our fleets and armies. . . .[49]

Achieving the Bath for his leading officers was McGrigor's last signal achievement. Weary of his arduous duties of 35 years of service, he was anxious to retire. In 1847, when he was 76 years of age, in fact, he had requested permission to quit, but the Duke of Wellington objected, saying: "No, McGrigor, there is plenty of work in you yet."[50] Sir James continued to work at his post until April 16, 1850, when he again requested retirement.

After receiving a testimony for his services in Parliament from the secretary of war and colonies, Lord Panmure ("an officer," said Panmure, "to whom the public were indebted")[51] McGrigor left his position on May 31, 1851. Just before his retirement, in a special tribute paid to the grand old man, a testimonial banquet was held in McGrigor's honor at the Thatched House Tavern on St. James Street, for which 500 medical officers had signed a testimonial to honor their chief.[52]

McGrigor returned to civilian life with many honors. In addition to titles granted by the Crown, he received from the Ottoman sultan the Order of the Crescent, and from the Portuguese government the Order of Knight Commander of the Tower and Sword. Three times (1826, 1827, 1841), Sir James was elected Lord Rector of the University of Aberdeen. In addition, he was a Fellow of the Royal Societies of London and of Edinburgh, a Fellow of the Royal Colleges of Physicians of London, Dublin and Edinburgh. In 1825 he was awarded an honorary doctorate in laws from the University of Edinburgh. Like other physician generals before him, McGrigor was also physician extraordinary to his sovereign.

In retirement, McGrigor pondered accounts of the disasters that befell the British army during the Crimean War. He was indignant over the torrents of criticism from the press and from Parliament that were heaped upon his medical staff, particularly the public castigation of two protégés, John Hall and Andrew Smith, who were blamed for the inefficiency of the medical department in the Crimea. On June 2, 1855, as Parliamentary commissions investigated the causes of the breakdown of medical and commissary services on the shores of the

Black Sea, McGrigor's son, James, wrote to Hall, the principal medical officer at Balaclava, that "father has been shaken by the attacks on you."[53] And on November 9 to Andrew Smith, his successor as director general, McGrigor stated in sympathy: "As you readily believe, I have been exccedingly annoyed by the attacks made upon us by the infamous newspapers. . . ."[54] The familiar story of the blunders and fiascos of Wellington's former subordinates in the Crimean campaign, and a description of the intense suffering of the Allied armies that besieged the Russian stronghold of Sevastapol, are beyond the scope of this work. But it should be noted that even after McGrigor's post-Waterloo reforms, the mobile hospital system in the Crimea faltered badly in transferring serious casualties from the sustained siege to distant general hospitals in pest-ridden Scutari. Thus the medical service would be subject to another round of investigations and reforms. Yet still lacking was a germ theory of disease to replace the climatorial pathology that prevailed until the end of the century, for no significant advances occurred in medical science until the bacteriological revolution in medical knowledge of the Pasteur-Lister era.

The changes in the medical administration of the army that resulted from the Crimean War do emphasize the limits of McGrigor's achievements. McGrigor certainly cannot be blamed for the ineffectiveness of the medical department in the Near East, more than four years after his retirement. But during his own tenure of office as director general, for reasons beyond his control—the Crown's monopoly of military affairs, Wellington's domination of the officers, Parliament's tight-fisted economy measures for public services—he was unable to initiate improvements in many areas. McGrigor could not create a corps of hospital orderlies, he was unable to establish a medical college for army surgeons or a school of tropical medicine, nor could he ever persuade Wellington to acquiesce in an ambulance system. McGrigor's staff was depleted by budget cuts, and regiments overseas often had inadequate medical care. Even in the construction of army hospitals, McGrigor and his staff had to accept the decisions of the Royal Engineers, who ignored the medical department's suggestions about bed space, adequate ventilation, and suitable drainage in their architectural plans. Perhaps the most significant aspect of army medical services which McGrigor was unable to improve was the protection of the rank and file from contagious diseases by improvements in sanitation.

Victorian England was gradually being cleansed by the "Sanitary Awakening" that is associated with Edwin Chadwick. Yet the army lagged far behind in hygienic improvements during McGrigor's era. Due to Chadwick's relentless agitation in the 1840s for public health reforms, he convinced the nation's leaders that the government should assume greater responsibility for eliminating the sources of contagion emanating from unhealthy environments rather than passively accept the disastrous consequences of a disease like cholera. Chadwick's widely propagated message, explains his biographer, was that "man should have a scientific knowledge of the conditions through which his health might be affected and act upon that knowledge."[55] Prevention of disease, not cure alone, became the cry of Chadwick's followers. Gradually, the political machinery of inquiry into urban health conditions began to evolve. The Poor Law Commission (1842), and the Duke of Buccleuch's Commission (1844)[56] investigated unsanitary conditions in cities—impure water, defective sewerage, crowded housing, and inadequate garbage disposal. The results of such inquiries was the Public Health Law of 1848, by which local governments assumed more responsibility for essential public services, particularly in matters involving dangers from contagion that had been neglected by private enterprise. "Life cannot rightfully be wasted by neglect any more than it can rightfully be taken by violence," declared John Simon, president of the General Board of Health and one of Britain's foremost sanitarians. "In every community," he continued, "the failures of protection of life (due to the lack of effective public health measures) has ever been felt as a scandal."[57]

Although some British cities were gradually made cleaner places in which to live, the living quarters of enlisted men remained incredibly filthy. Soldiers were quartered in garrisons or "barracks establishments" which were usually apart from, but were sometimes in the midst of, civilian dwellings. These garrisons were separate little towns administered solely by the army, and hence they were immune from public legislation. In these segregated facilities, the troops were supposedly provided with adequate quarters and decent conveniences. But the hygienic ideal of the soldier's environment was far from the disgusting reality. While British towns were attempting to eliminate the squalor of their slums, and to provide improved housing, purer water and better waste disposal, army barracks generally remained miserable hovels. Under local government acts and public sanitary regulations, the state was empowered to inspect civilian dwellings and business establishments for the welfare of the community. But in the army, troops lived under such dirty and unwholesome conditions that few improvements in their habitat seems to have transpired since the French Revolution. "There was hardly a barracks in the Kingdom," declared Sir William Clay in 1855 during a Parliamentary debate, "that would bear for a moment comparison for comfort and accommodation with a gaol, a penitentiary, or a union workhouse."[58]

With the exception of McGrigor's statistical expert, Henry Marshall, who wrote from retirement about army mortality rates, no other reformer of the early Victorian era publicly evidenced an interest in the sanitary condition of the soldiers. None of the famous individuals associated with the public health movement of the period—Chadwick, Simon, Thomas Southwood Smith, William Farr—seemed concerned about such matters.[59] Not until 1858, the year of McGrigor's death, did Chadwick demonstrate his concern over the fearsome death rate in the Indian army.[60] Health conditions in the army, therefore, were not within the province of the sanitarians until the Crimean War revealed to Britain that its vaunted humanitarianism during the Age of Reform had neglected its military institutions. Over 4,700 died from combat, and 15,300 perished from disease during the campaign.[61] The revelations about the casualty rates created the impetus to medical reforms (as well as improvements in education, the penal code, and recruitment of officers) which McGrigor, for all his influence and prestige, could never achieve.

The official leader in the movement for army sanitary reforms after the Crimean War was the influential Sidney Herbert, secretary at war (1852–1855), secretary for the colonies (1855), and secretary for war (1859–1861).[62] Herbert had the political acumen and the utilitarian attitude necessary to make the subject of army medical reform such an urgent issue that no ministry could ignore it. But Herbert lacked the scientific training, the necessary industry, and especially the perseverance of a Chadwick, that were needed to champion this cause. Herbert's deficiencies in this area were compensated by his association with Florence Nightingale, the tireless publicist, the clever propagandist, the real instigator of medical reforms. Armed with the prestige and reputation accorded to no other female in the century, encouraged in her endeavors by Queen Victoria and supported by a cadre of civilian and military reformers, Nightingale began a crusade to ame-

liorate the miserable life of the enlisted man. She helped to wipe away
the dirty cobwebs of musty Dickensian officialdom at the Horse
Guards and at the War Office to reveal the deplorable living conditions of the rank and file.[63]

Due to her famed accomplishments in treating the sick in Scutari
hospitals during the Crimean campaign, her amazing energy, and her
devastating bluntness, Nightingale enlisted a band of medical doctors,
army officers, and public health officials in efforts to make the health
of the army a primary object of reform. Duplicating Chadwick's
statistical techniques in their investigations, the Herbert-Nightingale
group plagued the military authorities with indictments of such care-
lessness and inefficiency in health matters that even the reactionary
Horse Guards had to agree to changes. With Herbert as chairman,
and with Nightingale providing direction, the Royal Commission on
the Sanitary State of the Army (1857) demonstrated that the military
had been incredibly thoughtless with soldiers' lives. The commission
proved, to the shock and dismay of public opinion, that the death rate
in the peacetime army from 1839 to 1853 was almost four times
greater than that of the civilian male population of England and Wales
for approximately the same period. It demonstrated that even the high
mortality rate at Sevastapol was less than that of troops quartered at
home in their loathsome environment. Although the most valuable
contribution of these reformers was to suggest methods by which the
health of the rank and file could be improved (by improvements
in diet, barracks construction, latrine accommodations, exercise, rec-
reation, etc.), the scope of the inquiry was later broadened to include a
study of troops in India, and recommendations to control venereal
disease around army garrisons, to raise the status of army surgeons,
and to establish an army medical college.[64]

In view of these post-Crimean developments, how does one evalu-
ate McGrigor? Due to insufficient evidence about his family and about
aspects of his character, it is difficult to speculate about McGrigor's
private life. His public career, however, is amply documented. Mc-
Grigor was a shy, industrious man who achieved prominence by study,
toil, and by a keen dedication to public duty. He was a punctilious
and conscientious surgeon who rose through the hierarchy of officialdom by avoiding controversy and by initiating reforms of medical
services only after he was confident of support from the generals.
Luckily for his career, McGrigor happened to be at the right place at

the right time. In Flanders, he became acquainted with the Duke of York; in the West Indies with Abercrombie; in the East Indies with Wellington; and in Egypt with Baird and Beresford.

Since most of McGrigor's ideas about military medicine had been advanced by his mentor, Sir John Pringle, McGrigor can not be labeled as a major innovator in military medicine. He was not a famous surgeon, he did not make any significant contributions as a clinician, nor did he even pretend to be a scientist. Even his limited connection to public health movements when he was director general was brief and insignificant.[65] Yet he was the most important British army medical figure of the era because he had the vision, energy, and influence to reform the medical department. As the epitome of "an organization man," he merits praise for improving sanitary conditions and hospital arrangements, for initiating studies in preventive medicine, and for raising the dignity of army surgeons. When McGrigor retired after fifty-seven years of service, army doctors were receiving better training, information about many diseases was being collected, and the sickness and mortality rates of soldiers was significantly decreasing. McGrigor justly deserves to be remembered as "the father of the Royal Army Medical Corps."

Sir James McGrigor, who died at his residence at Harley Street, Cavendish Square on April 2, 1858, in his 87th year,[66] surely merited two major tributes to his memory. In London a large statue of McGrigor stands at the headquarters of the Royal Army Medical College at Millbank. In McGrigor's beloved Aberdeen is an obelisk of polished granite, 72 feet high, overlooking Duthie Park on the banks of the Dee. These monuments are fitting acknowledgements to a dedicated humanitarian and to a practical army medical administrator who attempted to alleviate the horrors of war.

# NOTES

## I. THE TRAINING OF AN ARMY SURGEON

1. Military medicine was defined by Fielding H. Garrison as "all that relates to military hygiene and sanitation, military surgery, medico-military administration, medico-military transport, recruiting, sanitary formations and training. The history of military medicine has two main aspects, the professional or scientific and the administrative. Progress in military medicine, as a branch of medical science, has turned upon two principal coefficients—the advancement of scientific surgery and the advancement of the science of infectious diseases. Bacteriology has done more for this phase of the subject than anything else." *Military Medicine* (Washington, 1922), p. 1.

2. "I am the eldest of three sons of Colquhoun McGrigor, Esq. a merchant of Aberdeen, by Ann the daughter of Lewis Grant, Esq. of Lethendrey in Strathspey, Inverness-shire, where I was born. My brother Robert followed his father's occupation and my younger brother, Lieut. Colonel McGrigor, who served with distinction in the East and West Indies, America, and other quarters, particularly at the capture of Seringapatam [India], died in Nottingham in 1841." *The Autobiography . . . of Sir James McGrigor . . .* , cited hereafter as McGrigor, p. 1.

3. Ibid., p. 2.

4. The doctors were Walter Farquhar and William Fordyce. See *Dictionary of National Biography*, hereafter D.N.B., 6, p. 1088; 7, p. 432.

5. For a discussion of the contributions to medicine from King's and Marischal, see G. A. G. Michell, "The Medical History of Aberdeen and the Universities," *The Aberdeen University Review*, 37 (1958), 225–238.

6. Ian Porter, *Alexander Gorden, M.D. of Aberdeen, 1752–1799* (London, 1958), p. 10. See also William B. Howie, "Medical Education in 18th Century Hospitals," *The Scottish Society of the History of Medicine* (1970), 1–20, and H. P. Tait, "Medical Education at the Scottish Universities to the Close of the 18th Century," *The Evolution of Medical Education in Britain*, ed. F. L. N. Poynter (London, 1966), pp. 53–67.

7. McGrigor, p. 5. McGrigor's four notebooks, entitled "Monro's Anatomy Lectures," dated October, 1790 to March, 1791, are in the Muniment Room of the Library, Royal Army Medical College.

8. Porter, p. 9.

9. Ella Hill Burton Roger, *Aberdeen Doctors at Home and Abroad* (Edinburgh, 1893), pp. 52–54. There is information about the Society in Anon., *Regulations, List of the Members and Catalogue of the Aberdeen Medico-Chirurgical Society*, 5th ed. (Aberdeen, 1812).

10. McGrigor, pp. 7–8.

11. Ibid., p. 9. McGrigor had letters of introduction to Walter Farquhar, and to Gilbert Blane, the famed naval surgeon.

12. McGrigor to David Grant, London, September 13, 179(3?). McGrigor Family Letters.

13. McGrigor, p. 9.

14. I am indebted to E. H. Cornelius, Librarian of the Royal College of Surgeons of England, for informing me that McGrigor was later examined by the Company of Surgeons on February 6, 1794.

15. For discussions of the organization of the army medical department in the 17th and 18th centuries, see Johnston's Roll, 1, pp. xxv–xlvii; Arnold Chaplin, *Medicine in the Age of*

*George III* (London, 1919), pp. 76–82; D. A. Gordon, *The Story of our Services Under the Crown* (London, 1879), pp. 88–113; Fred L. Smith, *A Short History of the Royal Army Medical Corps* (Aldershot, 1946), pp. 3–7; Peter Lovegrove, *Not Least in the Crusade—A Short History of the Royal Army Medical Corps* (London, 1938), pp. 4–8; H. A. L. Howell, "The Story of the British Army Surgeons and the Care of the Sick and Wounded from 1689–1702," ". . . from 1715 to 1748," ". . . from 1765 to 1783," *Journal of the Royal Army Medical Corps,* hereafter JRAMC, 22 (1914), 320–334, 455–471, 643–658. See also William R. E. Smart, "On the Medical Services of the Navy and Army from the Accession of Henry VIII to the Restoration," *British Medical Journal,* 1 (1874), 168–169, 199–200, 228–229, 264–266.

16. Donald Monro, *Observations on the Means of Preserving the Health of Soldiers and of Constituting Military Hospitals and On the Diseases Incident to Soldiers,* 2 vols. (London, 1780), 1, p. vii. For comparable developments in the Royal Navy see Louis H. Roddis, *James Lind, Founder of Nautical Medicine* (New York, 1950); Christopher Lloyd and Jack L. S. Coulter, *Medicine in the Navy, 1200–1900, Vol. 3, 1814–1815* (London, 1961); and Christopher Lloyd, ed. *The Health of Seamen, Selections from the Works of Dr. James Lind, Sir Gilbert Blane, and Dr. Thomas Trotter,* Naval Records Society, vol. 107 (London, 1965).

17. John Hennen, *Military Surgery* (London, 1820), p. 30.

18. Monro, pp. 4–71, passim.

19. Ibid., pp. 91–98, passim.

20. Ibid., pp. 120, 135–136.

21. Sir John Pringle, *Observations on Diseases of the Army in Camp and Garrison,* 1st ed. (London, 1752), ix.

22. For accounts of Pringle's contributions, see Dorothy Waley Singer, "Sir John Pringle and His Circle," *Annals of Science,* 6 (1948–50), 171–261; Sidney Selwyn, "Sir John Pringle, Hospital Reformer, Moral Philosopher and Pioneer of Antisepsis," *Medical History,* 10 (1960), 268–274; and Lester S. King, *The Medical World of the 18th Century* (Chicago, 1958), pp. 133–138.

23. George Newman, *The Rise of Preventive Medicine* (Oxford, 1932), pp. 177–178.

24. Pringle, p. 254.

25. Ibid., pp. 31–41, 148.

26. Ibid., pp. 91, 93.

27. Russell F. Kirk, *British Anatomy, 1525–1800* (Melbourne, 1965), p. 6.

28. Charles Newman, *The Evolution of Medical Education in the 18th Century* (London, 1967), p. 13.

29. F. F. Cartwright, *The Development of Modern Surgery from 1830* (London, 1967), p. 13.

30. Cited by John Sutherland, *Men of Waterloo* (London, 1966), p. 151.

31. Robert Hamilton, *The Duties of a Regimental Surgeon Considered,* 2 vols. (London, 1787), 1, p. 187.

32. H. Moises, *An Inquiry into the Abuses of the Medical Department in the Militia of Great Britain with some necessary Amendments proposed* (London, 1794), p. 15.

33. Report of the Commissioners for Inquiry into Naval and Military Promotion, *Parliamentary Papers,* hereafter P.P. (1840), 235, XXIII, 1, 195.

34. John Ranby, *Methods of Treating Gunshot Wounds,* 3rd ed. (London, 1781), p. 30.

35. There is information about Hunter's military career in Jessie Dobson, *John Hunter* (Edinburgh and London, 1967); Lloyd Stevenson, "John Hunter, Surgeon-General, 1790–1793," *Journal of the History of Medicine and Allied Sciences,* hereafter J. His. Med., 19 (1964), 239–254; and Allen O. Whipple, *The Story of Wound Healing and Wound Repair* (Springfield, 1963), pp. 73–75.

36. McGrigor, pp. 12–18.

37. Ibid., p. 18.

38. Ibid., pp. 19–20, 237–238.

## II. THE FLANDERS CAMPAIGN

1. In addition to McGrigor's *Autobiography,* the following contemporary works on the Flanders campaign are pertinent: *A Journal Kept in the British Army From the Landing of the*

*Troops Under the Command of the Earl of Moira at Ostend in January, 1794 to their Retreat to Eng-land the Following Year* (Liverpool, 1796); Robert Brown, *An Important Journal of a Detach-ment from the Brigade of Foot Guards* (London, 1795); Caroline M. Duncan-Jones, ed., *Trusty and Well Beloved, the Letters Home of William Harness, An Officer of George III* (London, 1957); Edward W. Harcourt, ed., *The Harcourt Papers*, 14 vols. (Oxford, n.d.), 4, pt. 2; Robert Jackson, *An Outline of the History of a Cure of Fever, Endemic and Contagious* (Edinburgh, 1798); Captain L. T. Jones, *An Historical Journal of the British Contingent in the Year 1794 with the Re-treat Through Holland in the Year 1795* (Birmingham, 1798); and Sir Harry Verney, Bart., *The Journals and Correspondence of General Sir Harry Calvert, Bart., G.C.B. and G.C.H., Com-prising the Campaign in Flanders and Holland in 1793–94* (London, 1853). There is also infor-mation in: Alfred H. Burne, *The Noble Duke of York* (New York, 1949), 34–266, passim.; Sir John Fortescue, *A History of the British Army*, 13 vols. (London, 1899–1930), 4, pt. 1, pp. 221–324, passim.; Ramsay Weston Phipps, *The Armies of the First French Republic*, 4 vols. (Oxford, 1926), 1, pp. 133–152; and particularly an unpublished manuscript in the War Office Library by Captain H. B. Moffat, "The Duke of York's Campaign 1793 and 1794" (1881).

2. Harcourt, 4, p. 511.
3. Duncan-Jones, pp. 56–57.
4. Harcourt, p. 517.
5. McGrigor, p. 27.
6. McGrigor, pp. 28–29.
7. McGrigor, pp. 29–30.
8. Duke of Wellington, *Supplementary Dispatches of the Duke of Wellington*, 15 vols. (London, 1834), 13, p. 2.
9. Jackson, p. 14.
10. Harcourt, p. 565.
11. Jones, p. 145.
12. War Office Papers, Public Records Office, hereafter, W.O. 1/897, ff. 95, 118.
13. McGrigor, p. 32.
14. Fergusson, p. 56.
15. McGrigor, p. 32.
16. Brown, p. 225.
17. McGrigor, p. 31.
18. Jones, pp. 75–76.
19. Harcourt, p. 586.
20. McGrigor, pp. 31–32.
21. Brown, p. 225.
22. Cited in a letter from Robert McGrigor to David Grant, April 15, 1795, McGrigor Family Papers.
23. McGrigor, pp. 33–39.
24. Philip Henry, 5th Earl Stanhope, *Notes of Conversations with the Duke of Wellington, 1831–1851* (London, 1888), p. 182.
25. Alice, Countess of Strafford, ed., *Personal Reminiscences of the Duke Frances, The First Earl of Ellesmere* (London, 1903), p. 161. For an account of Wellington's military career, see Elizabeth Longford, *Wellington, the Years of the Sword*, (New York, 1969).
26. Fortescue, p. 324.
27. There is a copy of a letter dated December 5, 1804 from an unidentified J. Thomson to McGrigor summarizing the regimental strength and casualties of the 88th from 1794 to 1802. According to this summary, the losses of the Rangers in Flanders during the cam-paign were about 50 percent. Miscellanies, McGrigor Papers.


### III. THE WEST INDIAN CAMPAIGN

1. E. P. Thompson, *The Making of the English Working Class* (New York, 1963), p. 10.
2. McGrigor, pp. 41–42.

3. Ibid., p. 43.

4. Ibid., p. 47.

5. For summaries of the French revolutionary wars in the West Indies, see C. L. R. James, *The Black Jacobins* (New York, 1963), pp. 85–222; T. G. Steward, *The Haitian Revolution from 1791 to 1804* (New York, 1914), passim; Bryan Edwards, *The History, Civil and Commercial of the British West Indies*, 5 vols., 5th ed., (London, 1819), vols. 1, 2, and 4; Fortescue, 4, Pt. I, 482 496; Sir Alan Burns, *History of the British West Indies*, (London, 1954), pp. 564–574; and J. Holland Rose, "The Conflict with Revolutionary France," *The Cambridge History of the British Empire*, 3 vols. (London, 1926–27), 2, pp. 63–69.

6. John Rollo, *Observations on the Diseases which appeared in the Army on St. Lucia in December, 1778; January, February, March, April, and May, 1779* (London, 1780), p. i. For an account of the navy's medical case histories during the early 18th century in the West Indies, see Lloyd and Coulter, 3, pp. 97–138, passim.

7. Dr. John Hunter, *Observations on the Diseases of Jamaica and On the Best Means of Preserving the Health of Europeans in that Climate* (London, 1788), pp. 45–70.

8. George Rosen, "Occupational Diseases of English Seamen During the 17th and 18th Centuries," *Bulletin of the History of Medicine*, hereafter Bull. Hist. Med., 7 (1935), 755.

9. John Bell, *An Inquiry into the Causes which Produce, and the Means of Preventing Disease Among British Officers, Soldiers, and Others in the West Indies* (London, 1791), p. vii.

10. War Office, *Regulations to be observed by Troops for the West Indies* (London, 1795). For a discussion of victualling a naval vessel and protecting the health of seamen (diet, clothing, standards of cleanliness, ventilation, fumigation), see Lloyd and Coulter, 3, pp. 70–93.

11. Fitzpatrick's recommendations are in W.O. 1/897, ff. 7–16, 171–185.

12. Fergusson, p. 67.

13. James Lind, *An Essay on Diseases Incidental to Europeans in Hot Climates with the Method of Preventing Their Fatal Consequences* (London, 1786), p. 143. Another popular contemporary work on climatology and epidemiology was written by John Clark, M.D. (1744–1805), an East India Company surgeon. In his *Observations on The Diseases which Prevail in Long Voyages to Hot Countries* (London, 1773), he states: "Although the dictates of humanity and the love of the service are sufficient inducements with British officers to attend to the health of their men; yet unfortunately they have, in general considered it the province of the medical department alone. And many surgeons must acknowledge how often they have had occasion to regret that they have been foiled in preventing the prevalence and mortality of diseases, not only by the obstinacy and prejudices of the men; but also, not infrequently, by the inattention or neglect of their officers" (pp. ix–x.)

14. Rollo, p. i.

15. Bell, pp. 3–119, passim.

16. Hunter, p. 317.

17. Ibid., p. 13.

18. For an account of the voyage, see Rev. Cooper Willyams, *An Account of the Campaign in the Year 1794* (London, 1795).

19. W. O. 7/98, f. 37.

20. Ibid., 7/102, ff. 4–5, 10–11.

21. Papers Relating to the Expeditions to the West Indies under the Command of Sir Charles Grey and Sir John Jervis, P.P., XL (180), 1794–95, 43. (Hereafter cited as *Grey-Jervis*.)

22. Lloyd and Coulter, 3, p. 171.

23. J. K. Laughton and J. Y. F. Sullivan, *Journal of Rear-Admiral Bartholomew James, 1752-1828*, Naval Records Society, 6 (London, 1896), p. 241.

24. *Grey-Jervis*, pp. 36–39. See also C. L. Dunne, *The Chirurgical Candidate* (London, 1808), pp. 182–183.

25. See Sir Frederick Maurice, ed., *The Diary of Sir John Moore*, 2 vols. (London, 1904), 1, pp. 193–195.

26. For information about Abercrombie, see Lord Dunfermaline, *Lt. General Sir Ralph Abercrombie, K.B., 1793–1801* (Edinburgh, 1801) pp. 42–56; J. H. Hutchinson, "Memoir on the Life of the Much Lamented Lt. General Sir Ralph Abercrombie," *Miscellanies, 1760–*

*1801*, (Dublin, 1801); D.N.B., 1, pp. 43–46; and Carola Oman, *Sir John Moore* (London, 1953), pp. 132–160.

27. Rose, p. 63. See also Julian S. Corbett, ed., *Private Papers of George, Second Earl Spencer*, 1, Naval Records Society, 26 (London, 1913), pp. 150–157.

28. *Grey-Jervis*, pp. 103–107.

29. Ibid., p. 89.

30. With reference to hospital ships, Lloyd and Coulter state (3, pp. 67–69): "The use of hospital ships goes back to the sixteenth century. They were always old, slow ships seconded for such purposes, serving as prison hulks in the last stage of decay. They were never specifically built for the purpose, but were reconditioned inboard when their fighting days were over, the guns removed and the whole space of the flush decks directed to the use of the sick and their nurses. By the end of the century they carried, in addition to an executive officer . . . and a crew, a full hospital staff, consisting of a physician, a surgeon, three assistant surgeons, with landsmen as nurses, a baker, a washerman, a clerk, two servants, and sometimes a dispenser. . . . With their ancient hulls, rotting timbers, low deck space (5 feet 10½ inches) and grim atmosphere, they can never have been very salubrious craft." (Apparently no hospital ship accompanied the Abercrombie expedition.) Naval surgeons had various means of fumigating ships—burning pots of sulphur, charcoal, brimstone, or gun powder or even pots of tar or tobacco. Sometimes a mixture of vitriol and nitre was placed in a saucer to be warmed over a burning lamp.

31. Ibid., p. 66.

32. McGrigor, p. 49.

33. Robert Grant to ?, Aberdeen, February 23, 1796: "I had also a letter lately from my brother James from Barbados where he had arrived perfectly well in the 25 Dec- . . ." McGrigor Family Letters.

34. George Pinckhard, M.D., *Notes on the West Indies, including Observations Relative to the Creoles of Spain of the West Colonies and the Indians of South America, interspersed with Remarks upon the Seasoning or Yellow Fever of the Climate*, 2 vols. (London, 1816), 2nd ed., 1, p. 167.

35. Ibid., p. 98.

36. McGrigor, pp. 59–60.

37. Ibid., p. 70.

38. William Wright, *Memoir of the late William Wright, M.D.* (Edinburgh, 1828), pp. 103–106, 383–398.

39. Colin Chisholm, *Essay on the Malignant Pestilential Fever Introduced into the West India Islands from Boullam, or the Coast of Guinea as It Appeared in 1793, 1794, 1795, 1796* (London, 1801), p. 242.

40. Hector M'Lean, *An Enquiry into the Nature and Cause of the Great Mortality Among the Troops at St. Domingo* (London, 1797), pp. viii–ix.

41. Ibid., p. 214.

42. Ibid., pp. 229–230.

43. Ibid., p. 235.

44. William Lempriere, *Partial Observations on the Diseases of the Army in Jamaica As They Occurred Between the Years 1792 and 1797*, 2 vols. (London, 1799), 2, p. 4.

45. Ibid., p. 296.

46. Robert Jackson, *A Treatise on the Fevers of Jamaica With Some Observations on the Intermitting Fever of America and an Appendix Containing Some Hints on the Means of Preserving the Health of Soldiers in Hot Climates* (London, 1791). For Jackson's career, see Major H. A. L. Howell, "Robert Jackson, M.C., Inspector of Health," JRAMC, 16 (1911), 121–139.

47. Pinckhard, 2, p. 60.

48. Ibid., p. 414.

49. Cited in Maurice, 1, p. 236.

50. Cited in Beatrice Browning, *Life and Letters of Sir John Moore* (New York, 1923), p. 65.

51. W.O. 1/86, f. 5.

52. W.O. 1/85, f. 257.

53. Britain declared war on Denmark, allied to France, in 1801.

54. James, pp. 200–209. On Santo Domingo, from 1801–4, out of 25,000 men, the French lost over 20,000 men, mostly to yellow fever.

55. Edwards, 4, p. 117.

56. Ibid., 2, p. 428.

57. Chisholm, 1, p. 451.

58. Fortescue 4, pt. I, p. 565.

59. Robert Jackson, "Comparative Return of Sick of Army Serving in the Windward and Leeward Islands from 1803 to 1814," *Transactions of the Medical Society of London*, 1 (1810), 281–296.

60. M'Lean, p. xiii.

61. Concerning the use of black soldiers for duty in the West Indies, the Duke of York wrote to the king, on November 12, 1796: "Sir Ralph Abercrombie states in the strongest manner the great advantage which your Majesty's service has derived already from the few black corps which have been employed, and the great saving of British soldiers which may be made should a certain number of blacks be constantly kept in your Majesty's service. Five thousand are the number which it is wished may be kept up between the Leeward Islands, four hundred at Jamaica and five hundred at St. Domingo, but in the first instance it is proposed to procure three thousand five hundred, of whom five and twenty hundred to be stationed on the Leeward Islands, four hundred at Jamaica, and five hundred at St. Domingo, and to form them into battalions of eight companies of five hundred men each. As it is found impossible to enlist them, and as the Islands do not seem disposed to give them, it is necessary that they should be bought." A. Aspinall, *The Later Correspondence of George III*, 5 vols. (Cambridge, 1968–70), 2, p. 515.

62. A particularly significant consequence in medical history was the publication of *Observations Upon Bulam, Vomito-Negro or Yellow Fever* (1815) by William Pym. As a surgeon with the Grey expedition from 1794–96, Pym first encountered yellow fever on Martinique. Later, as superintendent of quarantine at Malta and at Gibraltar, deputy inspector of army hospitals, and eventually as president of the Board of Health on Malta during the Napoleonic wars, he continued his studies of differentiating fevers. His description "is the first clear account of the disease now known as yellow fever" (D.N.B., 16, p. 527). Pym claimed that yellow fever "is a different disease from the bilious remitting fever; that it is not produced by, nor in any way connected with marsh miasmata. . ." (Pym, *Observations*, p. 1). Furthermore, he held that yellow fever was highly infectious, that its infectious powers were increased by heat and were destroyed by cold, that it attacked natives of a warm climate in a comparatively mild form, and that like smallpox, it attacked the human frame only once. In 1828, Pym supervised quarantine procedures on Gibraltar during a plague of yellow fever. Knighted for his services, Pym in 1832 was chairman of the Central Board of Health in England during the cholera epidemic.

63. McGrigor, p. 75.

64. Ibid., pp. 76–80.

65. *The Times*, October 3, 1796, p. 3.


## IV. THE EAST INDIAN CAMPAIGN

1. For information on this episode, see James Duggan, *The Great Mutiny* (New York, 1967), pp. 55–117; and A. Temple Patterson, "The Naval Mutiny at Spithead, 1797," *The Portsmouth Papers*, 5 (1968), 3–15.

2. McGrigor, p. 90.

3. Ibid.

4. Ibid., p. 91.

5. McGrigor to David Grant, Jersey, June 27, 1797, McGrigor Family Letters.

6. McGrigor to Robert Grant, Jersey, February 10, 1798, ibid.

7. McGrigor to Robert Grant, Jersey, May 10, 1798, ibid.

8. On August 4, 1847 McGrigor bequeathed 64 volumes of his personal army medical records, the McGrigor Papers, covering a period from 1797 to 1814, which contain regi-

mental case histories, dissection reports, letter books, prescription books, registers of the weather, and drafts of his articles to the Aberdeen Medico-Chirurgical Society.

9. James Carmichael Smyth, *A Description of the Jail Distemper, As Appeared Among the Spanish Prisoners at Winchester in the Year 1790* (London, 1795); idem, *The Effect of Nitrous Vapours in Preventing and Destroying Contagions, From a Variety of Trials* (Philadelphia, 1799). For a description of this experiment aboard the *Union*, see J. J. Keevil, "Archibald Menzies, 1754–1842," Bull. Hist. Med., 22 (1948), 796–811. For a commentary on the nearly disastrous effects of this experiment with nitrous vapors on patients, see Lloyd and Coulter, 3, pp. 76–77.

10. Smyth, *Nitrous Vapours*, p. 120.

11. *Annals of Medicine*, 2 (1797), 390.

12. Ibid., 388–389.

13. Ibid., 3 (1798), 344–346.

14. Ibid., 347.

15. Ibid., 348–349.

16. McGrigor to Robert Grant, Jersey, May 10, 1798, McGrigor Family Letters.

17. The definitive account of the impact of the French Revolution upon strategy in the Indian Ocean is by C. Northcote Parkinson, *War in the Eastern Seas 1793–1815* (London, 1954).

18. W.O. 1/897, ff. 627–633.

19. Ibid., f. 637.

20. *Annals of Medicine*, 1 (1801), 353–354.

21. Ibid., 354.

22. McGrigor to Robert Grant, Cape Town, March 27, 1799, McGrigor Family Letters.

23. *Annals of Medicine*, 1 (1801), 356.

24. Ibid., 361.

25. *Edinburgh Medical and Surgical Journal*, hereafter Edin. Med. Surg. J., 1 (1805), 268–279.

26. *Annals of Medicine*, 1 (1801), 369.

27. Details on these activities are in Parkinson, pp. 156–169.

28. W.O. 1/897, f. 739. Fitzpatrick to William Huskisson, Under-Secretary of State, War Office, December 7, 1799.

29. Edin. Med. Surg. J., 1 (1805), 272.

30. McGrigor, p. 102.

31. Parkinson, p. 173; A. B. Rodgers, *The War of the Second Coalition, 1798–1808* (Oxford, 1964), p. 251. A participant in the campaign, Lt. Col. Robert Thomas Wilson (*History of the British Expedition to Egypt*, London, 1802, p. 7) stated: "The greatest misfortune was the total want of information respecting Egypt. Not a map to depend upon could be procured, and the best draught from which information could be formed and which was distributed to the generals proved ridiculously incorrect."

32. Details about the Red Sea expeditions are in Rodgers, pp. 265–268; Parkinson, pp. 173–183; Wilson, pp. 161–166; Fortescue, 4, pt. 2, 857–866; Duncan-Jones, pp. 90–163; *The Asiatic Annual Register, 1802* (London, 1803), pp. 83–86; Theodore Houk *The Life of General, the Rt. Honourable Sir David Baird Bart.* (London, 1832), pp. 237–251.

33. McGrigor, p. 107.

34. Ibid., pp. 107–109. There is a harrowing account of efforts to cure the loathsome guinea worm disease on the voyage by McGrigor's assistant Ninian Bruce, in Edin. Med. Surg. J, 2 (1806), 145–150.

35. Edin. Med. Surg. J., 1 (1805), 277.

36. McGrigor, p. 111.

37. James McGrigor, *Medical Sketches of the Expedition to Egypt from India* (London, 1804), pp. 4–5 (hereafter cited as *Sketches*).

38. For information about the desert crossing, see *Asiatic Register* (1802), pp. 84–86; Houk, pp. 301–368; and Wilson, pp. 164–166.

39. *Sketches*, p. 10.

40. Lt. Col. G. A. Kempthorne, "The Egyptian Campaign of 1801," JRAMC, 55

(1930), 221–223. I am grateful to Lt. General Sir Neil Cantlie, director general of the Army Medical Services (1948–52), for the opportunity to see a chapter on the Egyptian campaign in his manuscript on the history of the army medical department.

41. D. J. Larrey, *Relation, Historical and Surgical, of the Expedition of the Army of the Orient in Egypt and Syria,* Alexander Rose, trans., *The Military Surgeon,* 99 (1946), 330. For information on French military medicine in this period, see: E. H. Ackernecht, *Medicine at the Paris Hospital, 1794–1848* (Baltimore, 1967) pp. 25-37, 141–142; A. G. Chevalier, "Hygienic Problems of the Napoleonic Armies," *Ciba Symposium,* 3 (1941–42), 974–980; idem, "Physicians of the French Revolution," ibid., 7 (1945–46), 238–268; anon., "Dominique Jean Larrey (1766–1842)—Surgeon-in-Chief of the Grande Armée," *Journal of the American Medical Association,* 185 (1963), 104–105; anon., "Pierre François Percy," *British Medical Journal,* 1 (1905), 37–39; L. J. Bégin, *Etudes Sur le Service de Santé Militaire* (Paris, 1860); Dr. Brice and Captain Bottet, *Le Corps de Santé Militaire en France, Son Évolution, Ses Campagnes, 1708–1888* (Paris, 1907); J. Des Cilleuls, "Le Service de Santé Militaire des Origines à Nos Jours," *Revue Internationale des Services de Santé des Armées de Terre, de Mere, et de l'Air* (Paris, 1961), 1–129; idem, J. Pesme, J. Hassenforder, G. Hugonot, *Le Service de Santé Militaire* (Paris, 1961); Henry James Dible, *Napoleon's Surgeon* (London, 1970); Garrison, pp. 160–170; R. G. Dunbar, "The Introduction of the Practice of Vaccination into Napoleonic France," Bull. Hist. Med., 10 (1941), 635–650; Reginald Fitz, "Napoleon's Camp at Boulogne," *Annals of Medical History,* 2 (1919), 148–156; George Jean Granger, *Recherches Sur l'en Seignement de la Médicine Militaire à Strabourg au XVIIIe Siécle* (Strasbourg, 1967); Mme. Graux and M. Beylard, "L'Hospital des Armées Scrive de Lille," *Revue Historique de L'Armée,* 1 (1972), 88–105; J. Rieux, and J. Hassenforder, *Histoire Du Service de Santé Militaire et Val-De-Grace* (Paris, 1961), pp. 18–42; G. Rosen, "Hospitals, Medical Care and Social Policy in the French Revolution," Bull. Hist. Med., 30 (1956), 124–149; Andre Soubiran, *Le Baron Larrey, Chirugien de Napoléon* (Paris, 1966); David M. Vess, "The Collapse and Revival of Medical Education in France: A Consequence of Revolution and War, 1789–1795," *History of Education Quarterly,* 7 (1967), 71–92; Dora B. Weiner, "French Doctors Face War, 1792–1815," Charles K. Warner, ed., *From the Ancient Regime to the Popular Front* (New York, 1969), pp. 51–73; E. Robert Wiese, "Larrey, Napoleon's Chief Surgeon," *Annals of Medical History,* n.s., 1 (1929), 435–450.

42. Max Mayerhoff, "A Short History of Ophthalmia during the Egyptian Campaigns of 1798–1807," *British Journal of Ophthalmology,* 16 (1932), 140.

43. *Sketches,* p. 21.

44. Ibid., pp. 149, 153, 157.

45. Wilson, 2, p. 121.

46. Ibid., pp. 247–249.

47. Ibid., pp. 123, 253–254.

48. Mayerhoff, "A Short History . . . ," p. 143.

49. Ibid., p. 150. See also R. Fraser, "The Rise of Specialism and Special Hospitals," F. N. L. Poynter, ed., *The Evolution of Hospitals in Britain* (London, 1964), p. 173.

50. See McGrigor's comments about ophthalmia prevalent in army garrisons in England in Edin. Med. Surg. J., 3 (1807), 52–55, 395–400. See also John Vetch, *An Account of the British Army in Egypt* (London, 1807).

51. Ibid., pp. 115–117.

52. *Sketches,* p. 23.

53. Ibid., pp. 47–48.

54. Ibid., pp. 2–3, 52.

55. Bombay Military Proceedings, Z/P/3252, pp. 1412–1413, India Office Library.

56. *Sketches,* p. 55.

57. Wright, p. 143.

58. *Sketches,* p. vii. There are other medical accounts of the Egyptian campaign such as: Henry Dewar, *Observations on Diarrhea and Dysentery As Those Diseases appeared in the British Army During the Campaign in Egypt in 1801* (London, 1803).

59. Sketches, pp. vi, xiii, 68. John Huxham (1694–1768), a systematist like Hermann Boerhaave (1668–1738), wrote the famous *Essay on Fevers* (1739). George Cleghorn (1716–

1789) was the trailblazer for the army in climatological studies with his *Observations of the Epidemic Disease in Minorca* (1751).

60. *Sketches*, p. 68.
61. Ibid., pp. 71–97, passim.
62. Ibid., p. ix.
63. Ibid., pp. 56–57.
64. Ibid., p. 56.
65. Ibid., pp. 88–91.
66. Ibid., pp. 94–95.

## V. ADMINISTRATOR OF ARMY HOSPITALS

1. McGrigor, p. 151.
2. Ibid., p. 153.
3. Ibid., p. 158.
4. Ibid., p. 157.
5. Ibid., p. 160.
6. Ibid., pp. 182–184, 192–200.
7. Ibid., p. 215.
8. Ibid., p. 210.
9. Ibid., pp. 214–215.
10. Adam Neale, *The Spanish Campaign of 1808* (Edinburgh, 1828), pp. 181–185.
11. McGrigor, p. 215.
12. Christopher Hibbert, *Corunna* (London, 1967), p. 195.
13. James McGrigor, "Observations on the Fever which Appeared in the Army from Spain on Their Return to This Country in January, 1809," Edin. Med. Surg. J., 6 (1810), 9.
14. McGrigor, p. 216.
15. McGrigor, pp. 217–218. For a discussion of the Royal Hospital, Haslar, see Lloyd and Coulter, 3, pp. 207–260.
16. McGrigor, "Observations," 20. That not all of McGrigor's subordinates were such fine examples of the medical profession is indicated in his letter to Major General Arthur Whethan, lieutenant governor of Plymouth, May 13, 1809, regarding the conduct of Assistant Surgeon John Caldwell of the 8th Royal Veteran Battalion: "it really will be an act of cruelty to the soldiers . . . to leave them to him for a single hour more. . . . Mr. Caldwell has been drunk in every situation and at every hour of the day. At a time when sobriety was particularly required from him in addition to the sick of his own battalion, he had charge of some of the sick from Spain, who were in a state of distress at that time, I found him badly drunk in the hospital at an early hour of the morning." Correspondence Book # 2160, pp. 280–281, McGrigor Papers.
17. W.O. 1/641, ff. 23–41, passim.
18. There is information about the board's policies in the following: W.O. 1/711, f. 1 (hospital corps); 7/101, ff. 18–20 (on surgeon's pay); 1/896, ff. 183–184 (mates' pay); 7/104, f. 58 (on medical returns); 7/103, ff. 85–86; 7/104, ff. 121–122 (quarantine procedures); 7/104, f. 101 (surgeon's kit); 7/105, f. 26 (standard pharmacopiae); 7/106, f. 129 (barracks). There is additional information scattered in 40/12, 40/13, and 40/20. Data on the hospital inspection system is contained in letters from Keate to the Horse Guards in 1798–99 (# 14566, 15166, 1602, 17566, 1661, 1602c, 1538b, 1946b), the Earl Grey Papers. See copies of instructions to regimental surgeons, diet tables, and regimental chest of medicines cited in JRAMC, 60 (1933), 141–149, 222–228; and G. A. Kempthorne, "The Army Medical Service at Home and Abroad, 1803–1808," JRAMC, 61 (1933), 144–146.
19. A copy of the Royal Warrant is in Fifth Report of the Commissioners of Military Inquiry—Army Medical Department, P.P., 1808 (6) V, 1, 96–97, Appendix # 3 (hereafter cited as *Fifth Report*).
20. Robert Jackson, *A Letter to the Commissioners of Military Inquiry; Explaining the Con-*

*stitution of a Medical Staff, the Best Form of Economy for Hospitals* . . . (London, 1808), p. 12.

21. W.O. 1/641, ff. 31–33, 46.

22. For summaries of Jackson's career, see H. A. L. Howell, "Robert Jackson, M.D., Inspector of Hospitals," JRAMC, 16 (1911), 121–239; *Gentlemen's Magazine*, 97, I, (1827), 566; Edin. Med. and Surg. J., 29 (1829), 110–118; Leroy Crummer, "Robert Jackson, M.D., Late Inspector-General of Army Hospitals," *The Military Surgeon*, 3, (1935), 425–431. There are reports about Jackson and some of his letters to the board in W.O. 30/83, ff. 116–126 and in W.O. 40/16, passim. See also Papers relating to the Army Medical Board, P.P., 1810 (101), XIV, 244, Appendix #8 (hereafter cited as *Army Medical Board*).

23. *Fifth Report*, p. 79.

24. Ibid., p. 80.

25. Ibid., p. 82. For an account of the Ordnance Medical Corps see John Rollo, *A Short Account of the Royal Artillery Hospital at Woolwich* (London, 1801). See also John Bell, *A Memorial Concerning the Present State of Military and Naval Surgery* (London, 1800), pp. 2–39, in which the author calls for the establishment of an army medical college.

26. Edward N. Bancroft, *A Letter to the Commissioners of Military Inquiry Containing Animadversions on Some Parts of the Fifth Report and an Examination of the Principles on the Medical Department of Armies* . . . (London, 1808), pp. 2–91, passim.

27. (London, 1808), pp. 8, 37.

28. W.O. 1/641, ff. 181–182, June 23, 1809.

29. Ibid., ff. 199–204. The Board of General Officers consisted of the following: Lt.-General Sir Thomas Trigge, Lt.-General Oliver De Lancey, Lt.-General Robert Brownrigg, Major-General Harry Calvert, and Lt.-General James Willoughby Gordon.

30. Letter, August 6, 1808, McGrigor Family Letters.

31. McGrigor, pp. 226–227.

## VI. THE EXPEDITION TO THE SCHELDT

1. There are accounts of this expedition in Fortescue, 7, pp. 61–96; Chaplin, pp. 91–99; T. H. McGuffie, "The Walcheren Expedition and the Walcheren Fever," *English Historical Review*, 62 (1947), 191–202; Anthony Brett-James, "The Walcheren Failure," *History Today*, 13 (1964), 811–820, and 14 (1964), 60–69; and G. A. Kempthorne, "The Walcheren Expedition and the Reform of the Medical Board," JRAMC, 62 (1934), 133–138. There are six volumes of Parliamentary Papers on this subject: Scheldt Expedition, 1810, vi, 6 (P.P., Sch., vi, 6); Scheldt Expedition, 1810, vii, 7 (P.P., Sch., vii, 7); Scheldt Expedition, 1810, viii, 8 (P.P., Sch., viii, 8); Expedition to the Scheldt, 1810, i (P.P., Sch., i); Scheldt, 1810, ii (P.P., Sch., ii); Scheldt, 1810, v (P.P., Sch., v). (Note that this is not the usual citation for P.P.; like a writer for the *English Historical Review* who used these papers, I have used page numbers in order to clarify the citations.)

2. Lt. Colonel St. Clair, *A Soldier's Recollection of the West Indies and Americas with a Narrative of the Expedition to the Island of Walcheren*, 2 vols. (London, 1814), 2, p. 282.

3. P.P., Sch., vi, 6, pp. 16–17.

4. Cited in Brett-James, p. 62.

5. P.P., Sch., vii, 7, p. 51; ibid., vi, 6, p. 84.

6. For contemporary accounts by the medical staff, see McGrigor, pp. 226–250; G. P. Dawson, *Observations on the Walcheren Disease* (Ipswich, 1810); J. B. Davis, *A Scientific and Popular View of the Walcheren Fever* (London, 1812); and G. Hargrove, *An Account of the Island of Walcheren and South Beveland against which the British Expedition Proceeded in 1809* (Dublin, 1812).

7. Hargrove, pp. 53–54, 63, 70, 77.

8. P.P., Sch., vi, 6, p. 17.

9. Richard Feibel, "What Happened at Walcheren: The Primary Sources," Bull. Hist. Med., 42 (1968), 64–65.

10. P.P., Sch., vi, 6, pp. 140–141.

11. Ibid., pp. 14–15.

12. Thomas Wright, *History of the Walcheren Remittent Fever* (London, 1811), p. xv.

13. P.P., Sch., vi, 6, pp. 9, 80.

14. Ibid., pp. 6–7, 80.

15. Ibid., vii, 7, p. 46.

16. Ibid., pp. 46–47.

17. Ibid., p. 47.

18. Ibid., p. 53.

19. Ibid., pp. 48–49, 53.

20. Ibid., pp. 47–48.

21. Ibid., vi, 6, pp. 107–110.

22. McGrigor, p. 228.

23. Ibid., pp. 233–239.

24. Ibid., p. 240.

25. McGrigor to Coote, September 18, Middleburgh, Letter Book 2167, p. 16, McGrigor Papers.

26. McGrigor, p. 241.

27. McGrigor to Brig. General ?, October 4, Letter Book 2167, p. 42, McGrigor Papers.

28. McGrigor to Coote, October 4, ibid., p. 39.

29. P.P., Sch., vi, 6, pp. 23–25.

30. McGrigor to Surgeon-General, October 3, Letter Book 2167, pp. 38–39, McGrigor Papers.

31. P.P., Sch., vi, 6, pp. 27–28.

32. McGrigor to Surgeon-General, November 14, Letter Book 2167, pp. 116–117, McGrigor Papers.

33. McGrigor to General Don, November 14, ibid., p. 220.

34. P.P., Sch., vi, 6, pp. 109–110.

35. McGrigor, p. 244.

36. P.P., Sch., i, sup. 4.

37. McGrigor, pp. 248–250.

38. Papers Relating to the Formation of the New Army Medical Department, P.P., 1810 (101), 14, 23–25, 157.

39. McGrigor, p. 253. For the "Regulations for the Conduct of the whole Medical Board of the Army . . . , 24 February, 1810," see Papers Relating to the Formation of the New Army Medical Department, P.P., 1810 (101), 14, 157, 2–22. That McGrigor may have been a candidate for the new Medical Board is suggested by letters written in November and December, 1809 found in W.O. 4/409, ff. 54, 102, 104. Sir William Franklin replaced Dr. Theodore Gordon on July 12, 1810. Sir Charles Ker, who retired on December 28, 1815, was not replaced.

40. There are letters to McGrigor from the Medical Board about its directives in W.O. 7/107, ff. 19, 23, 48–49, 65, 76–77, 97, 112, 179. McGrigor's answers to the board from April 4, 1810 to November 16, 1810 on various administrative matters are in Letter Book 2161, McGrigor Papers.

41. McGrigor to Mrs. Grant, September 13, 1811, McGrigor Family Letters. Mary Grant had many brothers who joined the armed forces. One, Sir James Grant, was Arthur Wellesley's principal medical officer at Waterloo. Another, McGrigor's more famous brother-in-law, Lt. Colonel Colquhoun Grant, is the subject of a lively and well researched biography. See Jock Haswell, *The First Respectable Spy, The Life and Times of Colquhoun Grant, Wellington's Head of Intelligence* (London, 1969).

42. McGrigor, p. 252.

43. W.O. 7/107, f. 337.

44. McGrigor, p. 254.

## VII. WITH WELLINGTON IN THE PENINSULA

1. See Leo M. Zimmerman and Ilza Veith, *Great Ideas in the History of Surgery* (New York, 1967), pp. 388–772; Sir Thomas Longmore, *Treatise on the Transport of Sick and Wounded*

*Troops* (London, 1869), 26–35; and Dora W. Weiner, "French Doctors Face War, 1792–1815," Charles K. Wagner, ed., *From the Ancient Regime to the Popular Front* (New York, 1969), pp. 51–73.

2. Fergusson, p. 62. I have attempted to trace Fergusson's career as deputy inspector of hospitals in Beresford's Portuguese army through two documentary collections—the Fergusson Papers in the Royal Army Medical College and the Fergusson Papers in the Historical Library, Yale Medical Library. But the evidence is too fragmentary for a coherent account about Portuguese medical services. However, there is some information in Andrew Halliday, *The Present State of Portugal and of the Portuguese Army* (Edinburgh, 1812); Robert Southey, *History of the Peninsular War*, 6 vols. (London, 1827), 4, pp. 356–363; and Manuel R. F. Giao, "British Surgeons in the Portuguese Army during the Peninsular War," JRAMC, 62 (1934), 299–303.

3. Book 1, p. 3, McGrigor Papers.

4. James Elkington, *The Journal of James Goodall Elkington, Assistant Surgeon*, 2 vols. in mss., vol. 1, October 13, 1810, Library, Royal Army Medical College.

5. Cited in G. A. Kempthorne, "The Medical Department of Wellington's Army, 1809–1814," JRAMC, 54 (1930), 65–72, 131–146, 213–220.

6. W.O. 7/109, f. 134, February 14, 1811.

7. Ibid., f. 134, July 9, 1811.

8. Walter Henry, *Events of a Military Life*, 2 vols. (London, 1843), 1, p. 16.

9. John Donaldson, *Recollections of the Eventful Life of a Soldier* (London, 1856), p. 149.

10. William Grattan, *Adventures of the Connaught Rangers from 1808 to 1814*, 2 vols. (London, 1847), 1, pp. 104–105.

11. Kempthorne, p. 144.

12. Lt. Col. John Gurwood, comp., *The Dispatches of Field Marshal the Duke of Wellington*, 12 vols. (London, 1834–38), hereafter Dispatches, 5, p. 276.

13. Ibid., 6, p. 531.

14. Ibid., 5, pp. 329–330.

15. Ibid., 7, p. 256.

16. Ibid., 8, p. 302. For accounts of Wellington's strategic problems, see Jac Weller, *Wellington in the Peninsula, 1808–1814* (London, 1962); Michael Glover, *Wellington's Peninsula Victories* (New York, 1963); and D. J. Goodspeed, *The British Campaign in the Peninsula, 1808–1814* (London, 1958). The administration of Wellington's army is described by G. Davies, *Wellington and His Army* (London, 1954); and by S. G. P. Ward, *Wellington's Headquarters* (London, 1957).

17. W.O. 7/109, ff. 19–25, 32–35, 44, 70–74, 108–109.

18. Ibid., f. 69.

19. Cited in Kempthorne, p. 146.

20. Dispatches, 8, p. 365.

21. Book 1, Journal of Events, p. 1, McGrigor Papers.

22. McGrigor, pp. 256–257.

23. Book 1, p. 1, McGrigor Papers.

24. Ibid., pp. 7, 12–13.

25. Letter Book 2166, pp. 257–259, March 6, 1812, ibid.

26. Book 1, p. 3, McGrigor Papers.

27. McGrigor, pp. 257–259.

28. Ibid., p. 153.

29. Ibid., p. 259.

30. Ibid., p. 260.

31. Book 1, p. 49, McGrigor Papers.

32. McGrigor, p. 263.

33. McGrigor, ibid.

34. Ibid., pp. 263–264.

35. Ibid., p. 265; Book 1, p. 49, McGrigor Papers.

36. Book 2, p. 11, ibid. There is a request by McGrigor in Letter Book 2156, pp. 264–265, March 14, 1812, and p. 296, March 18, 1812 from Elvas to the commissary general for litter-bearers.

37. McGrigor, pp. 267–268.

38. Book 2, p. 46, McGrigor Papers.

39. McGrigor, p. 273.

40. Ibid., p. 274.

41. Ibid., p. 275.

42. McGrigor to Grant, April 8, 1812, Badajoz, McGrigor Family Letters.

43. McGrigor, pp. 278–279.

44. Ibid., p. 279.

45. Ibid., p. 297.

46. Letter Book 2166, pp. 257–259, McGrigor Papers.

47. Letter Book 3, pp. 6, 93, ibid.

48. Ibid., p. 82.

49. Ibid., p. 94.

50. Ibid., p. 129.

51. Letter Book, 2165, pp. 39–40, 44–45, ibid.

52. Dispatches, 9, p. 234.

53. Ibid., pp. 221–222.

54. McGrigor, p. 300.

55. Letter Book 2165, p. 72, McGrigor Papers.

56. McGrigor, p. 142.

57. McGrigor, p. 302.

58. Ibid., p. 303.

59. Ibid., pp. 204–206.

60. Ibid., pp. 306–307.

61. Ibid., pp. 310–311.

62. Ibid., pp. 313–314.

63. W.O. 1/256, f. 178, November 19, 1812, Ciudad Rodrigo.

64. Letter Book 2165, pp. 177–178, Castello Bom 24 December, 1812, McGrigor Papers.

65. James McGrigor, "Sketch of the Medical History of the British Armies in the Peninsula of Spain and Portugal During the Late Campaign," *Medico-Chirurgical Transactions*, 6 (1815), 387.

66. McGrigor, p. 321.

67. Ibid., p. 325.

68. Letter Book 2165, p. 161, 2 December, 1812, Castello Bom, McGrigor Papers.

69. McGrigor, pp. 322–323.

70. Letter Book 2165, p. 210, January 13, 1813, Castello Bom, McGrigor Papers.

71. Ibid., p. 211, January 13, 1813.

72. McGrigor, "Sketch of the Medical History," p. 388.

73. Letter Book 2165, pp. 216–217, February 7, 1813, Castello Bom, McGrigor Papers.

74. Dispatches, 10, p. 109, 10 February, 1813, Freneda.

75. McGrigor, p. 328.

76. Dispatches, 10, p. 400, May 25, 1813, Matilla.

77. Letter Book 2165, pp. 74–75, McGrigor Papers.

78. Ibid., pp. 145, 147, November 8, 1812.

79. Ibid., pp. 177–181, December 24, 1812.

80. Ibid., pp. 191–192, December 30, 1812.

81. Dispatches, 9, p. 451, September 27, 1812, Villa Toro.

82. Ibid., p. 633.

83. Johnston's Roll, 1, pp. 112, 137.

84. Book 12, pp. 10–12, May 1813, McGrigor Papers.

85. Letter Book 2157, p. 82, August 20, 1813, ibid.

86. Cited in "Letter to the Rt. Hon. the Secretary of War on the Medical Department of the Army from Sir George Ballingall," JRAMC, 42 (1924), 380.

87. Sir George Larpent, ed., *The Private Journal of F. S. Larpent, Esq., Judge-Advocate General of the British Forces in the Peninsula*, 3 vols. (London, 1853), 1, pp. 244–249.

88. Cited by Kempthorne, p. 216.

89. McGrigor to General Thomas Graham, Mss. 3611, f. 265, National Library of Scotland, hereafter Nat. Lib. Scot.

90. Letter Book 2157, pp. 148–149, McGrigor Papers.

91. George James Guthrie, *Commentaries on the Surgery of the War with Portugal, Spain, France, and the Netherlands from the Battle of Rolica, in 1808, to that of Waterloo, in 1815 with Additions Relating to those in the Crimea in 1854–1855* (London, 1855), p. 146.

92. Dispatches, 11, pp. 446–447, January 14, St. Jean de Luz.

93. McGrigor, "Sketch of the Medical History," p. 298. Although McGrigor provided casualty figures from combat and disease for the British army in the Peninsula from January, 1812, to May, 1814, only one other source estimates the casualty rate from August, 1808, through December, 1811. W. Barwick Hodge, "On the Mortality arising from Military Operations," *Journal of the Royal Statistical Society*, 19 (1856), 219–231 (hereafter J. Royal Stat. Soc.) states that from 1793 to 1815 in the British army 5,605 officers and 84,791 troops were killed or wounded, but provides no break-down of figures for deaths due to disease or casualties for the Peninsular War. David Stewart, *Sketches of the Character, Manners, and Present State of the Highlanders of Scotland* (Edinburgh, 1822), 2 vols., explains in the appendix to vol. 2 that 7,872 soldiers (rank and file, drummers, sergeants) were killed during the Peninsular War and that 36,961 were wounded, but he neglects to list figures for deaths from sickness. Garrison (p. 167) states: "The death-rate during 1808–1814 was 118/1,000 . . . ." Then, apparently using McGrigor's exact figures, Garrison adds in the same sentence: "the total losses 24,930 out of 61,511 for disease and 8,889 from battle casualties." Gore (p. 162) remarks: "The mean strength in the Peninsula of officers and men for forty-one months ending May, 1814 (i.e. from January, 1811, to May, 1814) was 66,772; the deaths during the same period numbered 35,535, of which 9,948 fell in battle or died of wounds; 225 per thousand of the 61,511 men were on the average on the sick list and the annual mortality was the rate of 161 per thousand." The best analysis of casualty rates for the Peninsular War came from T. R. Edmonds, "On the Mortality and Sickness of Soldiers Engaged in War," *Lancet*, 2 (1837–38), 143–148, who claimed that "the numbers killed and wounded during the years 1808, 1809, and 1810, did not amount to more than a sixth part of the number killed and wounded during the remaining period of the war" (p. 149). Edmonds added that the average strength of the British army in the Peninsular for the first three years was 30,000 and for the last three years and five months was 61,511. He estimated that about 22½ percent of the rank and file were absent from duty due to sickness, that sickness from wounds amounted to only 1½ percent, and that a rough comparison between deaths and sickness was one death to every two sick soldiers. Major Greenwood, "British Loss of Life in the Wars of 1794–1815 and in 1914–1918," J. Royal Stat. Soc., 105 (1942), 1–16, generalizes that "the cost to the armed forces of the country [including Waterloo and the naval battles] was, in round numbers, 64,000 for the Navy, 144,600 for the Army, 210,000 lives. In the Navy deaths from diseases (excess deaths over peace-time rates) more than doubled the losses from enemy action, in the Army they were eight times as numerous" (p. 4). For comparison of casualty rates by specific major battles for the French and for the Allied armies, see Gaston Bodart, *Losses of Life in Modern Wars* (Oxford, 1916), pp. 105–119.

94. Letter Book 2157, p. 363, McGrigor Papers.

95. Guthrie stated in his famous book on military surgery (p. x) that "the precepts laid down [in this work] are the result of the experiences acquired in the war in the Peninsula . . . which altered, nay overturned, nearly all those which existed previously to that period, on all points to which they relate."

96. McGrigor, p. 353.

## VIII. WATERLOO

1. McGrigor, p. 353.
2. Ibid., p. 357.
3. Dispatches, 12, p. 75.
4. McGrigor, pp. 357-363.
5. Ibid., p. 359.
6. Ibid., p. 364.
7. Dispatches, 12, p. 358. The bibliography on the Waterloo campaign is enormous. I have relied upon: Longford, 393–491; Fortescue, vol. 10, passim, 232–241; Dispatches, vol. 12; Supplementary Dispatches, vols. 10, 11; Sutherland, passim; John Naylor, *Waterloo* (London, 1960); David Howarth, *Waterloo: Day of Battle* (New York, 1968); Jac Weller, *Wellington at Waterloo* (New York, 1968); Anthony Brett-James, ed., *The Hundred Days* (New York, 1964); idem, ed., *Edward Costello, The Peninsular and Waterloo Campaigns* (New York, 1968); Edith Saunders, *The Hundred Days* (New York, 1964); Michael Glover, *Wellington as Military Commander* (New York, 1968); B. H. Liddell Hart, ed., *The Letters of Private Wheeler, 1809–1828* (Boston, 1951); John Selby, ed., *Thomas Morris, The Peninsular and Waterloo Campaigns* (New York, 1968); A. Euan Smith, ed., *Henry Houssaye, 1815—Waterloo*, 3 vols., 26th ed. (London, 1895–1905); John Kincaid; *Adventures in the Rifle Brigade, in the Peninsula, France, and in the Netherlands, from 1809 to 1815* (London, 1892); S. C. I .Wood, ed., *William Hay, Reminiscences, 1808–1815 Under Wellington* (London, 1901); William Siborne, *History of the Waterloo Campaign*, 2 vols. (London, 1844); James Tomkinson, ed., *The Diary of a Cavalry Officer in the Peninsula and Waterloo Campaigns, 1809–1816* (London, 1894); Cavalié Mercer, *Journal Kept Through the Campaign of 1815* (London, 1870); Edward Cotton, *A Voice from Waterloo* (London, 1849).
8. Dispatches, 10, p. 69.
9. George James Guthrie, *Treatise on Gun-Shot Wounds*, 2nd ed. (London, 1820), p. vi. For information about the medical aspects of Waterloo, see: G. A. Kempthorne, "The Waterloo Campaign," JRAMC, 60 (1933), 204–207; H. A. Howell, "The British Medical Arrangements During the Waterloo Campaign," *Proceedings of the Royal Society of Medicine, Section on Medical History*, 17 (1923–24), 39–50; J. M. Matheson "Comments on Medical Aspects of the Battle of Waterloo," *Medical History*, hereafter Med. Hist., 10 (1966), 52–58; H. E. R. Stephens, "The Influence of Wars on the Craft of Surgery," JRAMC, 62 (1934), 40–46; Owen H. Wangensteen, Jacqueline Smith, and Sarah D. Wangensteen, "Some Highlights in the History of Amputation Reflecting Lessons in Wound Healing," Bull. Hist. Med., 41 (1967), 97–123; anon., "Waterloo," *British Medical Journal*, 1(1915), 1050; H. P. Elkington, "Some Episodes in the Life of James Goodall Elkington," JRAMC, 16 (1911), 79–104; Howarth, pp. 149–155, 210–221; Naylor, pp. 180–191; Guthrie, *Commentaries*, pp. 1–188; Dispatches, vol. 8; Supplementary Dispatches, vol. 10; *General Orders, the Duke of Wellington*, 9 vols. (London, 1818), vol. 7; Charles Dalton, *The Waterloo Roll Call*, 2nd ed., (London, 1971), pp. 231–233; Anthony Bowlby, *The Hunterian Oration on British Military Surgery in the Time of Hunter and the Great War* (London, 1919), pp. 5–36; Hennen, pp. 235–240; C. A. Eaton, *Narrative of a Residence in Belgium During the Campaign of 1815* (London, 1817); B. R. Ward, ed., *A Week at Waterloo in 1815. Lady De Lancey's Narrative* (London, 1906); John Thomson, *Report of Observations Made in the British Military Hospitals in Belgium after the Battle of Waterloo* (Edinburgh, 1816); anon., *Narrative of a Residence in Belgium during the Campaign of 1815* (London, 1817); R. D. Gibney, ed., *Eighty Years Ago, or the Recollections of an Old Army Doctor* (London, 1896); Jane Vansittart, *Surgeon James's Journal* (London, 1964); Charles Bell, *Letters of Sir Charles Bell Selected from His Correspondence with His Brother George Joseph Bell* (London, 1870); Gordon Gordon-Taylor, and E. W. Walls, *Sir Charles Bell, His Life and Times* (Edinburgh, 1965), pp. 87–95, 190–199. There is some data in W.O. 1/856, f. 133; 1/661, f. 89; and 3/609, f. 223.
10. Cited by Longford p. 421.
11. Brett-James, *Costello*, p. 151.

12. Selby, p. 67.

13. Vansittart, p. 20.

14. Gibney, p. 195.

15. Cited by Naylor, p. 173.

16. Ibid., pp. 172–173. Comparative British losses from major Peninsular battles (which provide some conception of the difficulties encountered by the medical department at Waterloo) are: Talavera (5,365), Albuera (4,159), Badajoz (2,983), Salamanca (3,187), Vitoria (3,475), and Toulouse (4,568). Weller, *Peninsula*, pp. 204, 359.

17. Ibid., p. 175. "The paralysis of the army in the dark," writes Howarth, "seems strange in retrospect. Wellington, who rode back across the battlefield, and then sat down to his dinner and went to sleep, gave no order and made no suggestion about the wounded until the following evening. Nor did any other senior officer, so far as can be known." p. 210.

18. Wood, p. 202.

19. Gibney, p. 200.

20. Isaac James to Robert James, Brussels, 29 June, 1815, Muniment Room, Royal Army Medical Corps Library.

21. Vansittart, p. 35.

22. Anon., *A Narrative*, p. 157.

23. Elkington, p. 99.

24. Bell, pp. 246–247.

25. Brett–James, *Costello*, p. 153.

26. Cited by Brett-James, *Hundred Days*, p. 196.

27. Wood, p. 209.

28. Cited by Brett-James, *Hundred Days*, pp. 201–202.

29. Brett-James, *Costello*, p. 155.

30. James Simpson, *Paris After Waterloo* (London, 1853), p. 4.

31. Cited by Dible, p. 238.

32. Ibid., pp. 240–242.

33. For Guthrie, see the unsigned articles in D.N.B., 8, pp. 818–819; *Lancet*, 1 (1850) 726–736; *British Journal of Surgery*, 3 (1915), 5–7; *Journal of the American Medical Association*, 200 (1967), 408–409.

34. Guthrie, *Treatise*, p. vi.

35. Dible, p. 119.

36. Ibid., p. 121.

37. Cited by Naylor, p. 178.

38. Wood, p. 70.

39. Matheson, p. 206.

40. Cited in Gordon Gordon-Taylor and Walls, p. 94.

41. Guthrie, *Commentaries*, p. 154.

42. Edin. Med. Surg. J., 12 (1816), p. 221.

43. Howell, p. 56.

44. Howarth, pp. 153–154.

45. Ibid., p. 154.

46. Marquess of Anglesey, *One-Leg, The Life and Letters of Henry William Paget, 1st Marquess of Anglesey* (London, 1961), p. 150.

47. Cited by Longford, p. 483.

48. Brett-James, *Costello*, p. 156.

49. Guthrie, *Commentaries*, p. vi.

50. Thomson, pp. 7–25.

51. Cited by Brett-James, *Hundred Days*, p. 183.

52. Wood, pp. 76–77.

53. Cited by Longford, p. 485.

## IX. McGRIGOR'S POST-WATERLOO REFORMS

1. Erwin H. Ackerknecht, *Medicine at the Paris Hospital, 1794–1848* (Baltimore, 1967), pp. 18–19. I am indebted to the author for the ideas which I have summarized in this paragraph.

2. S. W. F. Holloway, "Medical Education in England, 1830–1858: A Sociological Analysis," *History*, 49 (1964), 195.

3. Richard H. Shryock, "Medicine and Public Health," Guy S. Métraux and François Crouzet, eds., *The Nineteenth-Century World* (New York, 1963), pp. 198–203.

4. Edin. Med. Surg. J., 3 (1817), pp. 124–125.

5. William Munro, *Records of Service and Campaigning in Many Lands*, 2 vols. (London, 1887), I, p. 5.

6. W.O. 43/23, #8223, f. 4. July 2, 1830.

7. Edin. Med. Surg. J., 62 (1844), 1–7; McGrigor to Tufnell, December, 1846, Item #233, Muniment Room, Royal Army Medical Corps Library.

8. *Lancet*, 2 (1850), 427.

9. Sketch of the Duties of the Medical Department, W.O. 43/57, ff. 18–20.

10. Original Minute Books of Officers Benevolent Society; Report of the Army Medical Officers Benevolent Society, 22 May, 1828, Muniment Room, Royal Army Medical Corps Library.

11. Edin. Med. Surg. J., 38 (1832), 223–224; *A Catalogue of the Library of the Army Medical Department* (London, 1833).

12. Edin. Med. Surg. J., 38 (1832), 221–222.

13. Letters to Sir James McGrigor, bound volume, unnumbered, presented June, 1836, Muniment Room, Royal Army Medical Corps Library.

14. McGrigor to Grey, July 27, 1837, Earl Grey Papers.

15. McGrigor to Aberdeen Medico-Chirurgical Society, August 4, 1847, McGrigor Papers.

16. McGrigor, p. 94.

17. Medical Sketches, pp. 52–53.

18. For a summary of Marshall's influence on military medicine, see my article, "Henry Marshall (1775–1851) and the Health of the British Army," Med. Hist. 14 (1970), 260–276.

19. Statistical Report on the Sickness, Mortality, and Invaliding among the Troops in the West Indies, P.P., 1837–38, X, 417, pp. 5–77.

20. Ibid., p. 84.

21. Ibid., p. 101.

22. Ibid., p. 102.

23. Ibid., p. 103.

24. Ibid., appendix, 2–7.

25. Edin. Med. Surg. J., 50 (1838), 466.

26. *Lancet*, 2 (1837–1838), 575.

27. *Times*, August 29, 1838, p. 6.

28. *Quarterly Review*, 66 (1840), 116.

29. *United Service Journal*, 2 (1864), 406.

30. McGrigor, pp. 381–382.

31. Statistical Report . . . among the Troops in the United Kingdom, the Mediterranean, and British North America, P.P., 1839 (166), XIV, 129; Statistical Report . . . among the Troops in Western Africa, St. Helena, Cape of Good Hope, and Mauritius, ibid., 1840 (228) XXX, 135; and Statistical Report . . . among Her Majesty's Troops serving in Ceylon, the Tenasserin Provinces, and the Burmese Empire, ibid., 1842 (358), XXVII, 147.

32. McGrigor, p. 96.

33. *General Regulations and Orders for the Army* (London, 1816), p. 6.

34. Report . . . Promotion and Retirement, p. 278.

35. Ibid.

36. London *Gazette* of 1831, pp. 402–404. There is evidence about McGrigor's frustrated

efforts to obtain a peerage in 1825–26 in his letters to the Duke of York and to Lord Liverpool in Additional Manuscripts, British Museum, hereafter Mus. Add. Mss. 38301, ff. 121–127, 265.

37. Report . . . Promotion and Retirement, p. 268.
38. Ibid., p. 205.
39. Ibid., p. 271.
40. Ibid., p. 279.
41. Ibid., p. lxii. Other generals on the commission were Rowland Hill, Richard Vivian, Henry Hardinge, A. Dickson, and James Kempt.
42. Hansard, *Parliamentary Debates*, 3rd Ser., 79, April 4, 1845, cols. 219–221 (hereafter cited as Hansard).
43. Ibid., 91, April 12, 1847, cols. 697, 700–707.
44. Ibid., 106, June 21, 1849, cols. 640–643.
45. Wellington to Grey, December 8, 1849, Earl Grey Papers (copy).
46. Grey to Wellington, February 12, 1850, and April 18, 1850 (copy), ibid. For an explanation of the classes of the Most Honourable Order of the Bath, see Charles M. Clode, *The Military Forces of the Crown, Their Administration and Government*, 2 vols. (London, 1869), 2, pp. 556–564.
47. *Lancet*, 2 (1848), 77.
48. Ibid., 2 (1849), 43.
49. Ibid., 2 (1850), 240. There is a summary of this development by J. B. Neal, "The Honorary Physicians and Surgeons to the Soverign," JRAMC, 97 (1951), 183–191.
50. McGrigor, p. 389.
51. Hansard, 115, March 28, 1851, col. 750.
52. For commentaries on McGrigor's career and retirement, see *Lancet*, II (1850), 424–431; *Gentleman's Magazine*, n.s., 4 (1858), 554–555; T. J. Pettigrew, *Medical Portrait Gallery*, 4 vols. (London, n.d.), 4, p. 9; *British Medical Journal*, 2 (1914), 187–188.
53. Cited by Percival R. Kirby, *Sir Andrew Smith, M.D., K.C.B., His Life, Letters and Work* (Capetown, 1965), p. 320.
54. Ibid., p. 312.
55. Maurice Marston, *Sir Edwin Chadwick* (London, 1925), p. 96.
56. The official name for the Duke of Buccleuch's commission was the Royal Commission to inquire into the State of Large Towns and Populous Districts.
57. Papers Relating to the Sanitary State of the People of England, P.P., XLVII (1858).
58. Hansard, 130, col. 1409.
59. I have found no references to military medicine (until after the Crimea) in the following works: Marston; S. E. Finer, *The Life and Times of Edwin Chadwick* (London, 1952); Richard Albert Lewis, *Edwin Chadwick and the Public Health Movement, 1832–1854* (London, 1952); Michael W. Flinn, ed., *Edwin Chadwick. Report on the Sanitary Condition of the Labouring Population of Great Britain* (Edinburgh, 1965); Dorsey Dee Jones, *Edwin Chadwick and the Early Public Health Movement in England* (Des Moines, 1931); F. N. L. Poynter, "Thomas Southwood Smith—the Man (1788–1861)," *Proceedings of the Royal Society of Medicine*, 55 (1962), 381–392; John Simon, *Public Health Reports, First Annual Report, 1849*, 2 vols. (London, 1887); C. Fraser Brockington, *A Short History of Public Health* (London, 1966); Lambert Royston, *Sir John Simon, 1816–1904, and English Social Administration* (London, 1966); Major Greenwood, *Some Pioneers of Social Medicine* (London, 1948); M. E. M. Walker, *Pioneers of Public Health* (London, 1930); E. Asher Underwood, "The Field Workers in the English Public Health Movement, 1847–1875," *Bulletin of the Society of Medical History*, 6 (1948), 31–48; Jeanne L. Brand, "John Simon and the Local Government Board Bureaucrats, 1871–1876," Bull. Hist. Med. 37 (1963), 184–194; W. J. Bishop and G. Bishop, comps., *A Bio-Bibliography of Florence Nightingale* (London, 1962).
60. Finer, p. 491. However, Chadwick was instrumental in staffing the Crimean Sanitary Commission (1855).
61. C. E. Vulliamy, *Crimea, The Campaign of 1854–1856* (London, 1939), p. 341.
62. For Herbert's career, see Lord Stanmore, *Sidney Herbert, Lord Herbert of Lea*, 2 vols. (London, 1906).

63. For Nightingale's influence, see Zachary Cope, *Florence Nightingale and the Doctors* (Philadelphia, 1959); Lucy Ridgeley Seymer, *Selected Writings of Florence Nightingale* (New York, 1954); Cecil Woodham-Smith, *Florence Nightingale, 1820–1910* (New York, 1950); idem, *The Reason Why* (New York, 1952). For some of Nightingale's writing on the subject, see her *Army Sanitary Administration and Its Reform Under the Late Lord Herbert* (London, 1862); *Notes on Hospitals* (London, 1859); *Mortality of the British Army at Home, at Home and Abroad and During the Russian War as Compared with the Mortality of the Civil Population* (London, 1858); *Notes on Matters Affecting the Health, Efficiency, and Hospital Administration of the British Army* (London, 1858).

64. Apparently the first inquiry into army living quarters was compiled by the Committee on Barracks Accommodation for the Army, P.P., XXXVII (1855). Other Parliamentary Papers on the subject are: Report from the Select Committee on the Army Before Sebastapol, IX (1854–55); Proceedings of the Sanitary Commission Dispatched to the Seat of the War in the East, IX, Sess. I, (1857). The Herbert-Nightingale Commission was officially titled Report of the Commissioners Appointed to inquire into the Regulations Affecting the Sanitary Condition of the Army, the Organization of Military Hospitals and the Treatment of Sick and Wounded, XXXIII (1857–58). See also the Health of the Army in Turkey and in the Crimea, XXXVIII (1857–58); the Royal Commission on Improving the Sanitary Condition of Barracks and Hospitals, XVI (1861); Royal Commission on the Sanitary State of the Army (East India), XIX (1863); A Bill for the Prevention of Contagious Disease, I (1864), 473; and A Bill for the Further Prevention of Contagious Diseases, II (1866), 219; etc.

65. McGrigor was appointed to a provisional board of health on June 21, 1831, but the board's functions were terminated in November, 1831, to be replaced by a Central Board of Health. McGrigor was not a member of the new board. Brockington, p. 67.

66. *Times*, April 6, 1856, p. 6; London *Gazette*, August 16, 1856, pp. 2042–43. McGrigor was survived by his wife, two sons, and a daughter.

# BIBLIOGRAPHY

## MANUSCRIPTS

ABERDEEN MEDICO-CHIRURGICAL SOCIETY LIBRARY

1. Sir James McGrigor Papers, 64 vols.

BRITISH MUSEUM

2. Liverpool Papers, Add. Mss. 43190.
3. McGrigor Letters, Add. Mss. 38301.

INDIA OFFICE LIBRARY

4. Bombay Military Proceedings Z/P 3250, 3251, 3252, 3253.
5. Bombay Public Proceedings, P/354,23; P/3402/52–57.

MCGILL UNIVERSITY LIBRARY

6. Sir Henry Hardinge Papers.

NATIONAL LIBRARY OF SCOTLAND

7. Lord Lynedoch Papers, Add. Mss. 3610.
8. McGrigor Letters, Add. Mss. 3903.

PUBLIC RECORD OFFICE, WAR OFFICE PAPERS

9. 1/84, 281. West Indies, Forces under Sir Ralph Abercrombie.
10. 1/85, 269; 305; 601–614. West Indies, Forces under Sir Ralph Abercrombie.
11. 1/86, 28–29; 257. West Indies, Forces under Sir Ralph Abercrombie.
12. 1/171, 561–567. Formation of a Medical Corps.
13. 1/172. Medical Reports on the Flanders Campaign.
14. 1/229, 583. Casualties, Sir John Moore's Army.
15. 1/242–1/276. Wellington's Dispatches from the Peninsula.
16. 1/292, 267–271. Ophthalmia, Prevalence of, Egypt, Malta.
17. 1/346. Expedition to Egypt.
18. 1/357, 319–387. Assembly of Indian Army in Egypt.
19. 1/358, 268–315. Red Sea Expedition, 1801.
20. 1/359, 141–148. Red Sea Expedition, 1801.
21. 1/375, 357–358. Red Sea Expedition, 1801.
22. 1/556, 80. West Indies, Sailing of Expedition, 1795.
23. 1/623, 45–47. Hospital Ships, Provisions for, Proposal for.

24. 1/633, 157–165; 205–220; 451–455; 527. Hospital Ships.
25. 1/641, 13–46. System of Inquiry into Military Hospitals.
26. 1/642, 181–187. In Spain, Treatment of Invalids, 1809.
27. 1/651, 227–235. Miscellaneous Letters, Spain.
28. 1/659, 571. Preference of Regimental to General Hospitals.
29. 1/661, 89. Commander in Chief, Miscellaneous, 1815.
30. 1/683, 313–353. American Rebellion, Administration of Hospitals.
31. 1/853, 163–167; 597–601. Hospitals of, Peninsula.
32. 1/865, 133. Miscellaneous Letters, 1815.
33. 1/894, 463. Operations In June, 1801, Egypt.
34. 1/896. Inspector of Health, Medical, 1794.
35. 1/897. Reorganization of Military Hospitals, Inspector of Health, Barracks and Troops Ships, 1794, Reorganization of Military Transports, 1795.
36. 1/1072, 387–408. Surgeon-General, Regimental Inspector of Hospitals Duties Of, 1792–94.
37. 3/31, 68–77. Military Superintendence of Military Hospitals.
38. 3/205, 113. General Regulations for Military Hospitals.
39. 3/333, 100. Regimental Establishment of Military Hospitals, 1806.
40. 3/609. Commander In Chief's Papers, 1815.
41. 4/401–4/409. Medical Department, 1805–1810. Miscellaneous Letters, Medical Reports.
42. 4/164, 280; 403. Regimental System, Re-organization Of, 1796.
43. 4/291, 120–133. Medical Arrangements, Low Countries.
44. 4/432, 266–268. Miscellaneous Letters, Medical Department.
45. 4/408. System of Inquiry into Medical Hospitals.
46. 6/147, 229–381. West Indies, Forces under Sir Ralph Abercrombie.
47. 7/96–7/109. Letter Books, Medical Department.
48. 18/16. Military Hospitals.
49. 18/180. Military Hospitals.
50. 18/181. Military Hospitals.
51. 18/199. Military Hospitals.
52. 25/3909, 27. Service Record of James McGrigor.
53. 26/22, 209. Physicians, Instructions as to Duties, 1759.
54. 26/37, 358. Army Medical Board, Establishment, Duties of, 1798.
55. 30/83. Copybook, Medical Reports, 1799–1803.
56. 30/84. Copybook, Medical Reports, 1799–1803.
57. 40/7. Unmarked Papers. Medical Department, 1795.
58. 40/10. Medical Arrangements for Holland.
59. 40/11. Helder Expedition. Medical Arrangements.
60. 40/12. On the Means of Preserving the Health of Troops in Tropical Climates, Observations of the Surgeon-General, Medical Report on the West Indies.
61. 40/13. Helder Expedition, Medical Arrangements, Hospitals Ships, Inquiries in Military Medical Arrangements, Instructions for General Hospitals.

62. 40/14. Establishment of a Medical Department at Malta, 1801, General Vaccination of the Troops, Isle of Wight.
63. 40/15. Memorial of Hospital Staff Surgeons for Increased Pay, Treatment of The Sick in Hospitals under Dr. Jackson and Dr. Borland.
64. 40/16. Remarks Of The Physician-General and Surgeon-General on the Report of the Depot Hospitals, Memorial of Hospital Staff Surgeons in England, Isle of Wight.
65. 40/20. Plan for the Formation of a College of Medical Candidates for the Army and Navy, Proposed Regulations for Medical Officers, Instructions to Principal Medical Officers Abroad.
66. 40/22. Proposal for Reorganization of Army Medical Board, 1805.
67. 40/25. Dr. Bancroft's Charge of Inefficiency against the Army Medical Department, Observations on Medical Staff of Army.
68. 40/27. Difficulty in Obtaining Properly Qualified Men for the Army Medical Service.
69. 40/28. Report of Abuses on Isle of Wight, Memorandum on the Organization of the Medical Staff of the Army.
70. 43/23. Miscellaneous Letters, Army Medical Department.
71. 43/28. Miscellaneous Letters, Army Medical Department.
72. 43/38. Letters of Director-General.
73. 43/57. Miscellaneous Letters, Army Medical Department.
74. 43/72. Army Medical Department, Reorganization.

ROYAL ARMY MEDICAL COLLEGE LIBRARY

75. James G. Elkington Papers.
76. Letters To Sir James McGrigor.
77. Minute Books of the Officers' Benevolent Society.
78. Sir James McGrigor's Notebooks.
79. Sir John Hall Papers.
80. William Fergusson Papers.

SIR CHARLES MCGRIGOR LIBRARY, UPPER SONACHAN, DALMALY, ARGYLL

81. McGrigor Family Letters.

UNIVERSITY OF DURHAM—PRIOR'S KITCHEN

82. Earl Grey Papers, The 3rd Earl.

WAR OFFICE LIBRARY

83. H. B. Moffat Mss. The Duke of York's Campaign in 1793 and 1794 (1881).

YALE UNIVERSITY—YALE MEDICAL LIBRARY

84. William Fergusson Papers.

## PERIODICALS

85. *Aberdeen Journal*, 1787–1796.
86. *Aberdeen Magazine*, 1789–1791.
87. *Annals of Medicine*, 1797–1798.
88. *Annual Register*, 1795–1796.
89. *Asiatic Annual Register*, 1800–1804.
90. *British Medical Journal*.
91. *Colburn's United Service Magazine*.
92. *Edinburgh Medical and Surgical Journal*.
93. *Gentlemen's Magazine*, 1810, 1827, 1858.
94. *Lancet*.
95. London *Gazette*, 1812, 1831, 1850.
96. *London Medical and Physical Journal*, 1802–1819.
97. *Medico-Chirurgical Transactions*, 1815.
98. *Military Panorama or Officer's Companion*, 1813.
99. *Quarterly Review*, 1840.
100. *Royal Military Chronicle*, 1810–1811.
101. *The Times*.
102. *Transactions of the Medical Society of London*, 1810.
103. *Transactions of the Provincial Medical and Surgical Association*, 1835.

## PRINTED PRIMARY SOURCES

104. Alice, Countess of Strafford, ed. *Personal Reminiscences of the Duke Francis, The First Earl of Ellesmere*. London, 1903.
105. Annesley, James. *Sketches of the Most Prevalent Diseases of India*. London, 1825.
106. Anon. *A Catalogue of the Library of the Army Medical Department*. London, 1833.
107. ———. *A Journal Kept in the British Army From the Landing of the Troops Under the Earl of Moira at Ostend, January, 1794 to Their Retreat to England the Following Year*. Liverpool, 1794.
108. ———. *A Narrative of a Residence in Belgium During the Campaign of 1815*. London, 1817.
109. ———. *A Short Narrative of the Late Campaign of the British Army Under the Orders of the Rt. Hon., the Earl of Chatham*. London, 1810.
110. ———. *Regulations, List of the Members and Catalog of the Aberdeen Medico-Chirurgical Society*. 5th ed. Aberdeen, 1812.
111. Army Medical Board. *Instructions for the Regulations of Regimental Hospitals*. London, 1812.
112. ———. *Instructions of the Army Medical Board of Ireland to Regimental Surgeons*. Dublin, 1813.
113. ———. *Instructions to Regimental Surgeons for Regulating the Concerns of the Sick, and of the Hospitals*. 3rd. ed. London, 1808.

114. Bancroft, Edward, N. *A Letter to the Commissioners of Military Inquiry*. London, 1808.

115. ————. *An Exposure and Refutation of Various Misrepresentations Published by Dr. McGrigor and Dr. Jackson in Their Separate Letters to the Commissioners of Military Inquiry*. London, 1808.

116. Bell, Charles. *Letters of Sir Charles Bell Selected from Correspondence with His Brother George Joseph Bell*. London, 1870.

117. Bell, George. *Rough Notes by an Old Soldier*, 2 vols. London, 1867, vol. 1.

118. Bell, John. *An Inquiry into the Causes which Produce, and the Means of Preventing Disease among British Officers, Soldiers, and Others in the West Indies*. London, 1791.

119. ————. *A Memorial Concerning the Present State of Military and Naval Surgery*. London, 1800.

120. Breen, Henry H. *St. Lucia, History, Descriptive and Description*. London, 1791.

121. Brocklesby, Richard. *Oeconomical and Medical Observations in Two Parts, for the Year 1758 to the Year 1764 Inclusive. Tending to the Improvements of Military Hospitals and to the Cure of Camp Disease Incident to Soldiers*. London, 1764.

122. Brown, Robert. *An Important Journal of a Detachment from the Brigade of Foot Guards*. London, 1795.

123. Burroughs, George Frederick. *A Narrative of the Retreat of the British Army from Burgos*. London, 1814.

124. Cannon, Richard. *Historical Records of the 88th Regiment of Foot, or Connaught Rangers*. London, 1838.

125. Chisholm, Colin. *Essay on the Malignant Pestilential Fever Introduced into the West Indian Islands from Boullam, or the Coast of Guinea as It Appeared in 1793, 1794, 1795, 1796*. London, 1801.

126. Clark, James. *A Treatise on the Yellow Fever as It Appeared in the Island of Dominica in the Years, 1793, 1794, 1795, 1796*. London, 1797.

127. Clark, John. *Observations on the Diseases Which Prevail in Long Voyages to Hot Countries*. London, 1773.

128. Cleghorn, George. *Observations of the Epidemical Diseases of Minorca. From the Year 1744 to 1749*. London, 1751.

129. Cotton, Edward. *A Voice From Waterloo*. London, 1849.

130. Dalton, Charles. *The Waterloo Roll Call*. 3rd. ed. London, 1971.

131. Davis, J. B. *A Scientific and Popular View of the Walcheren Fever*. London, 1812.

132. Dawson, G. P. *Observations on the Walcheren Disease*. Ipswich, 1810.

133. Dewar, Henry. *Observations on Diarrhea and Dysentery as Those Diseases Appeared in the British Army during the Campaign in Egypt*. London, 1803.

134. Donaldson, John. *Recollections of the Eventful Life of a Soldier*. London, 1856.

135. Duncan-Jones, Caroline, M., ed. *Trusty and Well Beloved, the Letters Home of William Harness an Officer of George III*. London, 1957.

136. Dunfermaline, Lord. *Lt. General Sir Ralph Abercrombie, K.B., 1793–1801.* Edinburgh, 1801.
137. Dunne, C. L. *The Chirurgical Candidate.* London, 1808.
138. Edwards, Bryan. *The History, Civil and Commercial of the British West Indies.* 5 vols., 5th ed. London, 1819, vols. 1, 2, 4.
139. Farrell, Charles. *Observations on Ophthalmia and Its Consequences.* London, 1811.
140. Fergusson, William. *Notes and Recollections of a Professional Life.* London, 1846.
141. Fitzpatrick, Jeremiah. *An Essay on Goal Abuses and on the Means of Redressing Them.* Dublin, 1784.
142. Grattan, William. *Adventures of the Connaught Rangers from 1808 to 1814.* 2 vols. London, 1847.
143. Gurwood, John, comp. *The Dispatches of Field Marshal the Duke of Wellington.* 12 vols. London, 1834–1838.
144. Guthrie, George James. *Treatise on Gun-Shot Wounds.* 2nd ed. London, 1820.
145. ———. *Commentaries on the Surgery of the War in Portugal, Spain, France, and the Netherlands from the Battle of Rolica, in 1808, to that of Waterloo, in 1815 with Additions Relating to Those in the Crimea in 1854–1855.* 5th ed. London, 1855.
146. Halliday, Andrew. *The Present State of the Portuguese Army.* Edinburgh, 1812.
147. Hamilton, David. *A Treatise of a Military Fever.* London, 1737.
148. Hamilton, Robert. *The Duties of a Regimental Surgeon Considered.* 2 vols. London, 1787.
149. Hansard. *Parliamentary Debates.* 3rd Ser.
150. Harcourt, Edward W., ed. *The Harcourt Papers.* 14 vols. Oxford, n.d., vol. 4.
151. Hargrove, G. *An Account of the Island of Walcheren and South Beveland against which the British Expedition Proceeded in 1809.* Dublin, 1812.
152. Henderson, Stewart. *A Letter to Officers of the Army under Orders to, or that May Hereafter Be Sent to the West Indies on the Means of Preserving Health and Preventing that Fatal Disease the Yellow Fever.* London, 1795.
153. Hennen, John. *Military Surgery.* 2nd. ed. London, 1820.
154. Henry, Philip. Philip, 5th Earl Stanhope. *Notes of Conversations with the Duke of Wellington, 1831–1851.* London, 1888.
155. Henry, Walter. *Events of a Military Life.* 2 vols. London, 1943.
156. Hodge, W. Barwick. "On the Mortality Arising From Military Operations," *Journal of the Royal Statistical Society,* 19 (1856), 219–231.
157. Houk, Theodore. *The Life of General, the Rt. Honourable Sir David Baird.* London, 1832.
158. Hunter, John. *A Treatise on the Blood, Inflammation and Gun-Shot Wounds.* 2 vols. Philadelphia, 1796.
159. Hunter, John, Dr. *Observations on the Diseases of Jamaica and on the Means of Preserving the Health of Europeans in that Climate.* London, 1786.

160. Hutchinson, J. H. "Memoir on the Life of the Much Lamented Lt. General Sir Ralph Abercrombie," *Miscellanies, 1760–1801*. Dublin, 1801.

161. Irving, James. "A Concise View of the Progress of Military Medical Literature in this Country," *Edinburgh Medical and Surgical Journal*, 63 (1845), 285–302; ibid., 64 (1845), 83–98, 115–129, 375–389; ibid., 65 (1846), 34–39.

162. Ives, John. *A Voyage From England to India in the Year MDCCLIV*. London, 1773.

163. Jackson, Robert. "Comparative Return of Sick of Army Serving in the Windward and Leeward Islands from 1803 to 1814," *Transactions of the Medical Society of London*, 1 (1818), 281–296.

164. ———. *A Letter to the Commissioners of Military Inquiry, Explaining the Constitution of a Medical Staff*. London, 1808.

165. ———. *A Letter to the Rt. Hon. Sir David Dundas, K.B.* London, 1809.

166. ———. *An Outline for the Political Organization and Moral Training of the Human Race*. Stockton, 1823.

167. ———. *An Outline of the History and Cure of Fever, Endemic and Contagious*. Edinburgh, 1798.

168. ———. *Remarks on the Constitution of the British Army with a Detail of Hospital Management*. London, 1803.

169. ———. *Remarks on the Epidemic Yellow Fever, which has appeared at intervals on the South Coast of Spain since the year 1800*. London, 1821.

170. ———. *A Sketch of the History and Cure of Febrile Diseases*. Stockton, 1817.

171. ———. *A System of Arrangements and Discipline for the Medical Department of Armies*. London, 1805.

172. ———. *A Systematic View of the Formation, Discipline and Economy of Armies*. London, 1804.

173. ———. *A Treatise on the Fevers of Jamaica*. London, 1791.

174. Jones, J. J. *Journal of Sieges, 1810–1814*. London, 1846.

175. Jones, L. T. *An Historical Journal of the British Contingent in the Year 1794 with the Retreat Through Holland in the year 1795*. Birmingham, 1798.

176. Kennedy, William. *Annals of Aberdeen*. 2 vols. London, 1818.

177. Kincaid, John. *Adventures in the Rifle Brigade, in the Peninsula, France, and in the Netherlands, from 1809 to 1815*. London, 1895.

178. Larpent, George, ed. *The Private Journal of F. S. Larpent, Esq., Judge-Advocate General of the British Forces in the Peninsula*. 3 vols. London, 1853, vol. 1.

179. Larrey, D. J. *Relation, Historical and Surgical, of the Expedition of the Army of the Orient in Egypt and Syria*. Rose, Alexander, trans. *The Military Surgeon*, 99 (1946), 323–337, 790–804; 100 (1947), 68–78, 175–187, 256–264, 523–534; 101 (1947), 66–78, 144–158, 232–244, 321–330, 516–528.

180. Lempriere, William. *Partial Observations on the Diseases of the Army in Jamaica, as They Occurred Between the Years 1792 and 1797*. 2 vols. London, 1799.

181. Lind, James. *An Essay on Diseases Incident to Europeans in Hot Climates with the Method of Preventing Their Fatal Consequences*. London, 1768.

182. Longmore, Thomas. *Treatises On the Transport of Sick and Wounded Troops*. London, 1869.

183. Luscombe, Edward T. *Practical Observations on the Means of Preserving the Health of Soldiers*. Edinburgh, 1820.

184. MacLean, Charles. *An Analytical View of the Medical Department of the British Army*. London, 1810.

185. McGrigor, James. *A Letter to the Commissioners of Military Inquiry in Reply to some Animadversions*. London, 1808.

186. ———. *Medical Sketches of the Expedition to Egypt from India*. London, 1804.

187. ———. *The Autobiography and Services of Sir James McGrigor Bart., Late Director-General of the Army Medical Department*. London, 1861.

188. Mercer, Cavalié. *Journal Kept Through the Campaign of 1815*. London, 1870.

189. Milburne, Henry. *A Narrative of Circumstances Attending the Retreat of the British Army under the Command of the Late Lieut. General Sir John Moore*. London, 1809.

190. Millar, John. *Observations on the Prevailing Diseases of Great Britain*. London, 1798.

191. ———. *Observations on the Change of Public Opinions in Religion, Politics, and Medicine*. London, 1788.

192. Milligen, J. G. V. *The Army Medical Officer's Manual Upon Active Service*. London, 1819.

193. M'Lean, Hector. *An Inquiry Into the Nature and Causes of the Great Mortality Among the Troops at St. Domingo*. London, 1797.

194. Moises, H. *An Inquiry into the Abuses of the Medical Department in the Militia of Great Britain with Some Necessary Amendments Proposed*. London, 1794.

195. Monro, Donald. *Observations on the Means of Preserving the Health of Soldiers and of Constituting Military Hospitals and on the Diseases Incident to Soldiers*. 2 vols. London, 1780.

196. Moseley, Benjamin. *A Treatise on Tropical Diseases, on Military Operations and on the Climate of the West Indies*. London, 1789.

197. ———. *Observations on the Dysentery of the West Indies*. Kingston, 1780.

198. Munro, William. *Records of Service and Campaigning in Many Lands*. 2 vols. London, 1887, vol. 1.

199. Neale, Adam. *Letters From Portugal and Spain*. London, 1809.

200. ———. *The Spanish Campaign of 1808*. Edinburgh, 1828.

201. Nightingale, Florence. *Army Sanitary Administration and Its Reform Under the Late Lord Herbert*. London, 1862.

202. ———. *Mortality of the British Army at Home, At Home and Abroad and During the Russian War as Compared With the Mortality of the Civilian Population*. London, 1858.

203. ———. *Notes on Matters Affecting the Health, Efficiency, and Hospital Administration of the British Army*. London, 1858.

204. ———. *Notes on Hospitals*. London, 1859.
205. Parliamentary Papers. *Papers Relating to the Expedition to the West Indies under the Command of Sir Charles Grey and Sir John Jervis*, 1794–1795, XL (810).
206. ———. *Fifth Report of the Commissioner of Military Inquiry, Army Medical Department*, 1808 (6), V, 1.
207. ———. *Return of the Sick of the Army Employed in Spain and Portugal*, 1810 (144), XIII, 301.
208. ———. *Papers Relating to the Army Medical Board*, 1810 (101), XIV, 1.
209. ———. *Papers Relating to the Formation of the New Army Medical Department*, 1810 (101), 14, 157.
210. ———. *Scheldt Expedition*, 1810, vi, 6.
211. ———. *Scheldt Expedition*, 1810, vii, 7.
212. ———. *Scheldt Expedition*, 1810, viii, 8.
213. ———. *Expedition to the Scheldt*, 1810, i.
214. ———. *Expedition to the Scheldt*, 1810, ii.
215. ———. *Expedition to the Scheldt*, 1810, v.
216. ———. *Report From the Select Committee to Consider the Validity of the Doctrine of Contagion in the Plague*, 1819 (499) II, 537.
217. ———. *Report of the Commission into Naval and Military Promotion*, 1840 (235) XXIII, 1.
218. ———. *Statistical Report on the Sickness, Mortality and Invaliding Among the Troops in the West Indies*, 1837–38 (138), X, 417.
219. ———. *Statistical Report . . . Among the Troops in the United Kingdom, Mediterranean, and British North America*, 1839 (166), XIV, 129.
220. ———. *Statistical Report . . . Among the Troops in Western Africa, St. Helena, Cape of Good Hope, and Mauritius*, 1840 (228), XXX, 135.
221. ———. *Statistical Report . . . Among Her Majesty's Troops serving in Ceylon, Tenasserim Province and the Burmese Empire*, 1842 (358), XXVII.
222. ———. *Instructions Issued by the Army Medical Board to the Medical Officers of the Army Serving in India, Relative to the Medical Treatment of Soldiers Attacked with Cholera*, 1847–48 (190), XLI, 29.
223. ———. *Report from the Select Committee on the Army Before Sebastopol*, 1854–55, IX.
224. ———. *Committee on Barracks Accommodations for the Army*, 1855, XXXVII.
225. ———. *Proceedings of the Sanitary Commission Dispatched to the Seat of the War in the East*, 1857, IX, Sess. I.
226. ———. *Report of the Commissioners Appointed to Inquire Into the Regulations Affecting the Sanitary Condition of the Army, the Organization of Military Hospitals, and the Treatment of the Sick and Wounded*, 1857–58, XXXIII.
227. ———. *Health of the Army in Turkey and In the Crimea*, 1857–58, XXXVIII.
228. ———. *Papers Relating to the Sanitary State of the People of England*, 1858, XLVII.
229. ———. *Royal Commission on Improving the Sanitary Condition of Barracks and Hospitals*, 1861, XVI.

230. ———. *Royal Commission on the Sanitary State of the Army* (East India), 1863, XIX.

231. ———. *A Bill For the Prevention of Contagious Diseases*, 1864, I, 473.

232. ———. *A Bill For the Further Prevention of Contagious Diseases*, 1866, II, 219.

233. Pettigrew, W. J. *Medical Portrait Gallery*. 4 vols. London, n.d.

234. Pinckhard, George. *Notes on the West Indies, Including Observations, Relative to the Creoles of Spain, of the West Colonies and the Indians of South America, Interspersed With Remarks Upon the Seasoning or Yellow Fever of the Climate*, 2 vols., 2nd. ed., London, 1816.

235. Pringle, John. *Observations on Diseases of the Army in Camp and Garrison*, 1st. ed. London, 1752.

236. Pym, William. *Observations upon Bulam, Vomito-Negro or Yellow Fever*. 2nd. ed. London, 1848.

237. Ranby, John. *Methods of Treating Gunshot Wounds*. 3rd. ed. London, 1781.

238. Reide, Thomas Dickson. *A View of the Diseases in Great Britain, America, the West Indies, and on Board King's Ships and Transports*. London, 1793.

239. Rollo, John. *A Short Account of the Royal Artillery Hospital at Woolich*, London, 1801.

240. ———. *Observations on the Diseases which Appeared in the Army on St. Lucia in December, 1778; January, February, March, April and May, 1779*. London, 1780.

241. Rowley, William. *Medical Advice for the Army and Navy in the Present American Expedition*. London, 1776.

242. Siborne, William. *History of the Waterloo Campaign*, 2 vols. London, 1844.

243. Simpson, James. *Paris After Waterloo*. London, 1853.

244. Smyth, James Carmichael. *A Description of the Jail Distemper, As Appeared Among the Spanish Prisoners at Winchester in the Year 1780*. London, 1795.

245. ———. *The Effect of Nitrous Vapours in Preventing and Destroying Contagions, From a Variety of Trials*. Philadelphia, 1799.

246. Somerville, Robert. *Memoir on the Medical Arrangements to be Observed in Camps*. London, 1796.

247. Southey, Robert. *History of the Peninsular War*. 6 vols. London, 1827, vol. 4.

248. St. Clair, Lt. Col. *A Soldier's Recollection of the West Indies and America with a Narrative of the Expedition to the Island of Walcheren*. 2 vols. London, 1814.

249. Stewart, David. *Sketches of the Character, Manners, and Present State of the Highlanders of Scotland*. 2 vols. Edinburgh, 1824.

250. Thomson, John. *Report on Observations in British Military Hospitals After the Battle of Waterloo*. Edinburgh, 1816.

251. Tomkinson, James, ed. *The Diary of a Cavalry Officer in the Peninsula and Waterloo Campaigns, 1809–1815*. London, 1894.

252. Verney, Sir Harry. *The Journals and Correspondence of General Sir Harry*

*Calvert, Bart. G.C.B., and G.C.H. Comprising the Campaign in Flanders and Holland in 1793–94.* London, 1853.

253. Vetch, John. *An Account of the British Army in Egypt.* London, 1807.

254. Walsh, Thomas. *Journal of the Late Campaign in Egypt.* London, 1803.

255. War Office, *General Regulations and Orders For the Army.* London, 1816.

256. ———. *Regulations to be Observed by Troops For the West Indies.* London, 1795.

257. Wellington, the 3rd Duke of, ed., *Supplementary Dispatches and Memoranda of Field Marshal Arthur, the Duke of Wellington.* 15 vols. London, 1858–72.

258. Wellington, the Duke of. *General Orders.* 9 vols. London, 1818.

259. Willyams, Cooper. *An Account of the Campaign in the Year 1794.* London, 1795.

260. Wilson, Robert, Thomas. *History of the British Expedition to Egypt.* London, 1802.

261. Wright, Thomas. *A Letter to the Members of the Legislature Who Feel A Real Interest in the Welfare of Thousands of Our Brave Soldiers Who Have Suffered by Sickness at Walcheren.* London, 1810.

262. ———. *A History of the Walcheren Remittent Fever.* London, 1811.

263. Wright, William. *Memoir of the Late William Wright, M.D.* Edinburgh, 1828.


SECONDARY WORKS

264. Ackernecht, E. H. *Medicine at the Paris Hospital, 1794–1848.* Baltimore, 1967.

265. Aldington, Richard. *The Duke.* New York, 1943.

266. Allardyce, Mabel D. *The Library of the Medico-Chirurgical Society of Aberdeen.* Aberdeen, 1943.

267. Allison, R. S. *Sea Diseases. The Story of a Great National Experiment in Preventive Medicine in the Royal Navy.* London, 1943.

268. Anderson, Peter J. *Selections From the Records of Marischal College and University.* Aberdeen, 1934.

269. Anglesey, Marquess of. *One-Leg. The Life and Letters of Henry William Paget, 1st Marquess of Anglesey.* London, 1961.

270. Anon. "Dominique Jean Larrey (1776–1842)—Surgeon in Chief of the Grande Armée," *Journal of the American Medical Association,* 185 (1963), 104–105.

271. ———. "George James Guthrie," ibid., 200 (1967), 408–409.

272. ———. "Pierre François Percy," *British Medical Journal,* 1 (1905), 37–39.

273. Aspinall, A. *The Later Correspondence of George III.* 5 vols. London, 1968–70.

274. Bayne-Jones, Stanhope. *The Evolution of Preventive Medicine in the United States Army, 1609–1939.* Washington, D.C., 1968.

275. Bégin, L. J. *Etudes sur le Service de Santé Militaire.* Paris, 1860.

276. Billroth, Theodore. *Historical Studies on the Nature and Treatment of Gunshot Wounds from the 15th Century to the Present Time.* Rhoads, C. P., trans. New Haven, 1933.

277. Bishop, William James. *A Bio-Bibliography of Florence Nightingale.* London, 1962.

278. Blanco, Richard L. "A Long and Bloody War," in *Great Military Campaigns,* ed. Raymond F. Locke. Los Angeles, 1970, pp. 117–170.

279. ———. "Henry Marshal (1775–1851) and the Health of the British Army," *Medical History,* 14 (1970), 260–276.

280. ———. "James McGrigor and the Army Medical Department," *History Today,* 21 (1971), 132–140.

281. ———. "Reform and Wellington's Post-Waterloo Army," *Military Affairs,* 29 (1965), 123–131.

282. Bodart, Gaston. *Losses of Life in Modern Wars.* Oxford, 1946.

283. Bowlby, Anthony. *The Hunterian Oration on British Military Surgery in the Time of Hunter and the Great War.* London, 1919.

284. Brand, Jeanne L. "John Simon and the Local Government Board Bureaucrats, 1871–1876," *Bulletin of the History of Medicine,* 37 (1963), 184–194.

285. Brett-James, Anthony. *The Hundred Days.* New York, 1964.

286. ———. "The Walcheren Failure," *History Today,* 13 (1963), 811–820; 14 (1964), 60–68.

287. ———, ed. Edward Costello. *The Peninsula and Waterloo Campaigns.* New York, 1968.

288. Brice, Dr., and Bottet, Captain. *Le Corps de Santé Militaire en France, Son Evolution, Ses Campagnes, 1708–1888.* Paris, 1907.

289. Brockington, C. Fraser. *A Short History of Public Health.* London, 1966.

290. Browning, Beatrice. *The Life and Letters of Sir John Moore.* New York, 1923.

291. Bunbury, Henry. *Narrative of Some Passages in the Great War with France, 1799–1810.* London, 1854.

292. Burne, Alfred, H. *The Noble Duke of York,* New York, 1949.

293. Burns, Alan. *History of the British West Indies.* London, 1954.

294. Carr-Saunders, A. M. and Wilson, P. A. *The Professions.* Oxford, 1933.

295. Cartwright, F. F. *The Development of Modern Surgery From 1830.* London, 1967.

296. Chandler, David, G. "The Egyptian Campaign of 1801," *History Today,* 11 (1962), 117–123, 177–186.

297. Chaplin, Arnold. *Medicine in the Age of George III.* London, 1920.

298. Chevalier, A. G. "Hygienic Problems of the Napoleonic Armies," *Ciba Symposium,* 3 (1941–42), 974–980.

299. ———. "Physicians of the French Revolution," ibid., 7 (1945–46), 238–268.

300. Clode, Charles M. *The Military Forces of the Crown.* 2 vols. London, 1869.

301. Cope, Zachary. *Florence Nightingale and the Doctors.* Philadelphia, 1959.

302. ———. *Some Famous General Practitioners and Other Medical History Essays.* London, 1961.
303. Copeman, W. S. C. *The Apothecaries of London.* London, 1967.
304. Corbett, Julian S., ed. *Private Papers of George, Second Earl Spencer.* 2 vols. Naval Records Society, vols. 26, 28. London, 1913–14.
305. Crawford, D. G. *History of the Indian Medical Service, 1600–1913.* 2 vols. London, 1914.
306. Crummer, LeRoy. "Robert Jackson, M.D., Late Inspector-General of Army Hospitals," *The Military Surgeon,* 3 (1935), 425–431.
307. Davies, G. *Wellington and His Army.* London, 1954.
308. Des Cilleuls, J. "Le Service de Santé Militaire des Origenes à nos jours," *Revue Internationale des Services de Santé des Armées de Terre, de Mere, et de l'Air,* n.v. (1961).
309. ———, Pesme, J., Hassenforder J., Hugonot, G. *Le Service de Santé Militaire.* Paris, 1961.
310. Dible, Henry. *Napoleon's Surgeon.* London, 1970.
311. *Dictionary of National Biography.* 2nd ed., 27 vols. London, 1908.
312. Dobson, Jessie. *John Hunter.* Edinburgh and London, 1957.
313. Duggan, James. *The Great Mutiny.* New York, 1967.
314. Dunbar, R. G. "The Introduction of the Practice of Vaccination into Napoleonic France," *Bulletin of the History of Medicine,* 10 (1941), 633–650.
315. Elkington, H. P. "Some Episodes in the Life of James Goodall Elkington," *Journal of the Royal Army Medical Corps,* 16 (1911), 79–104.
316. Feibel, Richard. "What Happened at Walcheren: The Primary Sources," *Bulletin of the History of Medicine,* 42 (1968), 62–72.
317. Finer, S. E. *The Life and Times of Edwin Chadwick.* London, 1952.
318. Fitz, Reginald, "Napoleon's Camp at Boulogne," *Annals of Medical History,* 2 (1919), 148–156.
319. Flinn, Michael, W. ed. *Edwin Chadwick, Report on the Sanitary Condition of the Labouring Population of Great Britain.* Edinburgh, 1965.
320. Forrest, C. W. *Sepoy Generals: Wellington to Roberts.* London, 1901.
321. Fortescue, John. *A History of the British Army,* 13 vols. London, 1899–1930, vols. 4, 7, 8, 9, 10.
322. Fox, Richard H. *Dr. John Fothergill and His Friends.* London, 1917.
323. Fulford, Roger. *Samuel Whitbread.* London, 1967.
324. Furber, Holden. *Henry Dundas, First Viscount Melville, 1742–1811.* London, 1931.
325. Garrison, Fielding H. *Military Medicine.* Washington, D.C., 1922.
326. Giao, Manoel, R. F. "British Surgeons in the Portuguese Army During the Peninsular War," *Journal of the Royal Army Medical Corps,* 62 (1934), 299–303.
327. Gibney, R. D., ed. *Eighty Years Ago, or the Recollections of an Old Army Doctor.* London, 1896.
328. Glover, Michael. *Wellington as Military Commander.* New York, 1949.
329. ———. *Wellington's Peninsular Victories.* New York, 1963.

330. Glover, Richard. *Peninsular Preparation. The Reform of the British Army 1795–1809.* Cambridge, 1961.
331. Goodspeed, D. J. *The British Campaign in the Peninsula, 1808–1814.* London, 1958.
332. Gordon, G. A. *Army Surgeons and Their Work.* London, 1870.
333. Gordon-Taylor, Gordon, and Walls, E. W. *Sir Charles Bell, His Life and Times.* Edinburgh, 1965.
334. Gore, Albert. *The Story of Our Services Under the Crown.* London, 1870.
335. Granger, George Jean. *Recherches sur l'en Seignement de la Médicine Militaire à Strasbourg au XVIIIe Siecle.* Strasbourg, 1967.
336. Graux, Mme., and Beyland, M. "L'Hospital des Armées Scrive de Lille," *Revue Historique de L'Armée,* 1 (1972), 88–105.
337. Greenwood, Major. "British Loss of Life in the Wars of 1794–1815 and in 1914–1918," *Journal of the Royal Statistical Society.* 105 (1942), 1–16.
338. ———. *Some Pioneers of Social Medicine.* London, 1948.
339. Grey, Denis. *Spencer Percival, the Evangelical Prime Minister, 1782–1812.* Manchester, 1963.
340. Guedalla, Philip. *Wellington.* New York, 1934.
341. Hamilton, Bernice. "The Medical Profession in the 18th Century," *Economic History Review,* 2nd ser., 4 (1951), 141–169.
342. Haswell, Jock. *The First Respectable Spy, The Life and Times of Colquhoun Grant, Wellington's Head of Intelligence.* London, 1969.
343. Herold, J. Christopher. *Bonaparte in Egypt.* New York, 1968.
344. Hibbert, Christopher. *Corunna.* London, 1967.
345. Higham, Robin, ed. *A Guide to the Sources of British Military History.* London, 1972.
346. Holloway, S. W. F. "Medical Education in England, 1830–1848: A Sociological Analysis," *History,* 49 (1964), 299–324.
347. Howarth, David. *Waterloo: Day of Battle.* New York, 1968.
348. Howell, H. A. L. "Robert Jackson, M.D., Inspector of Hospitals," *Journal of the Royal Army Medical Corps,* 16 (1911), 121–139.
349. ———. "The British Medical Arrangements During the Waterloo Campaign," *Proceedings of the Royal Society of Medicine,* 17 (1923–24), 39–50.
350. ———. "The Story of the British Army Surgeon and the Care of the Sick and Wounded," *Journal of the Royal Army Medical Corps,* 22 (1914), 320–334, 445–471, 643–658.
351. Howie, William B. "Medical Education in 18th Century Hospitals," *Scottish Society of the History of Medicine,* n.v. (1970), 1–20.
352. Hunter, Richard, and Malcalpine, Ida. *George III and the Mad Business.* New York, 1969.
353. James, C. L. R. *The Black Jacobins.* New York, 1963.
354. Jones, Dorsey Dee. *Edwin Chadwick and the Early Public Health Movement.* Des Moines, 1931.
355. Jourdain, H. F. N., and Fraser, Edward. *The Connaught Rangers.* 2 vols. Edinburgh, 1893, vol. 1.

356. Keevil, J. J. "Archibald Menzie, 1754–1842," *Bulletin of the History of Medicine*, 22 (1940) 796–811.
357. ———, Lloyd, Christopher, and Coulter, Jack, L. S. *Medicine and the Navy, 1200–1900.* 4 vols. London, 1957–63. (Note: Keevil wrote vols. 1 and 2; Lloyd and Coulter wrote vols. 3 and 4.)
358. Kempthorne, G. A. "The American War, 1812–1814," *Journal of the Royal Army Medical Corps*, 62 (1934), 139–140.
359. ———. "The Army Medical Service at Home and Abroad, 1803–1808," ibid., 61 (1933), 144–146, 223–232.
360. ———. "The Army Medical Service in India, 1840–1853," ibid., 56 (1931), 220–228, 299–310.
361. ———. "The Army Medical Services, 1816–1825," ibid., 60 (1933), 299–310.
362. ———. "The Egyptian Campaign of 1801," ibid., 55 (1930) 217–230.
363. ———. "The Medical Department of Wellington's Army," ibid., 54 (1930), 65–72, 131–146, 213–220.
364. ———. "The Walcheren Expedition and the Reform of the Medical Board," ibid., 62 (1934), 133–138.
365. ———. "The War on the Continent, 1793–1795," ibid., 64 (1935), 339–351.
366. ———. "The Waterloo Campaign," ibid., 60 (1933), 204–207.
367. King, Lester. *The Medical World of the Eighteenth Century.* Chicago, 1958.
368. ———. *The Growth of Medical Thought.* Chicago, 1963.
369. ———. *The Road to Medical Enlightenment, 1650–1695.* London, 1970.
370. Kirby, Percival, R. *Sir Andrew Smith, M.D., K.C.B., His Life, Letters and Work.* Capetown, 1965.
371. Kirk, Russell R. *British Anatomy, 1525–1800.* Melbourne, 1965.
372. Laffin, John. *Surgeons in the Field.* London, 1970.
373. Larpent, George, ed. *The Private Journal of F. S. Larpent, Judge Advocate General of the British Forces in the Peninsula.* 3 vols. London, 1853, vol. 1.
374. Laughton, J. K., and Sullivan, J. Y. F. *Journal of Rear-Admiral Bartholomew James.* Naval Records Society, vol. 6. London, 1898.
375. Lewis, Richard A. *Edwin Chadwick and the Public Health Movement, 1832–1854.* London, 1952.
376. Liddell, Hart, B. H. ed. *The Letters of Private Wheeler, 1809–1829.* Boston, 1951.
377. Lloyd, Christopher, ed. *The Health of Seamen; Selections From the Works of Dr. James Lind, Sir Gilbert Blane, and Dr. Thomas Trotter.* Naval Records Society, vol. 107. London, 1965.
378. Longford, Elizabeth. *Wellington, the Years of the Sword.* New York, 1969.
379. Lovegrove, Peter. *Not Least in the Crusade—A Short History of the Royal Army Medical Corps.* London, 1938.
380. Ludoveci, Anthony, M., ed. *On the Road With Wellington.* London, 1924.
381. Marston, Maurice. *Sir Edwin Chadwick.* London, 1925.
382. Matheson, Cyril. *Life of Henry Dundas, First Viscount Melville.* London, 1933.

383. Matheson, J. M. "Comments on the Medical Aspects of the Battle of Waterloo," *Medical History*, 10 (1960), 52–58.

384. Maurice, Frederick, ed. *The Diary of Sir John Moore*, 2 vols. London, 1904, vol. 1.

385. Mayerhoff, Max. "A Short History of Ophthalmia during the Egyptian Campaigns of 1798–1807," *British Journal of Ophthalmology*, 16 (1933), 129–152.

386. McDonald, Donald. *Surgeons Twoe and a Barber. Being Some Account of the Indian Medical Service (1600–1947).* London, 1950.

387. McGuffie, T. H. "The Walcheren Expedition and the Walcheren Fever," *English Historical Review*, 62 (1947), 191–202.

388. Mitchell, G. A. G. "The Medical History of Aberdeen and the Universities," *Aberdeen University Review*, 37 (1958), 191–238.

389. Mitra, S. M. *The Life and Letters of Sir John Hall.* London, 1911.

390. Naylor, S. M. *Waterloo.* London, 1960.

391. Neal, J. R. "The Honorary Physicians and Surgeons to the Sovereign," *Journal of the Royal Army Medical Corps*, 97 (1951), 183–191.

392. Newman, Charles. *The Evolution of Medical Education in the Eighteenth Century.* London, 1957.

393. Oman, Carola. *Sir John Moore.* London, 1953.

394. Palmer, Robert R. *The Age of Democratic Revolution.* 2 vols. Princeton, 1964, vol. 2.

395. Parker, George. *The Early History of Surgery in Great Britain.* London, 1920.

396. Parkinson, C. Northcote. *The Trade Winds.* London, 1954.

397. ———. *War in the Eastern Seas, 1793–1815.* London, 1954.

398. Parry, J. M., and Sherlock, P. M. *A Short History of the West Indies.* 2nd ed. London, 1963.

399. Patterson, A. Temple. "The Naval Mutiny at Spithead, 1797," *Portsmouth Papers*, 5 (1968), 3–15.

400. Peterkin, A. and Johnston, William. *Commissioned Officers in the Medical Services of the British Army.* 1660–1960. 2 vols. 2nd ed. London, 1968, vol. 1.

401. Phipps, Ramsay Watson. *The Armies of the First Republic.* 4 vols. Oxford, 1926.

402. Porter, Ian. *Alexander Gordon, M.D. of Aberdeen, 1752–1799.* Edinburgh, 1958.

403. Poynter, F. N. L. "Thomas Southwood Smith—The Man (1788–1861)," *Proceedings of the Royal Society of Medicine*, 55 (1962), 381–393.

404. ———. ed. *The Evolution of Hospitals in Britain.* London, 1964.

405. ———. ed. *The Evolution of Medical Education in Britain.* London, 1966.

406. Ragatz, Lowell, Joseph. *The Fall of the Planter Class in the British Caribbean, 1763–1833.* New York, 1928.

407. Reader, W. J. *Professional Men.* New York, 1966.

408. Rieux, J., and Hassenforder, J. *Histoire Du Service de Santé Militaire et Val-De-Grace.* Paris, 1961.

409. Roddis, James H. *James Lind, Founder of Nautical Medicine*. New York, 1950.
410. Rodger, Ella H. B. *Aberdeen Doctors at Home and Abroad*. Edinburgh, 1893.
411. Rodgers, A. B. *The War of the Second Coalition, 1798–1808*. Oxford, 1964.
412. Rolge, James. *The Naval Biography of Great Britain*. 4 vols. London, 1870.
413. Rose, J. Holland. "The Conflict With Revolutionary France," *Cambridge History of the British Empire*. 3 vols. London, 1926–27, vol. 2, pp. 63–69.
414. ———. "The Political Reaction of Bonaparte's Egyptian Expedition," *English Historical Review*, 173 (1929), 48–58.
415. Rosen, George. "Occupational Diseases of English Seamen During the 17th and 18th Centuries," *Bulletin of the History of Medicine*, 7 (1935), 751–758.
416. ———. "Health, Medical Care and Social Policy in the French Revolution," ibid., 30 (1956), 124–149.
417. Ross, Stephen T. *European Diplomatic History, 1789–1815: France Against Europe*. New York. 1969.
418. Royston, Lambert. *Sir John Simon, 1816–1904, and English Social Administration*. London, 1966.
419. Saunders, Edith. *The Hundred Days*. New York, 1964.
420. Selby, John, ed. *Thomas Morris. The Peninsular and Waterloo Campaigns*. New York, 1968.
421. Selwyn, Sidney. "Sir John Pringle, Hospital Reformer, Moral Philosopher, and Pioneer of Antisepsis," *Medical History*, 10 (1960), 268–274.
422. Seymer, Lucy Ridgeley. *Selected Writings of Florence Nightingale*. New York, 1954.
423. Shepherd, John A. *Simpson and Syme of Edinburgh*. Edinburgh, 1969.
424. Shryock, Richard H. "Medicine and Public Health," in Métraux, Guy S., and Crouzet, François, eds., *The Nineteenth Century World*. New York, 1963, pp. 193–253.
425. Simon, John. *Public Health Reports. First Annual Report, 1849*. 2 vols. London, 1887.
426. Singer, Charles, and Underwood, E. A. *A Short History of Medicine*. New York, 1962.
427. Singer, Dorothy Waley. "Sir John Pringle and His Circle," *Annals of Science*, 6 (1948–1950), 171–261.
428. Smart, William R. E. "On the Medical Services of the Navy and Army from the Accession of Henry VIII to the Restoration," *British Medical Journal*, 1 (1874), 168–169, 199–200, 228–229, 264–266.
429. Smith, A. Euan, ed. *Henry Houssaye, 1815—Waterloo*. 3 vols. 26th ed. London, 1895–1905.
430. Smith, Fred L. *Short History of the Royal Army Medical Corps*. Aldershot, 1946.
431. Soubiran, André. *Le Baron Larrey, Chirurgien de Napoléon*. Paris, 1966.
432. Stanmore, Lord. *Sidney Herbert, Lord Herbert of Lea*. 2 vols. London, 1906.

433. Stevens, H. E. R. "The Influence of War on the Craft of Surgery," *Journal of the Royal Army Medical Corps*, 62 (1934), 40-46.
434. Stevenson, Lloyd G. "A Note on the Relation of Military Service to Licensing in the History of the British Army," *Bulletin of History of Medicine*, 27 (1953), 420–427.
435. ———. "John Hunter, Surgeon General, 1790–1793," *Journal of the History of Medicine and Allied Sciences*, 19 (1964), 239–254.
436. Steward, T. G. *The Haitian Revolution of 1791 to 1804*. New York, 1914.
437. Sutherland, John. *Men of Waterloo*. London, 1966.
438. Thompson, E. P. *The Making of the English Working Class*. New York, 1963.
439. Tomkinson, James, ed. *The Diary of a Cavalry Officer in the Peninsular and Waterloo Campaigns, 1809–1816*. London, 1894.
440. Underwood, E. Asher. "The Field Workers in the English Public Health Movement, 1847–1875," *Bulletin of the Society of Medical History*, 6 (1948), 31–48.
441. Vansittart, Jane. *Surgeon James's Journal*. London, 1964.
442. Vess, David, M. "The Collapse and Revival of Medical Education in France: A Consequence of Revolution and War," *History of Education Quarterly*, 7 (1967), 71–92.
443. Vulliamy, C. E. *Crimea, the Campaign of 1854–1856*. London, 1939.
444. Walker, M. E. M. *Pioneers of Public Health*. London, 1930.
445. Wangensteen, Owen H., Smith, Jacqueline, and Wangensteen, Sarah D. "Some Highlights in the History of Amputation Reflecting Lessons in Wound Healing," *Bulletin of the History of Medicine*, 41 (1967), 97–123.
446. Ward, B. R., ed. *A Week at Waterloo in 1815. Lady De Lancey's Narrative*. London, 1906.
447. Ward, S. G. P. *Wellington's Headquarters*. London, 1957.
448. Warren, Edmund, ed. *Lt. General Sir William Warren, Letters from the Peninsula*. London, 1909.
449. Watson, J. Steven. *The Reign of George III*. Oxford, 1963.
450. Weiner, Dora B. "French Doctors Face the War, 1792-1815," in Charles K. Warner, ed. *From the Ancient Regime to the Popular Front*. New York, 1963, pp. 51–73.
451. Weller, Jac. *Wellington at Waterloo*. London, 1960.
452. ———. *Wellington in the Peninsula, 1808–1814*. London, 1962.
453. Whipple, A. O. *The Story of Wound Healing and Wound Repair*. Springfield, 1963.
454. Widdes, J. H. S. "Robert Adair," *British Journal of Medical Science*, 6 (1948), 121–125.
455. Wiese, E. Robert. "Larrey, Napoleon's Chief Surgeon," *Annals of Medical History*, n.s., 1 (1929), 435–450.
456. Wilkin, W. H. *The Life of Sir David Baird*. London, 1902.
457. Winslow, Charles-Edward A. *The Conquest of Epidemic Disease*. New York, 1967.

458. Wood, S. C. I., ed. *William Hay, Reminiscences, 1808–1815, Under Wellington*. London, 1901.
459. Woodham-Smith, Cecil. *Florence Nightingale*. London, 1950.
460. ———. *The Reason Why*. London, 1953.
461. Zimmerman, Leo M., and Veith, Ilza. *Great Ideas in the History of Surgery*. New York, 1967.

# BIBLIOGRAPHIC ESSAY ON BRITISH
# MILITARY MEDICINE, 1750–1850

Note: The numbers cited in parentheses—e.g. (400)—refer to the sources listed in the Bibliography.

Historians have neglected the study of British military medicine in the eighteenth and nineteenth centuries. No bibliography on the subject is available, few books or articles about medical practice in the army are extant, memoirs by army surgeons (with a few exceptions) have limited value, and chronological gaps in the official records of the army medical department hinder research. Yet one guide to the service careers of medical officers, some essays on the history of the Royal Army Medical Corps, and material from related medical and biographical works provide enough material for a historical investigation of British military medicine from 1750 to 1850.

Biographical data about army medical officers is in Peterkin and Johnston (400) which contains details on administration, officers' titles, and military hospitals from 1660 to the present. Although there are minor errors in volume 1, this guide is the best published source on the subject. A good summary of the literature from 1500 to 1845 was written by Irving (161). He overlooked some items but compiled a useful list of books on surgery, hygiene, and disease written by army medical men. A more recent attempt to survey the published work on military medicine by the noted medical historian, F. N. L. Poynter, is found in Higham (345). However, Poynter's essay overlooks much pertinent literature in the field, and it has limited value.

Some popular works which purport to outline the history of the Royal Army Medical Corps are Gordon (332), Gore (334), and Lovegrove (379). But these books have little information. Laffin (372) must be used with caution; he ignores numerous developments in military medicine, fails to mention many famous books on the subject, and he credits the famed surgeon, John Hunter, with writing a book on West Indian disease that was actually written by Dr. John Hunter, the physician. Yet some valuable essays are available. Smart (428) traces the development of army medicine from the Tudors to the Stuarts, and Howell (350) carries the story to 1789. Kempthorne, a medical officer with a flair for history, compiled articles (358–366) about the medical department from the French Revolution to the Crimean War. Naval medicine is a separate research area, but naval surgeons, like their contemporaries in the army, often encountered problems in protecting large bodies of men. Books on naval medicine that have ramifications for military medicine are Allison (267), Lloyd (377), and Roddis (409). Nothing is available for the army that matches the excellent four volume work by Keevil, Lloyd, and Coulter on medicine in the Royal Navy which has abundant information and full bibliographies (357).

Particularly helpful to the researcher are works about medicine in civilian society of the eighteenth and nineteenth centuries. C. Singer and Underwood (426) wrote a medical history with chapters on this era; Zimmerman and Veith (461) summarize the accomplishments of leading medical men; and Brockington (289), Finer (317), Greenwood (338), and Lewis (375) trace developments in public health. King (367–369) offers lucid commentaries about prominent medical thinkers of the Enlightenment; penetrating insights about the state of medicine are also found in Chaplin (297), Fox (322), Kirk (371), and particularly in Newman (392). Chaplin (297) remains the only general account of medicine in the late Hanoverian era. Improvements in medical education and in hospital organization are discussed by specialists in Poynter (404, 405). Ackernecht (264) offers a splendid account of the influence of Paris hospitals. Cope (302) summarizes medical education in London; Porter (402) and Howie (351) offer valuable information about medical practice in Scotland. The status of the medical profession is deftly analysed by Carr-Saunders and Wilson (294), and in a plodding essay by Hamilton (341). Witty commentaries about the medical profession are in Reader (407). The apothecaries have Copeman (303) as their historian. Fine works on progress in surgery are Cartwright (295), Dobson (312), Kirk (371), and Parker (395). Developments in wound treatment are examined by Billroth (276), Bowlby (283), Wangensteen et al. (445), and Whipple (453). For an insight into John Hunter's career, Dobson (312) is helpful. Pringle does not have a recent biographer, but Selwyn (421), D. Singer (427), and especially King (367, 368), provide the background. Changes in medical practice during the post-Waterloo era are traced by Cartwright (295), and by Poynter (404, 405). Two excellent articles that discuss the relationship of medical developments to the contemporary social and economic scene are Holloway (346), and Shryock (424).

Little published information from secondary sources is available about British military medicine before the French Revolution, although Howell (350), and Peterkin and Johnston (400) offer some clues. Pringle (235) wrote the great work on preventive medicine for the eighteenth century; and Ranby (237) left a classic on military surgery. Brocklesby's work on the Seven Years War (121) is the best volume on military medicine in English for the century. Monro's description of hospital conditions (195) is invaluable. Cleghorne (128) explained the treatment of disease in the Mediterranean, Robert Hamilton (148) commented on the responsibilities of regimental surgeons. John Clark (127) and Ives (162) wrote about conditions aboard transports in the Indian Ocean. Rowley (241), in what seems to be the only work about the American Revolution by a British medical officer, gave advice about how to survive in North America. For information about the West Indies, three are at least six good accounts of equal merit—Bell (118, 119), Dr. John Hunter (159), Jackson (173), Lind (181), Moseley (196), and Rollo (240). Volume 3 of Keevil, Lloyd and Coulter (357) is extremely helpful for information about Caribbean campaigns. John Hunter (158) wrote a famous work on wound treatment; information about his career as surgeon general is in Dobson (312), and Stevenson (434, 435). Developments in French military medicine during the Enlightenment are summarized by Begin (275), Brice and Bottet (288), and Granger (335).

The best published accounts about the life of a British medical officer during the French Revolution are by McGrigor (185–187). My article (280) summarizes his accomplishments. The life of William Fergusson has not been studied, although Fergusson's Papers are available at the Royal Army Medical College (80) and at the Yale Medical Library (84). His autobiography (140) is valuable for this pe. iod. Although Guthrie is the subject of some brief articles, he merits a biography. His major works (144, 145) should be consulted for information on military surgery. Robert Jackson was a prolific writer on many subjects (163–173), and his descriptions of disease, commentaries about hospital management and tirades against the Medical Board provide an insight into army medicine. Crummer (306) and Howell (348) wrote essays on Jackson's career. Like Guthrie, Jackson has been a neglected figure.

Military accounts of a campaign sometimes have data on medical problems. But, unfortunately, there is little medical information in the account of the Flanders campaign by Fortescue (321), or by Burne (292), who makes a feeble effort to glorify the Duke of York. The only medical account of this expedition was written by Kempthorne (365). Fergusson (140), McGrigor (187), and Jackson (167, 168, 172) participated in the venture. Other useful commentaries by observers about the effects of typhus are Anon. (107), Brown (122), Duncan-Jones (135), Harcourt (150), L. T. Jones (175), and Verney (252).

The West Indian campaigns have also been neglected. Fortescue (321), Edwards (138), and Rose (413), provide some material. Apparently, Willyams (250) left the only published work on the Grey-Jervis expedition. In Parliamentary Papers (205) are some documents related to that campaign. McGrigor (187), Fergusson (140), and Jackson (167, 170, 173) were on the Abercrombie expedition. The best medical account of the Abercrombie campaign is by Pinckhard (234). Useful information about surgeons in the tropics can be extracted from Rollo (240), William Wright (263), Chisholm (125), Dunne (137), and Henderson (152).

Campaigns in the Indian Ocean during the French revolutionary era are ably described by Parkinson (397); Rodgers (441) has information about strategic problems of the Egyptian invasion. McGrigor (186, 187) wrote the only medical accounts of the Red Sea Expedition. Houk (157), Wilson (260), and Forrest (320), are useful. A fine study of Napoleon's Egyptian campaign is by Herold (343); the British side of the action is ably summarized by Chandler

(296). Descriptions of the plague and of eye diseases are in Farrell (139), Mc-Grigor (186, 187), Kempthorne (362), Mayerhoff (385), Dible (310), and Vetch (253).

Material about the difficulties of the Medical Board is limited to an article by Kempthorne (359). Participants in the feuds of the board were Mc-Grigor (185, 187), Jackson (164, 165, 168, 171, 172), and particularly Bancroft (114, 115) who defended the board. An article by Kate Elizabeth Crowe, "The Walcheren Expedition and the New Army Medical Board: A Reconsideration" (*English Historical Review*, 88 [1973], 770–785) is a thoughtful analysis of the board's problems.

The Walcheren expedition has been studied. McGrigor (187), Dawson (132), Davis (131), Hargrove (151), and Wright (261, 262), described the Walcheren fever in detail. Kempthorne (364) compiled a satisfactory account of the fiasco; and Brett-James (286) provides a vivid description of the expedition. The best treatment, however, is by McGuffie (387) who deftly handles the vast documentation on the subject. Feibel (316) claims to have written a medical history of the expedition based upon primary sources, but he overlooked some memoirs and completely ignored the basic material in the Parliamentary Papers on the campaign (208–215). However, Feibel demonstrates a medical doctor's knowledge in identifying diseases.

Military aspects of the Peninsular War have been well covered, but, again, there is little medical information in recent works by Davies (307), M. Glover (329), R. Glover (330), Goodspeed (331), S. G. P. Ward (447), and Weller (452), which all keep to the traditional level of strategy and tactics in describing the campaigns. Wellington's dispatches (143, 257) have some material about hospital organization. Some data about Beresford's army is in Halliday (146), and Giao (326). McGrigor (187) is the best medical source about the campaigns. Guthrie (145) should be consulted for commentaries on surgical practice. Kempthorne (363) summarized the functions of the medical department in Spain.

Waterloo has been discussed by a host of historians, yet the medical aspects of the battle have been generally overlooked. A good essay on the medical treatment of Waterloo is by Howell (349); Kempthorne (362) is also useful. A recent essay by Matheson (383) merely repeats Howell and Kempthorne. The best primary sources by medical men are Charles Bell (116), Guthrie (145), Thomson (250), Gibney (327), B. R. Ward (446), and especially, Vansittart (441). Imaginative reconstructions about medical arrangements are by Howarth (347), Naylor (390), and particularly, Sutherland (437). Medical developments in Napoleon's armies are discussed by Chevalier (298, 299), Des Cilleuls (308, 309), Dible (310), Graux and Beylard (336), Sourbiran (431), and Weiner (450).

For the post-Waterloo era, Ackernecht (264), Holloway (346), and Shryock (424) present fine accounts of trends in civilian medicine. The only articles about the medical department in this period are by Blanco (279), and Kempthorne (360, 361). Chadwick's career is covered by Finer (317) and

Lewis (375); Simon by Royston (418), and Southwood Smith by Poynter (403). Nightingale is the subject of a large bibliography; one of the best treatments is by Woodham-Smith (459).

Although abundant source material exists, no satisfactory account about the medical department in the Crimean War has been written. Likewise, there is a need for a study of how army surgeons grappled with tropical diseases in the British Empire, particularly in India and South Africa, during the late Victorian era. An explanation of how the medical department evolved into the Royal Army Medical Corps by 1898 awaits an historian.

# INDEX